W9-BRH-702

For Reference

Not to be taken

from this library

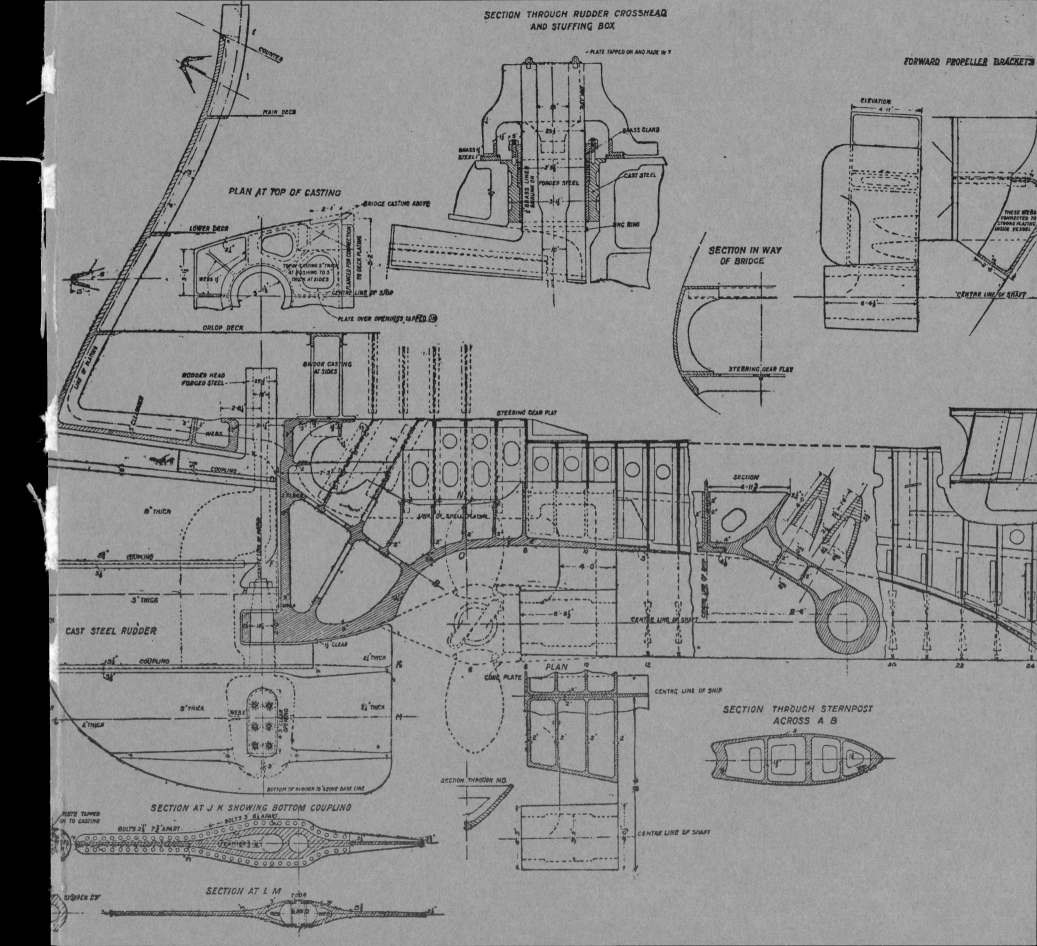

SECTION THROUGH RUDDER CROSSHEAD
AND STUFFING BOX

FORWARD PROPELLER BRACKETS

PLAN AT TOP OF CASTING

SECTION IN WAY
OF BRIDGE

CAST STEEL RUDDER

SECTION AT J K SHOWING BOTTOM COUPLING

SECTION AT L M

SECTION THROUGH STERNPOST
ACROSS A B

PLAN

THE ENGINE POWERED VESSEL

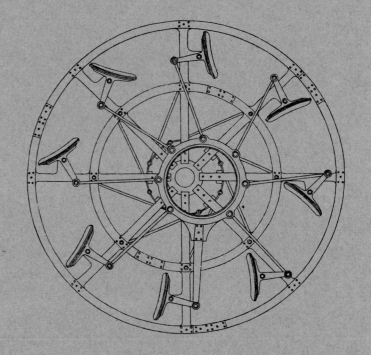

W. A. BAKER - TRE TRYCKARE

FROM PADDLE-WHEELER TO NUCLEAR SHIP ◖ CRESCENT BOOKS ◖ NEW YORK

Copyright © MCMLXV
by Tre Tryckare, Cagner & Co.

This edition published by
CRESCENT BOOKS
a division of Crown Publishers, Inc.,
by arrangement with Tre Tryckare AB.
a b c d e f g h

Library of Congress Catalogue Card
Number 65-21508

TRE TRYCKARE AB
Gothenburg, Sweden.
B28US11, 5722
Printed in Italy, 1972

The paintings on pages 4, 5, 8, 261, and 265
were reproduced from originals at The Maritime
Museum at Gothenburg.

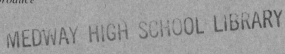

has been worked out by Tre Tryckare, Cagner & Co, Gothenburg, Sweden. This book is the result of comprehensive international teamwork covering several years in which nautical experts from different parts of the world have collaborated with the editorial staff of Tre Tryckare. In addition several marine museums and firms in the shipping trade, such as shipowners, yards and naval architects, have cooperated.

Supervising editors have been WILLIAM A. BAKER, Naval Architect and Curator at the Hart Nautical Museum at Boston, Massachusetts, and BENGT KIHLBERG, DGI, DIHR, Tre Tryckare, who has also been Art Director. Mr. Baker is also responsible for the text.

The editors' committee, which has selected the ships and done the editing work, also includes:
TAGE BLUM, Naval Architect and Lecturer at the Polytechnic Institute in Copenhagen, Denmark, G.A.J. BOVENS, Nautical Editor, Vlijmen, Holland, HOWARD I. CHAPELLE, Curator of the Division of Transportation at the Smithsonian Institution, Washington, D.C., USA, KNUD KLEM, Director of the Commercial and Maritime Museum at Kronborg, Helsingør, Denmark, STIG NOTINI, Captain and Director of the Maritime Museum at Gothenburg, Gothenburg, Sweden, H.P. SPRATT, I.S.O., B.SC., Science Museum, London, Great Britain, and GERHARD TIMMERMANN, Engineer and Head of Shipping and Fishing Section at the Altonaer Museum, Hamburg, West-Germany.

The original drawings were made in the studios of Tre Tryckare by, among others: BENGT BERGLUND, SIV ENGLUND, BILLY HELLSTEN, KARL ERIK INGEBY, FRITZ RODHE and RUNE SVENSSON. The illustrations have been drawn and lithographed under the direction of PER NIELSEN.

Furthermore some illustrations are reproduced from paintings, engravings and plans (see detailed list of sources on page 266). In some instances when, despite great endeavours, it has not been possible to obtain adequate and exact prototypes, Mr. Tage Blum has done some extensive reconstruction work.

Tre Tryckare owes a great debt of gratitude to the following persons, institutions and firms for invaluable help with advice and viewpoints and the supply of pictorial and textual material without which this book could not have been produced:

Beylen, J. van, Museum Keeper, Antwerp, Belgium - Christensen, Carl, Eureka, California, USA - Eriksson, Per, Head of Section at the Swedish Board of Shipping and Navigation, Stockholm, Sweden - Forshell, Hans, Commander, Gothenburg, Sweden - Hellner, A., Commander, Malmö, Sweden - Karlsson, Gösta, Museum Keeper, Gothenburg, Sweden - Molaug, Svein, Museum Director, Oslo, Norway - Munday, John, Curator at the National Maritime Museum, London, Great Britain - Notini, Stig, Captain, Gothenburg, Sweden - Petrejus, E.W., Museum Curator, The Hague, Holland - Pira, Evald, Civil Engineer, Stockholm, Sweden - Rosendahl, W., Managing Director of the New Steamship Co. of Waxholm, Stockholm, Sweden - Sell, Wolfgang, Hamburg, West-Germany - Stephens, William, Naval Architect, London, Great Britain - Sundström, Göran, Museum Keeper, Stockholm, Sweden - Svensson, Sam, Sea-Captain, Stockholm, Sweden - Vea, Erik, Museum Curator, Oslo, Norway

Chalmers Tekniska Högskolas Bibliotek, Gothenburg, Sweden - The Embassy of Japan, Stockholm, Sweden - The Embassy of the U.S.S.R., Stockholm, Sweden - Glasgow Museums & Art Galleries, Glasgow, Great Britain - Göteborgs Sjöfartsmuseum, Gothenburg, Sweden - Handels- og Søfartsmuseet på Kronborg, Helsingør, Denmark - Heeres Geschichtliches Museum, Vienna, Austria - Kungl. Sjöfartsstyrelsen, Stockholm, Sweden - Kungl. Tekniska Högskolans Bibliotek, Stockholm, Sweden - Lloyd's Register of Shipping, London, Great Britain - Marinens Pressdetalj, Stockholm, Sweden - The Mariners Museum, Newport News, Virginia, USA - Maritiem Museum "Prins Hendrik", Rotterdam, Holland - Maritime Museum, Haifa, Israel - Massachusetts Institute of Technology, Cambridge, Massachusetts, USA - Ministère des Armées, Paris, France - Museo Maritimo, Barcelona, Spain - Museo Maritimo "Alm. Ramalho Ortigao", Faro, Portugal - Museo Naval, Madrid, Spain - Museo Nazionale della Scienza e della Technica Leonardo da Vinci, Milan, Italy - Museo Storico Navale, Venice, Italy - National Maritime Museum, London, Great Britain - Nazional di S. Martino, Naples, Italy - Norsk Sjøfartsmuseum, Oslo, Norway - Peabody Museum, Salem, Massachusetts, USA - The Royal Scotch Museum, Edinburgh, Great Britain - San Francisco Maritime Museum, San Francisco, California, USA - Science Museum, London, Great Britain - Sjöfartsstyrelsen, Fartygsbyrån, Helsinki, Finland - Société Linguistique de Paris, Paris, France - Stadt- und Universitätsbibliothek, Hamburg, West-Germany - Statens Sjöhistoriska Museum, Stockholm, Sweden - Stevens Institute of Technology, Hoboken, New Jersey, USA - Suomen Akatemian Kielitoimista, Helsinki, Finland - Swiss Institute of Transport and Communications, Luzern, Switzerland - Universitetsbiblioteket, Gothenburg, Sweden - U.S. Department of Commerce, Maritime Administration, Washington, D.C., USA - U.S. Maritime Commission, Washington, D.C., USA - Verkehrshaus der Schweiz, Luzern, Switzerland

AB Götaverken, Gothenburg, Sweden - AB Lindholmens Varv, Gothenburg, Sweden - ASEA, Västerås, Sweden - Berninghaus, Ewald, Kölner Werft, Köln, West-Germany - Bethlehem Steel Company, Shipbuilding Division, Bethlehem, Pennsylvania, USA - The Fairfield Shipbuilding & Engineering Co., Ltd., Glasgow, Great Britain - Finlands Redareförening, Helsinki, Finland - Furness Shipbuilding Company Ltd., Billingham, Great Britain - Gibbs & Cox, Inc., New York, USA - Hamburg-Amerikalinie, Hamburg, West-Germany - Harland and Wolff Limited, Belfast, Great Britain - Hawthorn Leslie (Shipbuilders) Ltd., Hebburn-on-Tyne, Great Britain - Henry Company, Inc., J.J., New York, New York, USA - The Institution of Mechanical Engineers, London, Great Britain - Japan Catalogue Center, Tokyo, Japan - Kieler Howaldtswerke Aktiengesellschaft, Kiel, West-Germany - Kockums Mek. Verkstad AB, Malmö, Sweden - Koninklijke Nederlandsche Reedersvereeniging, 's-Gravenhage, Holland - Köln-Düsseldorfer Rheindampfschiffahrt, Köln, West-Germany - The Kure Shipbuilding & Engineering Co., Ltd., Kure, Japan - Malmö Bogseraktiebolag, Malmö, Sweden - N.V. Stoomvaart Maatschappij "Nederland", Amsterdam, Holland - Nederlandsche Dok en Scheepsbouw Maatschappij, Amsterdam, Holland - New Steamship Co. of Waxholm, Stockholm, Sweden - Newport News Shipbuilding & Drydock Co., Newport News, Virginia, USA - Nippon Yusen Kaisha, Tokyo, Japan - Norddeutscher Lloyd, Bremen, West-Germany - Norges Rederforbund, Oslo, Norway - Nydqvist & Holm Aktiebolag, Trollhättan, Sweden - Öresundsvarvet, Landskrona, Sweden - Rederiaktiebolaget Nordstjernan, Gothenburg, Sweden - Röda Bolaget, Gothenburg, Sweden - Shell Tankers (U.K.) Limited, London, Great Britain - St. Louis Shipbuilding, St. Louis, Missouri, USA - Stoomvaart Maatschappij Zeeland, Hoek van Holland, Holland - Thompson & Sons Limited, Joseph L., Sunderland, Great Britain - Trosviks Verksted, Brevik, Norway - Union-Castle Line, London, Great Britain - United Fruit Company, Boston, Massachusetts, USA - United States Lines, New York, New York, USA - United States Steel Corporation, Cleveland, Ohio, USA - Vickers-Armstrongs Limited, Barrow-in-Furness, Great Britain - Westfal-Larsen & Compani A/S, Bergen, Norway - Wilton-Fijenoord N.V., Schiedam, Holland - Zeise, Firma Theodor, Hamburg, West-Germany

6

PREFACE

Here is another of those beautifully illustrated volumes for ship-lovers, this time on the History of the Engine-Powered Vessel, produced by Tre Tryckare at the Scandinavian seaport of Gothenburg. Many books have been written about the history of merchant steamers and motor-ships, and in the course of time I must have read most of them, but I have never seen one so lavishly illustrated in colour, to show in such detail and exactitude the vessels represented. Tre Tryckare have here provided something new in maritime literature.

The earliest origins are traced back to the paddle-wheel, driven by the muscular force of men, horses or oxen, even before the Christian era, which only awaited the application of steam power as proposed by Denis Papin and patented by Jonathan Hulls, whose detailed plans for a steamboat, published in 1737, are the earliest known to us. From the pioneer experiments of Jouffroy d'Abbans, John Fitch, Symington and the CHARLOTTE DUNDAS, *Fulton and many others, came the first commercially successful steamboats: the* CLERMONT *in America, and the Scottish* COMET *in Europe.*

The first steam-auxiliary SAVANNAH *crossed the Atlantic in 1819, and the* SIRIUS *did so for the first time in 1838 under sustained steam power. There followed the transition from paddle to screw propulsion, and from wooden to iron hull construction, both embodied in the* GREAT BRITAIN *of 1843, and the premature super-liner* GREAT EASTERN *of the nineteenth century. Steel soon replaced iron, and early in our own century came the introduction of the Parsons marine steam turbine, the* TITANIC *disaster of 1912, and the* MAURETANIA *which held the Blue Riband for 22 years, the proudest record in the whole history of the service. Diesel had meanwhile produced his heavy-oil motor, and this was first used on the Atlantic in the Swedish liner* GRIPSHOLM.

Later we saw the first of the thousand-foot liners: the beautiful old NORMANDIE *and the two stately British* QUEENS. *After the Second World War came the* UNITED STATES *of phenomenal speed, the* SOUTHERN CROSS *with her funnel aft, like a tanker, and the* FRANCE *with curious smoke-disposal fins at her funnel tops. Gas turbines were tried as a new source of power, and nuclear propulsion has been introduced, notably on the Russian ice-breaker* LENIN *and on the* SAVANNAH *of 1959, the first atomic merchant ship. Supertankers of 100,000 tons and more have been built; not very beautiful ships perhaps, but with the efficient utility look of these modern times.*

The book has been edited by Mr. William A. Baker, an American naval architect, with the collaboration of experts invited from the principal maritime countries, to ensure that the work should be truly international in scope. To collect all the necessary detail has involved laborious international researches in archives, museum collections, all kinds of historical documentation and modern reference works. The resultant text, rich in technical detail for the nautical connoisseur, will also be a delight to the amateur ship-lover, for everyone in our maritime countries loves a ship; it is part of our life, our history.

The beautiful and technically accurate illustrations have been drawn with scrupulous care by Tre Tryckare's own staff of artists in the best tradition of Scandinavian taste and handicraft. Let me therefore commend this new volume to the reader, and let it speak for itself. To end on a personal note, I have been so much impressed by the thoroughness and enthusiasm of all concerned in this fine production, that it has been a real pleasure for me to collaborate and, above all, to have been invited to contribute this foreword.

SCIENCE MUSEUM, LONDON, JUNE 1965   H. PHILIP SPRATT, I.S.O.

In the designing of a ship there comes the time when the naval architect draws the final line on his plans. Pushing aside his pens, pencils, scales, curves, and slide rule—switching off the computer might be a more modern action—he thinks of all the compromises made to suit the capacity and speed requirements of the owner, the rules of the classification society, the regulations of governmental bureaus, and his own concepts. What could not be done on this ship will be included in the features of the next—the ideal ship is always one step in the future.

So it is with a book. The names of the participants are different but the effect is the same. That is why authors always have one more book to write.

You the reader may find in the following pages that your favorite ship is not included or perhaps seems to be slighted. A "first" in a given field is not necessarily the significant item. As development to modern times is considered the interval which permits a reasonable assessment of older items is absent. Hence for many modern ships we are faced with the efforts of one publicity writer versus another rather than a consideration of the real qualities of the ships.

For most of the ships included in this book it is easy to name equally good representatives of the types from countries other than those selected. It is almost impossible to cover the range of the history of engine-powered vessels with examples from one country alone. Experts in several countries helped to compile a list of about twice the number of vessels shown. To them my thanks for including many interesting but relatively obscure vessels normally overshadowed by the glamor ships. Some ships were eliminated from the list because of the lack of sufficient information, others to avoid too much emphasis on a given type or those for a certain run.

H. I. Chapelle of the Smithsonian Institution, Washington, D.C., and H. P. Spratt of the Science Museum, London, in addition to aiding with the initial list, read and commented on my manuscript. I am deeply indebted to them for their many suggestions.

Having dotted the last i and crossed the last t I can now lean back in my easy chair and dream of what might have been—but I will probably stretch a new sheet of paper on my drawing board and draw the keel line for the next ship.

WILLIAM AVERY BAKER, N.A.

In spite of the romance of sail, it is obvious that in one sense mechanically-propelled vessels came first. The simplest form of mechanical propulsion—the strength of men applied through paddles or the additional leverage provided by oars—served to move war and cargo ships in the ancient and medieval world. Men still resort to such means of propulsion for recreation. Large crews of oarsmen and the stores to feed them placed severe limitations on the design features and cargo capacity of vessels so propelled. Warships required oars for rapid manœuvering but the limitations on cargo capacity could be tolerated only when cargoes consisted of such high value commodities as silks and spices. Ordinary bulky cargoes were relegated early in history to the relatively slow but capacious sail-propelled vessels.

But other means of mechanical propulsion were tried. Before the Christian era, paddle-wheels turned by oxen propelled some of the boats that carried the Roman legions of Claudius Caudex to Sicily. A bas-relief of about A.D. 527 showed a war vessel having three pairs of paddle-wheels each turned by two oxen. On the opposite side of the world, Chinese sources mention man-operated paddle-wheels on warships in the 7th, 12th and 16th centuries. A manuscript of 1430 in Munich describes a warship fitted with four paddle-wheels mounted on crank-shafts turned by four men and later in the century Leonardo da Vinci sketched many schemes for propelling ships. These are obviously but a few of the early steps in man's search for a truly mechanical method of ship propulsion.

JONATHAN HULLS'S MACHINE — 1736

Although Hulls's "machine" or towboat was probably never built, his proposal was a practical application of Newcomen's engine. The scheme called for a paddle-wheel supported by a framework extending from the stern of the boat, a boiler forward, and an atmospheric engine located about amidships. Two driving wheels mounted on the paddle-wheel shaft were connected to that wheel by ratchets and to the engine by a system of ropes and pulleys. After each power stroke of the engine, the driving wheel was returned by a weight in the rope drive system. Thus, with one engine, continuous motion of the paddle-wheel could be obtained.

Men or animals provided the power for mechanical propulsion schemes proposed in England by William Bourne in 1578, David Ramsey in 1630, and Thomas Toogood and James Hayes in 1661 and 1662. Toogood and Hayes patented a scheme of jet propulsion employing a large bellows. None of these proposals, however, led to any practical results.

One of the first to recognize the power of steam and that it might be employed to move vehicles on land and vessels at sea was Saloman de Caus in France (1576-1635). Denis Papin, a French physicist (1647-1714), was among the earliest experimenters with steam engines. In 1690 he described a steam cylinder fitted with a piston—steam pressure in the cylinder moved the piston out and when this steam was condensed, atmospheric pressure outside moved the piston back. Papin proposed to fit three or four such cylinders in a boat and to obtain rotary motion of a paddle-wheel shaft by a toothed rack and ratchet mechanism. He apparently constructed a small steam-propelled carriage but in 1707, when he sailed in his own paddle-wheel driven boat down the Fulda river on his way to the mouth of the Weser, the wheels were turned by the crew and not by steam. Boatmen on the Weser, jealous of their rights on that river, confiscated his boat at Münden. Papin did construct a successful steam-operated water pumping device in which steam acted on a piston floating in a chamber on the water's surface.

Thomas Newcomen in England (1663-1729), following the ideas of Papin and others, completed in 1705 a successful "atmospheric" engine. Where Papin had proposed heating water directly in the cylinder to produce steam, unworkable from the practical point of view, Newcomen employed a separate boiler. To effect the return or "atmospheric" power stroke of the engine, the steam in his engine was condensed by a jet of cold water. Newcomen's engine was soon widely used for pumping water out of English coal and tin mines.

Dr. John Allen of England obtained in 1729 a patent for a scheme of jet propulsion using steam power. Two Newcomen atmospheric engines were to give motion by forcing water out through the stern of a vessel. His scheme was said to have been tried on a canal boat but men and not steam operated the pumps. Steam power was again proposed in 1736 when Jonathan Hulls obtained a patent for the "Invention of a machine for carrying ships and vessels out of or into any harbour or river against wind and tide". His "machine" would today be called a stern-wheel towboat.

Few men of the period, however, seriously considered applying steam power to the propulsion of ships. In a contest in 1753 for a prize offered by the Royal Academy of Sciences, Paris, the winner, the famous Daniel Bernoulli, proposed a system of large hinged paddles attached to a ship's side while Leonhard Euler and Mathon de la Cour proposed side paddle-wheels operated by geared or rope drives from capstans or windlasses. All were to be operated by man power as horse-driven machinery took up too much room to say nothing of the water and hay required for the horses. Yet in the 1755 Mémoires de la Société Royale de Nancy, Canon Joseph Gautier showed that the strength of a ship's crew was insufficient to give it great speed and that the only means of obtaining speed was by employing a steam engine. He calculated that food for 260 oarsmen would exceed the volume of coal required for a Newcomen engine to do the same amount of work.

By 1772 in France, an actual steam-propelled boat was being constructed. Comte J.B. d'Auxiron equipped this boat in 1774 with a two-cylinder atmospheric engine but misfortune struck, the boat sank before trials could be held and the project was abandoned. Jacques C. Périer operated a small steamboat on the Seine in 1775 but

BLASCO DE GARAY

Because of a note published in 1825 it was believed for many years that steam-driven paddle-wheels had been employed on a Spanish ship as early as 1543. The Spanish sea captain Blasco de Garay had submitted to Emperor Charles V a proposal for moving ships without the use of oars or sails. His scheme was tried with success in Barcelona harbor in June 1543 on the 209 ton ship TRINIDAD. *The report of the experiment mentioned clouds of steam. In 1858 published results of investigations showed that the ship was moved by two paddle-wheels each operated by 25 men and that the steam came from a large tank of hot water carried on deck for defensive purposes.*

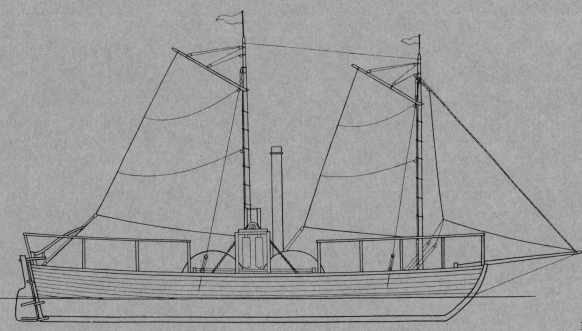

MILLER AND SYMINGTON — 1788

After having experimented with boats moved by the power of men or horses applied to paddle-wheels, Patrick Miller decided to try steam power. William Symington, who was then working on a steam-propelled carriage, built an engine having two vertical Newcomen atmospheric cylinders, 4 in. (0,102 m) diameter by about 18 in. (0,457 m) stroke, which was installed in one hull of a twin-hulled boat. The boiler was placed in the other hull. Two chain-driven paddle-wheels placed in tandem were fitted between the hulls. The boat, about 25 ft. (7,620 m) long and 7 ft. (2,134 m) wide, moved at about 5 miles (8,05 km) per hour on trials in October 1788. On 26 December 1789 a Forth and Clyde Canal boat fitted with similar machinery also performed successfully.

the vessel's power was so small that it could not breast the river's current. Marquis Claude de Jouffroy d'Abbans is generally accepted as the successful pioneer in the application of steam power to boats. In June 1778 on the Doubs river, he tried unsuccessfully a 43 ft. (13,106 m) 9 ton boat fitted with two flapped paddles working like duck's feet, one on each side of the boat, which were operated by chains from two inclined Newcomen atmospheric cylinders. His principles were correct but the engine and mechanism were too inefficient.

Experimental success came in 1783 with Jouffroy's second boat named PYRO-SCAPHE. Built of wood at Ecully, near Lyons, this boat was propelled by machinery constructed by Messrs. Frèrejean et Cie. of Lyons. A horizontal double-acting cylinder, 25.6 in. (0,650 m) diameter by 77 in. (1,956 m) stroke, was enclosed in the boiler and its piston rod was connected to a double ratchet device to produce the continuous rotating motion of the side paddle-wheels. These were 13.1 ft. (3,992 m) in diameter and had eight radial paddles or floats each.

PYROSCAPHE was operated successfully on 15 July 1783 when she managed to move against the current of the Saône river for 15 minutes. The boiler proved unable to generate sufficient steam for extended operations. Jouffroy failed in an attempt to gain government support for his work and the French Revolution put an end to his experiments for a time. On 23 April 1816, he obtained a patent for a steamboat design and then built CHARLES-PHILIPPE which he operated on the Seine.

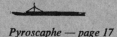

Pyroscaphe — page 17

On the western side of the Atlantic, John Fitch presented a steamboat model with drawings and a description of his proposed engine to the American Philosophical Society in Philadelphia on 27 September 1785. This scheme called for an endless paddle-chain on the port side of the boat and a single leeboard on the starboard side to keep the boat on course. There is no record that a boat so propelled was ever tried.

Fitch organized a company which provided the funds for the 45 ft. (13,716 m) long steamboat first tried on the Delaware river in August 1787; other successful runs were made before the winter lay up. She was propelled at about 3 miles (4,84 km) per hour by six overhead supported paddles on each side which were given a reciprocating motion by a single-cylinder double-acting condensing steam engine. Its horizontal cylinder was 12 in. (0,305 m) diameter by 36 in. (0,914 m) stroke. This engine success-fully propelled a 60 ft. (18,288 m) boat fitted with stern paddles on several trips during the second half of 1768. An 18 in. (0,457 m) diameter cylinder was substituted for further experiments in 1789 and in the spring of 1790 a carefully measured speed of 8 miles (12,87 km) per hour was attained.

The following advertisement appeared in Philadelphia newspapers on 14 July 1790:

"The STEAMBOAT is now ready to take passengers and is intended to set off from Arch Street Ferry, in Philadelphia, every Monday, Wednesday, and Friday for Burlington, Bristol, Bordentown, and Trenton, to return on Tuesdays, Thursdays, and Saturdays..."

During the remainder of the summer this boat named EXPERIMENT made 14 trips covering over 2000 miles (3219 km) in commercial service with few breakdowns. This service, however, operated at a loss, a larger steamboat was damaged in a storm before completion, and Fitch's steamboat company fell to pieces.

EXPERIMENT was propelled by three "duck leg" paddles at the stern operated by cranks and rods from a horizontal shaft fitted across the square stern of the hull. The engine was geared to a shaft having sprocket wheels and a chain or rope drive transmitted power to the stern shaft that operated the paddles. Steam was provided by a so-called pipe or tubular boiler in which the hot gases passed through tubes surrounded by water. Thus Fitch was able to eliminate some three tons of brickwork that normally was fitted around the common externally-fired boilers of the period.

James Rumsey of Berkeley Springs, Virginia, produced a steam-driven boat in 1787 which was a return to the jet principle. His engine consisted of a steam cylinder mounted directly over a water-pump cylinder with a common piston rod. He, like Fitch, employed a tubular boiler to supply steam. On 3 December 1787 Rumsey gave a public demonstration of his boat during which she was operated on the Potomac river for about two hours, attaining a speed of 3 miles (4,83 km) per hour against the cur-rent. After a second trial on 11 December, the boat was laid up and never moved again.

In 1788 and again in 1789, Patrick Miller of Dalswinton in Scotland conducted successful trials of twin-hulled boats fitted with engines built by William Symington. No further experiments were conducted as Symington's machinery apparently was not capable of the certainty of operation necessary for commercial application.

In the U.S.A., somewhere between 1790 and 1792, Samuel Morey produced a small steamboat that successfully moved against the current of the upper Connecticut river. After several other successful experiments in New York he built in 1797 a steamboat on the Delaware which was fitted with side paddle-wheels. Using Morey's words—"The shaft ran across the boat with a crank in the middle, worked from the beam of the engine with a shackle bar..."—an arrangement far in advance mechani-cally of the various schemes of his predecessors. This boat was exhibited at Philadelphia

Experiment — page 18

JAMES WATT 1736-1819

This famous Scottish engineer and inventor improved the efficiency of the Newcomen atmospheric engine by employ-ing a separate chamber in which to condense the steam. His first steam engine patent of 1769 also covered the use of steam jackets and insulation to keep the cylinder hot and an air pump worked off the engine to produce a vacuum in the separate condenser. His second patent of 1781 dealt with a scheme to obtain rotary motion thus making steam engines useful for more than pumping operations. In 1782 he patented the double-acting engine and the use of the expansive power of steam. Among Watt's other inventions were a linkage to obtain parallel motion of a piston rod without guides and the indicator, a device which measured the work done by a steam engine.

but nothing came of the project. Morey's backers ran into financial difficulties and he turned to other inventions which included an internal combustion engine. It is possible that this engine was installed in 1820 in a small boat named AUNT SALLY.

Thomas, Lord Dundas of Kerse, a governor of the Forth and Clyde Canal, attempted to obtain something better than horses for towing canal boats. Remembering the experiments of Miller and Symington, he commissioned the latter in 1801 to build a steam-propelled towboat for the canal. Symington had not worked on steamboats since Miller withdrew his support but new plans were soon drawn and patented. The result was CHARLOTTE DUNDAS, probably the first practical steamboat. Her wooden hull, built by Alexander Hart, had a single paddle-wheel in a covered stern recess. The resulting double stern was fitted with two rudders controlled by a horizontal steering wheel located near the bow. Her boiler was located to starboard and her 10 h.p. engine to port. The latter had a single horizontal double-acting cylinder 22 in. (0,559 m) in diameter by 4 ft. (1,219 m) stroke. The piston rod was guided in slides and the connecting rod was attached to a crank on the paddle-wheel shaft as on Morey's 1797 boat.

In March 1802, CHARLOTTE DUNDAS towed two 70-ton canal boats on the Forth and Clyde Canal against a strong head wind, when nothing else would move, a distance of 19½ miles (31,38 km) in six hours. The owners of the canal decided, however, that despite this successful trial, the damage to the canal's banks by a steamboat's wash would more than offset any gain from its use. CHARLOTTE DUNDAS was laid up in a creek off the canal and so ended a very promising experiment; she was finally broken up in 1861.

In attempting to describe the steamboat that gained the monopoly in New York waters for Robert Fulton and Robert R. Livingston, the first commercially successful steamboat, one researcher stated that he was "confronted not by a dearth of facts but by a superabundance of misinformation". Much of the misinformation arises from the fact that after the boat's few successful trips in 1807, Fulton rebuilt her for the 1808 season and further that Fulton's patent specifications of 1809 and 1810 do not conform with what is known of the boat.

There is further confusion regarding this boat's name. Although known in textbooks for years as CLERMONT, her official enrollment of 1807 reads "the ship or vessel called the North River Steamboat"; her second enrollment of 1808 reads "the ship or vessel called the North River Steamboat of Clermont". In spite of continuing arguments, she will here be called NORTH RIVER. As may be deduced from the previous pages, Robert Fulton did not "invent" this steamboat. His great contribution was his ability to combine the work of earlier experimenters into a successful boat, to improve the boat and its machinery as he went along, and to build effective steamboats at will.

The wooden hull of the first NORTH RIVER was constructed by Charles Brownne at Corlear's Hook, New York. Although similar in many respects to boats used for inland water navigation under oars and sail—long, narrow, shoal, flat bottomed, flaring sides, and with little sheer—Fulton based her proportions on resistance tests made by Colonel Mark Beaufoy between 1793 and 1798. Errors in his calculations, however, led him to make her so long and narrow that she was unsafe. NORTH RIVER'S 20 h.p. engine was constructed by Messrs. Boulton, Watt & Co. and was the third of their engines allowed to be exported from England. It had one vertical cylinder, 24 in. (0,610 m) in diameter by 4 ft. (1,219 m) stroke, which drove through bell-cranks and

Charlotte Dundas — page 19

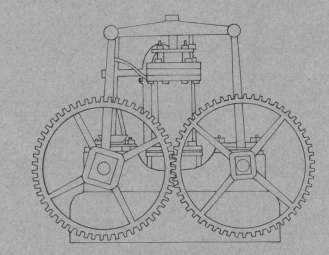

STEVENS'S TWIN-SCREW STEAMBOAT — 1804

Another early experimenter with steamboats in the U.S.A. was Colonel John Stevens of Hoboken who patented a tubular boiler in 1791. In 1802 he produced a "rotary" steam engine consisting of vanes on a shaft which were enclosed in a cylindrical casing; it drove a screw-propelled flat-bottom boat at about 4 miles (5,43 km) per hour. A believer in high pressure steam and screw propulsion, he built in 1803-04 the launch LITTLE JULIANA. The engine consisted of a single vertical cylinder, 4½ in. (0,114 m) diameter by 9 in. (0,229 m) stroke, with an overhead crosshead from which two connecting rods drove gearing attached to twin propeller shafts. This launch also made a speed of about 4 miles (5,43 km) per hour.

gearing designed by Fulton two side paddle-wheels 15 ft. (4,572 m) in diameter each having eight radial floats. Steam was supplied by an externally fired copper boiler mounted on brick-work.

The first NORTH RIVER left her temporary wharf in Greenwich Village, New York, at 1:00 P.M. on Monday, 17 August 1807, for a trip to Albany and arrived back in New York on Friday, 21 August. One viewer up the river described her as "looking precisely like a backwoods saw-mill mounted on a scow and set on fire". Kept as light as possible for this experimental voyage, Fulton now boarded in the sides, decked over the boiler and engine, furnished each cabin with twelve berths, and strengthened all the ironwork. Because of deliberate damage by sailing packets, the paddle-wheels were soon enclosed in heavy frames and they were also covered to prevent the splash of the paddles from drenching the passengers on deck.

This NORTH RIVER set off on her first commercial voyage on 4 September 1807 and operated on the Hudson until mid-November of that year when she was laid up for the winter. Unlike Fitch's EXPERIMENT, NORTH RIVER paid a profit but operating experience had shown that she would have to be strengthened for the next season. Rebuilt and enlarged, NORTH RIVER of 1808 was for all practical purposes a new boat which served on the Hudson until withdrawn in 1814. By 1810 Fulton had two more steamboats on the Hudson—CAR OF NEPTUNE and RARITAN—and in 1811 he designed NEW ORLEANS which became the first steamboat to operate on the Mississippi.

Henry Bell of Scotland holds the honor of introducing commercial steam navigation on the eastern side of the Atlantic. Proprietor of the Helensburgh Baths on the Clyde down-stream from Glasgow, Bell first thought of his steamboat as a means of attracting clients to his hotel. He did not believe that a steamboat necessarily would be an improvement over the usual sailing packets or horse-drawn stages but it would provide an additional form of amusement. After correspondence with Fulton, Bell had Messrs. John Wood & Co. of Glasgow build COMET in 1812. The lines drawing for her hull shows that her form was that of the typical small sailing packet of her day. She had two saloons which were far from luxurious. The second-class saloon forward provided only sitting headroom on benches along the sides but passengers could stand up under the small deck house covering the first-class one aft.

John Robertson of Glasgow constructed COMET's vertical single-cylinder, double-acting, jet-condensing engine which had a nominal horse-power of four. The original cylinder had a bore of 11.5 in. (0,292 m) and a stroke of 16 in. (0,406 m) but after a few months of service a new cylinder having a 1 inch (0,025 m) larger bore was fitted. Two side rods drove a pair of half side-levers from which a connecting rod transmitted power to a crankshaft. This was geared to two paddle shafts which had four radial paddles at each end. These gave trouble and were replaced by a single paddle-wheel on each side which propelled COMET at a speed of about 6 knots (11,12 km/hr.).

COMET's externally fired horizontal boiler set in brick-work was supplied by David Napier at a cost of £52. The funnel, 12 in. (0,305 m) in diameter and 25 ft. (7,620 m) tall, served also as a mast to carry a square sail; a staysail could be set on the fore stay.

On trials in August 1812, COMET steamed about 20 miles (32,19 km) in 3½ hours. A passenger service between Glasgow and Greenock proved financially unsuccessful and in 1813 Bell sent COMET on various trips around the coasts of Scotland. These trips created the desired interest in steam navigation and by 1815 ten steamboats were plying as packets on the Clyde. In 1816 COMET operated on the Firth of Forth and

North River — page 20

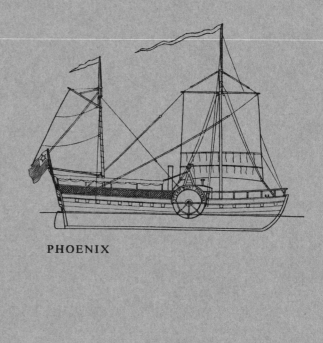

PHOENIX

Comet — page 21

PHOENIX — 1808

101 × 16 × 6.75 feet
30,784 × 4,877 × 2,057 m

Because of the Fulton-Livingston monopoly on the waters of the state of New York, PHOENIX became the first steamboat to venture upon the open sea. Built and engined in 1808 by Colonel John Stevens, she was forced to leave the Hudson river and, between 10 and 23 June 1808, she made the open sea voyage from New York harbor down the coast of New Jersey and up the Delaware to Philadelphia. PHOENIX operated between that city and Trenton until wrecked in 1814. Her original crosshead engine had two cylinders, 16 in. (0,406 m) diameter by 3 ft. (0,914 m) stroke but later in Philadelphia these were replaced by a single cylinder of 24 in. (0,610 m) in diameter and a flywheel was fitted to obtain smoother motion.

in 1818 Bell employed her to establish steam travel between Glasgow and the West Highlands. While on a voyage to Fort William in December 1820, COMET ran ashore at Craignish Point.

In 1962, the 150th anniversary of the building of COMET, a working reconstruction of her was built by a consortium of Clyde shipbuilding and engineering companies and operated on the Glasgow-Helensburgh route.

The first steam packet on the Thames and the first steamboat to cross the Channel to France was another vessel built on the Clyde. As MARGERY she was built by Messrs. Archibald MacLachlan & Co. for Glasgow merchants and launched in June 1814. In form and arrangement she followed the general pattern set by COMET—a typical sailing packet hull with one deck, one pair of paddle-wheels, and a tall funnel carrying a square sail. She also had a foremast which was not quite as tall as the funnel.

MARGERY's engine was of the side-lever type of 10 n.h.p. and was built by James Cook of Tradeston. Its single vertical cylinder was 22 in. (0,559 m) in diameter by 2 ft. (0,610 m) stroke. Steam at about 2 p.s.i. pressure (0,141 kg/cm²) was generated by a flat-sided iron boiler and was exhausted into a condenser. The paddle-wheels, 8.75 ft. (2,667 m) in diameter, had six radial floats each and turning at 32 revolutions per minute they gave MARGERY a speed of 6 knots (11,12 km/hr.).

Operated on the Clyde until November 1814, MARGERY was sold to London owners who started running her on the Thames between London and Gravesend on 23 January 1815. Her new owners soon ran into difficulties with the licensed watermen on the Thames who, under an old Act, had the exclusive right of carrying passengers on the river. The vessel's original captain had to be replaced by a freeman of the Watermen's Company and she was not allowed to go alongside a wharf at either end of her run but had to anchor in the stream while the watermen took her passengers to and from her in their wherries. MARGERY was out of service for repairs several times and was withdrawn at the end of the 1815 season.

Early in 1816, MARGERY was chartered or sold to Messrs. Andriel, Pajol et Cie. of Paris, refitted for service on the Seine, and renamed ELISE. After a stormy passage from the Thames around the coast to Newhaven in Sussex, ELISE left that port for Havre on 17 March 1816 against strong southerly head winds. This first Channel crossing by a steam-propelled vessel required seventeen hours. She stayed in Havre until 20 March and then proceeded up the Seine to Paris arriving there on the 29th. In spite of attempts to avoid it, ELISE and Jouffroy's CHARLES-PHILIPPE became competitors on the Seine; neither became a commercial success. The British records concerning ELISE ex-MARGERY were closed in October 1816; her timbers reportedly could be seen on the banks of the Seine as late as 1888.

In spite of difficulties with the watermen, other steam packets appeared on the Thames and the run was extended to Margate which was becoming a popular holiday resort. One of these was CALEDONIA, built on the Clyde in 1815 by Messrs. John and Charles Wood, which came to the Thames in 1816. While COMET and MARGERY had hulls shaped like the normal sailing packets, CALEDONIA reportedly had a flat bottom and a square bilge. Her original machinery of 28 h.p. proved defective and she was soon laid up.

Although James Watt, the inventor, never invested in steamboats, his son James, Jr. purchased CALEDONIA in April 1817 and fitted her with new machinery of 32 h.p., new boilers, and new paddle-wheels. This new machinery differed from that of previous vessels in that it consisted of two engines working on paddle-shaft cranks set 90° apart, a great improvement over the single-cylinder engine. The cylinders of

Elise (Margery) — page 22

Caledonia — page 23

CALEDONIA's new engines were 23 in. (0,584 m) in diameter by 30 in. (0,762 m) stroke; the paddle-wheels with eight radial floats each were 13 ft. (3,962 m) in diameter

On 15 October 1817, CALEDONIA crossed the North Sea from Margate to the Scheldt, and reached Rotterdam the next day. On the 23rd, Mr. Watt took her on a pleasure trip up the Rhine—she was the first steamboat on that river—and arrived at Coblenz on 13 November. Because CALEDONIA drew 4 feet 6 inches (1,37 m) and the river was at a low stage the journey ended there. After her return to England, CALEDONIA was employed in some speed experiments and was sold in 1818 to Danish owners, thus becoming the first steam-propelled vessel in that country. She operated on the Copenhagen-Kiel run and occasionally served as the royal yacht; she was broken up in 1841.

In 1816, another English steamboat crossed the North Sea to the Netherlands. This was William Wager's DEFIANCE which left Margate on 9 May for Veere and eventually Rotterdam. Reports are confusing about this vessel but she was apparently built in 1815/16 by Messrs. John Wood & Co. for service on the Clyde out of Glasgow. In appearance she followed the general pattern set by the earlier Clyde steam packets with the characteristic tall funnel doubling as a mast and a shorter mast forward. Unlike the earlier boats, though, she had a long deck house which had three side windows forward of the machinery space and four aft. A permanent awning structure on this house abaft the funnel provided sheltered deck space for the passengers. DEFIANCE seems to have had the new double engine installation pioneered by Messrs. Boulton, Watt & Co. Hers, however, were constructed by Robertson with horizontal cylinders; they were rated at 14 h.p.

Upon DEFIANCE's arrival in Rotterdam, Wager was made an honorary citizen of the city and King Willem visited the little vessel. Wager asked for a concession to operate four steamboats on the inland waters of the Netherlands for the carriage of passengers and package freight and found merchants ready to invest in his project. Rotterdam, nevertheless, was at that time unwilling to grant him the operating rights requested because of the effect on established stage coach and passenger boat services and the same proved true at Amsterdam.

Defiance — page 24

HORSE-POWER

James Watt found it necessary to introduce a unit to express the power developed by his steam engines. As his engines were replacing horses to work mining and other machinery it was natural that the average work performed by a horse should be the basis. Taking nearly double the average value and using a standard steam pressure and piston speed Watt calculated a "nominal horse-power" (n.h.p.). Early steam engines actually delivered this power and it remained a satisfactory unit until steam pressures and piston speeds increased. When this occurred the Watt indicator provided a means for measuring actual cylinder steam pressures and by using actual piston speeds the power "indicated" could be determined—hence "indicated horse-power" (i.h.p.). The power of a steam turbine is measured by the twist in the shaft near the propeller hence "shaft horse-power" (s.h.p.). The i.h.p. of a reciprocating steam engine must be reduced about 8-10% for shaft bearing friction to arrive at its s.h.p. The power delivered by a Diesel engine is measured by a brake unit attached to the shaft coupling hence "brake horse-power" (b.h.p.).

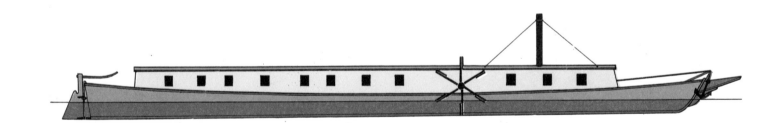

PYROSCAPHE · 1783

Marquis Claude de Jouffroy d'Abbans

148.5 × 14.8 feet ☾ 45,261 × 4,511 m

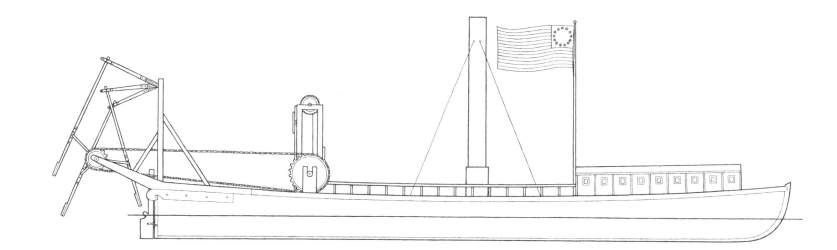

EXPERIMENT · 1788

John Fitch

60 × 12 feet ◖ 18,287 × 3,658 m

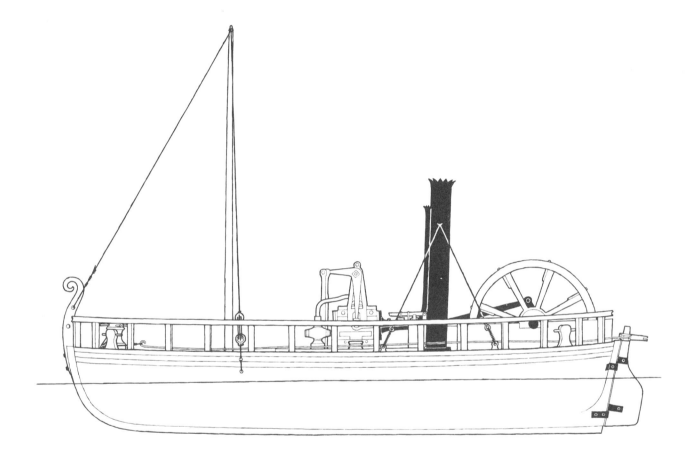

CHARLOTTE DUNDAS · 1801

Thomas, Lord Dundas

56 × 18 × 8 feet ◐ 17,068 × 5,486 × 2,438 m

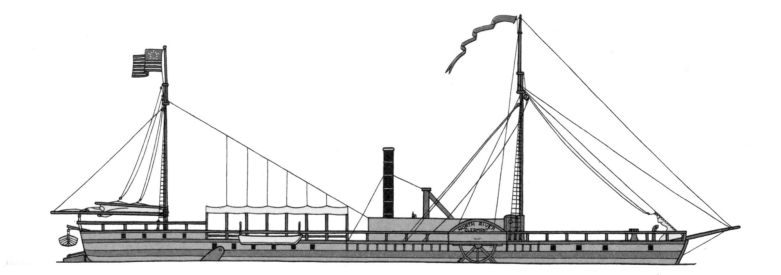

NORTH RIVER · 1807-1808

Robert Fulton and Robert R. Livingston

1807: 142 × 14 × 4 feet ℂ 79 T ℂ 43,280 × 4,267 × 1,219 m

1808: 149 × 17.92 × 7 feet ℂ 182 T ℂ 45,414 × 5,462 × 2,134 m

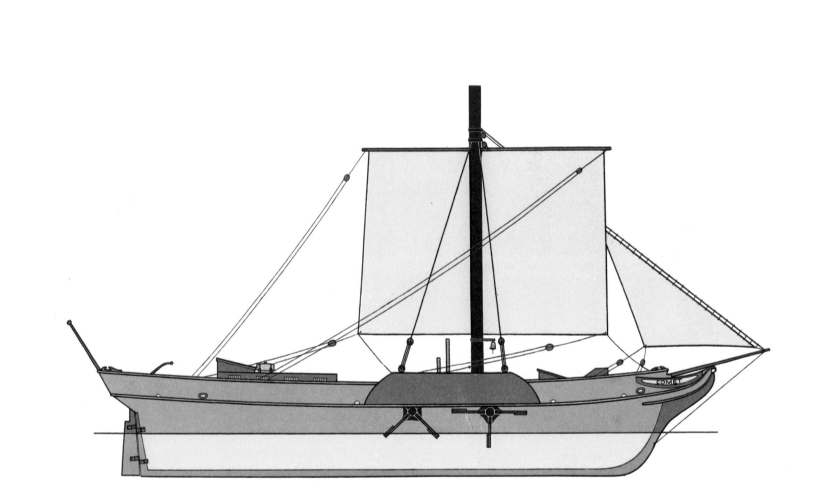

COMET · 1812

Henry Bell

43.5 × 11.25 × 5.6 feet ☾ 25 T ☾ 13,258 × 3,429 × 1,707 m

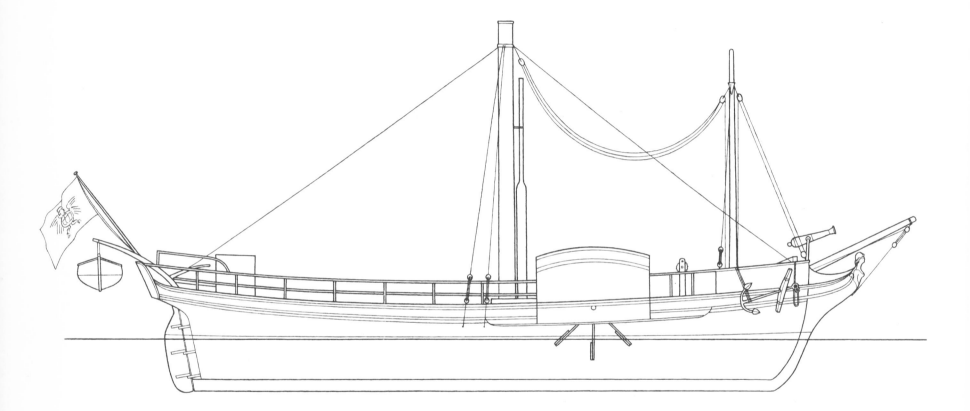

ELISE (MARGERY) · 1814

Andriel, Pajol et Cie. (Wm. Anderson and John McCubbin)

63 × 12 × 5.5 feet ◖ 38 T ◖ 19,202 × 3,658 × 1,676 m

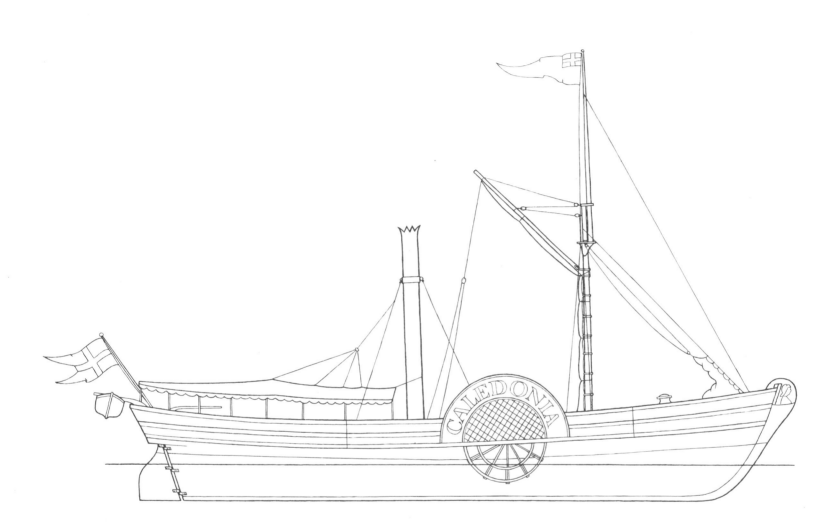

CALEDONIA · 1815

James Watt, Jr. — Steen Andersen Bille

94 × 27.67 × 9 feet ☾ 95 T ☾ 28,651 × 8,434 × 2,743 m

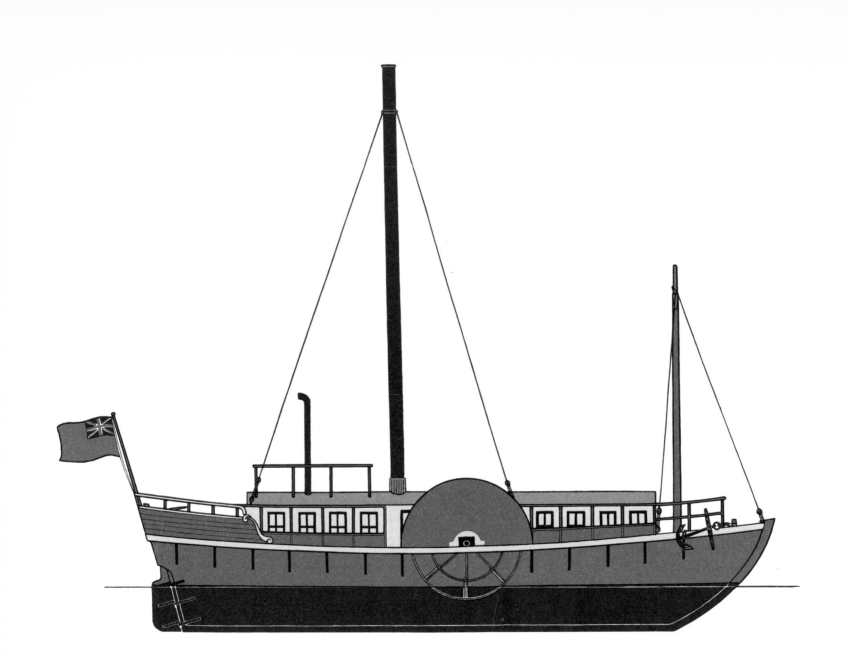

DEFIANCE · 1815-1816

William Wager

58.1 × 17.2 feet ◖ 51 T ◖ 17,709 × 5,242 m

157.0 × 33.5 × 10.25 feet
47,852 × 10,210 × 3,124 m

Robert Fulton's finest steamboat but not completed until after his death; her hull was designed by Henry Eckford and built by Isaac Webb. Her 75 h.p. engine had a single vertical cylinder 40 in. (1,016 m) diameter by 5 ft. (1,524 m) stroke which operated with a steam pressure of between 25 and 30 p.s.i. (1,758-2,109 kg/cm²). Paddle-wheels 18 ft. (5,486 m) in diameter drove the vessel at a speed of 8½ miles (13,67 km) per hour in still water. Axel Klinckowström, a Swedish nobleman who travelled in North America between 1818 and 1820, described her accommodations thus: "On the after deck is a lounge for female passengers which contains 24 berths... Under the deck aft is a
continued

These early steamboats that crossed the English Channel were soon followed by British engines and engineers as steamboat construction was started in various European countries. In 1816 John B. Humphreys installed a Boulton & Watt side-lever engine of 14 n.h.p. in PRINZESSIN CHARLOTTE VON PREUSSEN, the first steamboat to be built in Prussia. Her arrangement was similar to that of Patrick Miller's boat of 1788—twin hulls with a paddle-wheel working between them. These hulls were constructed of wood by John Rubie at Pichelsdorf near Spandau and launched on 14 September 1816. From stems to sterns one flush deck covered both hulls and the space between thus giving the passengers plenty of deck room; accommodations were arranged for the passengers below deck in each hull.

The Boulton & Watt engine in PRINZESSIN CHARLOTTE had one vertical cylinder 23.5 in. (0,597 m) diameter by 30 in. (0,764 m) stroke. Boulton & Watt also supplied her boiler but its disposition within the hulls is not known. She had one tall funnel which may also have served as a mast although there is no indication of a sail in the available illustrations of the vessel. PRINZESSIN CHARLOTTE was fitted with three rudders that were controlled by a large steering wheel located on deck aft. Designed for use on the Elbe, Havel, and Spree rivers she entered service on 6 November 1816.

Another early German steamboat was DIE WESER built in 1817 near Bremen for Friedrich Schroeder. She measured 85 ft. in length with a breadth of 14 ft. and a depth

Prinzessin Charlotte von Preussen — page 33

continued
spacious dining room with a row of two-high berths on each side; 100 to 120 passengers can be served in this room... A door from one end of the galley leads to the forward cabin in which there are three rows of two-high berths. Generally speaking, it can be said that the interior of the vessel and her fittings have an exquisite, and I can almost say, superfluous elegance... All stairs and floors are covered with carpets of painted fabric. In the ladies' lounge there are red satin curtains with rather pretty fringes, blankets and sheets of the best quality and all berths covered with white piqué spreads... The berths in the men's lounge are not so elegant but still quite handsome... As soon as supper is over, the passage fee is paid... After this procedure has taken place, berths are assigned by lot."

of 8 ft. (25,907×4,267×2,438 m). Messrs. Boulton, Watt & Company supplied both her engine and boiler. The engine, rated at 10 n.h.p., was of the side-lever type with one cylinder 22 in. (0,559 m) diameter by 24 in. (0,610 m) stroke. Boulton & Watt later supplied several 40 n.h.p. engines for steamboats built at Potsdam.

The first European country after England to build its own steamboats was Sweden where the transplanted British engineer Samuel Owen was active. Between 1801 and 1804 Baron Edelcrantz, a member of the Royal Swedish Custom Board, toured northern European countries and England studying public housekeeping problems. In England he purchased four steam engines and on returning to Sweden he brought some mechanics to assemble them. One of these was Samuel Owen who, after completing his work, returned to England with the intention of emigrating to the U.S.A. A letter from Baron Edelcrantz induced him to return to Sweden about the end of 1806. Following other employment Samuel Owen started his own engineering works at Kungsholmen in Stockholm in the spring of 1809. These, the first real engineering works in Sweden, were important perhaps more for the training of good skilled workmen than for the production of material goods.

Owen followed the progress of steam navigation in England and the U.S.A. obtaining descriptions and drawings of their steamboats and machinery which he was able to adapt and improve. He recognized the many disadvantages of paddle-wheels—that their efficiency is dependent on their immersion, that when a vessel heels one wheel may be lifted clear of the water, and that the wheels can be easily damaged by ice. Owen proposed to drive a steam vessel by a completely immersed wheel at the stern—a screw propeller. If power applied to a typical undershot water-wheel could move a ship he reasoned that it should be possible to turn something like a windmill under water to obtain the same result. After testing a small rowboat in which two men working a windlass turned a screw propeller through gearing he proceeded to adapt a larger sailing-type hull to test steam propulsion. The result was STOCKHOLMSHÄXAN (THE WITCH OF STOCKHOLM).

Taking a typical sloop from Lake Mälar Owen extended her keel aft and fitted a new sternpost thus providing an aperture for the propeller. Nearly 5 ft. (1,524 m) in diameter, the propeller had a cast iron frame and four wooden blades of birch fitted at an angle of 36° with the shaft line. The after end of the shaft was supported by the sternpost and it extended forward under the floor of a small cabin to the engine room.

According to one source STOCKHOLMSHÄXAN's 4 h.p. engine had a single oscillating cylinder turning the shaft through gearing because the limited space would not allow a fixed cylinder engine. A sketch made many years later by Samuel Owen's son shows, however, a single vertical cylinder with return connecting rods working cranks on a shaft passing under the cylinder. This may have been the arrangement of other early engines built by Owen. As customary at the time a flywheel was fitted to equalize the motion of the engine. Steam was supplied by a single internally-fired flue-type boiler whose size was limited by the available space. The smoke was carried off by a well-stayed funnel 16 ft. (4,877 m) high which was fitted with a water jacket at its lower end. STOCKHOLMSHÄXAN had a bowsprit and two masts of nearly equal height; the fore mast carried a square sail and the mizzen a gaff sail. The drawing of her is based on a modern model; no one knows her exact appearance.

Trials were held in July 1816 on a measured course of 180 fathoms (329,173 m) and it was found that the vessel's speed was 4 knots (7,41 km/hr.). It was also found, as expected, that the boiler was too small for sustained operation; the engine slowed down and finally stopped until a new head of steam could be raised. Owen concluded,

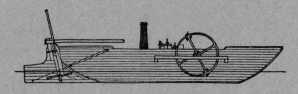

ELIZABETH — 1815

72.0 × 15.8 feet
21,945 × 4,816 m

The pioneer Russian steamboat that operated on the Neva river providing daily service between St. Petersburg (Leningrad) and Kronstadt. Robert Fulton had planned to add foreign monopolies to his monopoly on New York waters but Charles Baird, the English operator of a foundry in St. Petersburg, built ELIZABETH in 1815 and obtained the twenty year privilege of furnishing the city with commercial steamboat service. After experiments with a small boat fitted with a 4 h.p. engine Baird rebuilt a double-ended canal barge and installed a 20 h.p. side-lever engine having one cylinder 18 in. (0,457 m) diameter by 21 in. (0,533 m) stroke. An externally-fired boiler was located abaft the engine. To carry off the smoke ELIZABETH had what can only be described as a chimney—it was square in section and built of brick. ELIZABETH was propelled by two 12 ft. (3,658 m) paddle-wheels each having four gear-operated feathering floats which gave her a speed of about 6 miles (9,66 km) per hour.

The Witch of Stockholm — page 34

SAVANNAH — 1818 — 320 T

98.5 × 25.8 × 14.2 feet
30,022 × 7,855 × 4,328 m

SAVANNAH, the first ship to employ steam power during an Atlantic crossing, was converted while on the ways from a sailing packet ship. Stateroom berths were provided for 32 passengers and there were two saloons. She carried a full ship rig crossing topgallant yards with royals set flying and her single funnel had a swivel elbow top so as to direct smoke and sparks away from the sails and rigging. Her 90 i.h.p. machinery was definitely
continued

however, that a long, narrow, screw-propelled vessel of from 32 to 40 tons powered with an engine of from 10 to 15 h.p. could equal the speed of the paddle steamers in England and the U.S.A.

While tests were being conducted with STOCKHOLMSHÄXAN Samuel Owen built two other steamboats—EXPERIMENT for the Swedish crown prince Carl Johan and AMPHITRITE for his own use. During the 1820's a number of other steamers were built in Stockholm including the paddle-wheeler YNGVE FREY, a 30 ton vessel 91 ft. (27,736 m) long powered by a 22 n.h.p. engine. She operated on Lake Mälar between Stockholm and Arboga and was made famous in Scandinavia by Carl Jonas Love Almqvist's novel "Det går an" (It Will Do).

continued

auxiliary to her sails. Its single cylinder, 40⅜ in. (1,026 m) diameter by 5 ft. (1,524 m) stroke, was inclined at 20⁰ to permit a direct connection to the paddle shaft. The steam pressure was about 2 p.s.i. (0,141 kg/cm²). The paddle-wheels, 16 ft. (4,877 m) in diameter, had ten radial arms arranged to fold up like a fan and in 20 minutes they could be uncoupled for carrying on deck when not in use. With the paddle-wheels turning at 16 r.p.m. she had a speed of about 4 knots (7,41 km/hr.) in calm weather. Although SAVANNAH was intended for coastwise service her owners, the Savannah Steam Ship Company, decided, because of a business depression, to try to sell her abroad.

continued

SAVANNAH

Another British-built engine was installed in the first steam vessel to operate in the Mediterranean—FERDINANDO PRIMO. Captain Pierre Andriel, who in 1816 had taken ELISE ex MARGERY across the Channel from England to France to run on the Seine, was not able to make a commercial success of that operation. In 1818 he turned to Italy and the Mediterranean to try another steamboat venture. He formed the Società Napoletana Pietro Andriel and had FERDINANDO PRIMO's wooden hull built in the Stanislao Filosa shipyard near Forte Vigliena; she was launched on 24 June 1818. Accommodations were arranged for 50 passengers in a public saloon forward and there were 16 private cabins aft. A painting preserved in Naples shows her with a three-masted rig.

It is believed that James Cook of Tradeston, Scotland, furnished FERDINANDO PRIMO's 50 h.p. side-lever engines which had two vertical cylinders 27 in. (0,686 m) diameter by 3 ft. (0,914 m) stroke. One flat-sided iron flue boiler having one furnace supplied steam at about 2 p.s.i. (0,141 kg/cm²). Her 12 ft. (3,658 m) diameter paddle-wheels, located well forward, were constructed with iron spokes and rims; each was fitted with eight radial floats. At 22 r.p.m. they gave her a speed of 6 knots (11,12 km/hr.) at which speed she reportedly burned two tons of coal a day.

Under the command of Don Guiseppe Libetta and with a British mechanic aboard, FERDINANDO PRIMO left Naples on 27 September 1818 bound for Genoa at which port she attracted considerable public attention; she stopped en route at Livorno. Leaving Genoa on 30 October with ten passengers she arrived in Marseilles on 4 November being the first steam vessel to enter that port. Information concerning other voyages is very vague. In March 1820 FERDINANDO PRIMO was dismantled and scrapped.

After the visit of DEFIANCE to Rotterdam in 1816 several years elapsed before steps were taken to establish steamboat service in the Netherlands. Finally in 1823 Gerhard M. Roentgen and Cornelius van Vollenhoven founded the Nederlandsche Stoomboot Maatschappij to operate steamboats between Rotterdam and Antwerp; the incorporation papers were approved on 10 November 1823. Service was later established between Rotterdam, Nijmegen, and Cologne and eventually overseas to other countries.

When the company was organized Roentgen was still a naval officer but the king granted him a special discharge so that he might work on the development of steam vessels. He was responsible for the technical direction and construction survey of the company's first vessel NEDERLANDER. She was by no means an experimental vessel like so many of the early boats in other countries as Roentgen was able to draw on the accumulated experience of the English and U.S.A. builders.

During NEDERLANDER's construction period Roentgen submitted a prize winning paper to the Provinciaal Utrechts Genootschap (Society) in which he described and presented a drawing of a steam vessel with a 32 h.p. engine specially designed for carrying passengers on the Zuiderzee and the Maas, Rhine, and Scheldt rivers. He noted that the proposed hull lines were similar to those of Fulton's best boats but that the arrangement of the vessel followed English practice. As the early steamboats of the Netherlands were employed on protected inland waters it is not surprising that their forms were based on those used in the U.S.A. rather than the sailing vessel types employed in the rougher coastal waters of Great Britain. Roentgen's paper also contained descriptions and drawings for a ferry boat at Moerdijk—this was of WILHELMINA already in service—for a towboat to serve on the Rhine, and for an

continued
There were reasons for believing that a sale could be made to Russia. After a March 1819 trial trip in New York waters SAVANNAH proceeded to her home port employing her machinery for 41 hours of the 8½ day passage. With no cargo or passengers she started her eastbound Atlantic crossing under sail and steam at 5:00 A.M. on 24 May 1819; at 8:00 A.M. the paddle-wheels were taken on deck. After recoaling at Kinsale, she arrived in Liverpool on 20 June, 27 days 11 hours out; her engine was used about 85 hours during the crossing. Twenty five days later, SAVANNAH sailed for Stockholm where the king's offer of $100,000 in hemp and iron was declined and she continued on to St. Petersburg but a sale to the Russians could not be arranged. The high price of
continued

Ferdinando Primo — page 35

continued
European coal forced her to return home under sail but her engine was employed as she entered the mouth of the Savannah river. An attempt to sell SAVANNAH to the United States government also failed and in 1820 she was sold at auction. With her machinery removed she became a sailing-packet on the Savannah-New York run and ended her career on the shores of Long Island near Moriches on 5 November 1821. In view of her record it requires a stretch of the definition to classify SAVANNAH as a
continued

Nederlander — page 36

continued
"steam ship" but her machinery did operate without a breakdown during the periods of steaming. She was important in her day, however, as an indication, which few recognized, of the shape of things to come.

ocean-going steamship. Inasmuch as NEDERLANDER was the only steamboat under construction in the Netherlands at the time of the writing of the paper it is surmised that the first vessel described was based on her dimensions and details.

NEDERLANDER's hull offered no problems and was built in the yard operated by the widow of J. Hoogendijk at Capelle aan de IJssel. With the machinery, however, things were different. John Cockerill of Liége had built the engine for a second ferry boat at Moerdijk which, while considered of satisfactory construction, was not as good as the then current English engines. To serve as models for future construction two 20 h.p. engines were ordered from Henry Maudslay in England. While the government of the Netherlands was seeking to build up the country's industries by requiring the use of domestic products for vessels flying the Netherland's flag permission was granted the Nederlandsche Stoomboot Maatschappij to employ the English engines in their first two boats. Thus NEDERLANDER was fitted with a 20 h.p. Maudslay engine.

The trial trip of NEDERLANDER to Antwerp was set for 31 May 1823 but off the island of Schouwen faulty packing in some of the steam lines forced her to return to Rotterdam. This unfortunate event disappointed a crowd of over 4000 waiting at Antwerp, some of whom had traveled from as far as Brussels and Louvain. After a second and more successful trial NEDERLANDER carried King Willem I from Flushing to Antwerp on 16 June 1823 on one of his journeys to the southern part of the country. In regular service she connected with the coaches from Brussels to Antwerp and from Rotterdam to The Hague. In 1825 she was used in some unsuccessful towing trials of sailing vessels which led, however, to the building of the towboat HERCULES in the same year. NEDERLANDER was lengthened and modernized in 1835 for passenger service on the Rhine.

In the early 1820's in both England and India there was interest in the possibility of using steam power to shorten the passage time between the two countries. To aid in the establishing of steamship service a committee of influential persons residing in Bengal worked with the government of India in 1823 to provide the means for rewarding anyone who should make two successful voyages by steamship between England and India. A prize of 20,000 rupees was finally offered for the establishment of permanent communications with Calcutta before the end of 1826 with the provision that the passage time should not exceed 70 days.

ENTERPRISE was purchased while on the stocks and fitted out for the voyage by a group formed to compete for the prize. A wooden paddle steamer with one flush deck and a raised poop she was built in 1824 by Messrs. Gordon & Company, Deptford. She carried a three-masted fore-and-aft rig with lug sails and had one tall thin funnel located just abaft her mainmast.

Messrs. Maudslay, Sons and Field constructed the 120 n.h.p. side-lever engines installed in ENTERPRISE; their two cylinders measured 42 in. (1,067 m) diameter by 4 ft. (1,219 m) stroke. Steam at about 3 p.s.i. (0,211 kg/cm²) pressure was supplied by one large copper flue-type boiler that weighted 32 tons and cost £7000. Considering that the vessel would be operating where repairs or replacements were then impossible it was believed that the copper boiler would give better continuous service than one of iron. The paddle-wheels were 15 ft. (4,572 m) diameter and normally operated at 22 r.p.m. Means were provided for locking the wheels when the vessel was proceeding under sail alone and seven floats could be removed from each wheel to reduce their drag.

RISING STAR — 1821 — 428 T

123.6 × 27.8 × 6.1 feet
37,672 × 8,473 × 1,859 m

RISING STAR, built for Thomas Cochrane (later the 10th Earl of Dundonald) for use in the Chilean revolution against Spain, was the first steam ship to head westerly across the Atlantic. Launched on 5 February 1821 she ran trials in June attaining a speed of about 5 or 6 knots (9,27-11,12 km/hr.), and finally, after many machinery alterations, she sailed from Gravesend on 22 October for Valparaiso. Springing a leak off Portugal, she put back to Cork for repairs and finally reached Valparaiso in April 1822, the first steam vessel in the Pacific. By that time Chile was free and RISING STAR never served as a warship. From 1824 until wrecked in 1830 she served

continued

Enterprise — page 37

continued

several owners in commercial operations. In her hold between the fore and main masts RISING STAR had two paddle-wheels enclosed in a watertight casing which was open to the sea by apertures in her bottom structure. Her engines of 70 n.h.p., constructed by Messrs. Maudslay, Sons and Field, had two cylinders about 42 in. (1,067 m) diameter by 36 in. (0,914 m) stroke. Steam at about 2 or 3 p.s.i. (0,141-0,211 kg/cm²) pressure was supplied by marine flue boilers; it is possible that she had four of these as she had two funnels placed athwartships. It is not known how much her engines were used on her voyage to Valparaiso.

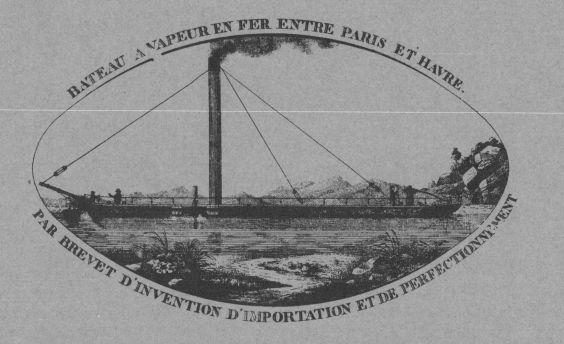

BATEAU A VAPEUR EN FER ENTRE PARIS ET HAVRE. PAR BREVET D'INVENTION D'IMPORTATION ET DE PERFECTIONNEMENT

106.8 × 17.2 × 7.2 feet
32,552 × 5,243 × 2,195 m

AARON MANBY was the first steamer to have an iron hull. The Horseley Ironworks, located near Tipton, Staffordshire, fabricated this hull in sections which were taken to London and assembled at the Surrey Docks, Rotherhithe, the work being completed on 30 April 1822. Successful trials were run on the Thames on 9 May 1822. Her single deck, flush from bow to stern, was of wooden construction and the interior of her cargo spaces was lined with wood. AARON MANBY's 30 n.h.p. engines had two oscillating cylinders about 27 in. (0,686 m) diameter by 3 ft. (0,914 m) stroke which operated on steam at 2 p.s.i. (0,141 kg/cm²) supplied by two flat-sided iron boilers. She had a 47 ft. (14,325 m) high funnel 3 ft. (0,914 m) in diameter which probably served as a mast. Although intended to have double paddle-wheels similar to those originally fitted on COMET she was finally fitted with one pair 12 ft. (3,658 m) in diameter that had four gear-operated feathering floats. At 25 r.p.m. these gave her a speed of 7 knots (12,97 km/hr.). AARON MANBY was built for a speculative venture to promote the use of iron steamers on the Seine. With a cargo of iron and linseed she crossed the Channel and arrived in Paris on 10 June 1822 being the first iron vessel to go to sea and the first vessel to sail directly from London to Paris. After years of service on the Seine she was at Nantes on the Loire in 1836 and was still working in 1842. Reported to be in good condition as late as 1849, AARON MANBY was finally broken up in 1855.

ENTERPRISE with 17 passengers aboard sailed from Falmouth on 16 August 1825 and 113 days later, having covered 13,700 miles (22046 km) she arrived in Calcutta. Although she failed to meet the stipulated time limit she was awarded half the prize. During the passage to India she was under steam power for 64 days, under sail for 39, and spent 10 days in ports refueling and taking on supplies. On leaving port she was loaded so deeply with coal that her speed was much less than expected. Her best average speeds for a day's run were about 8 knots (14,83 km/hr.) under steam alone, 8.79 knots (16,29 km/hr.) under sail alone, and 9.36 knots (17,46 km/hr.) using both steam and sails.

By the time ENTERPRISE arrived in Calcutta it was apparent that from a commercial point of view it was not feasible to continue the project and return the ship to England. She was sold to the government of Bengal for £40,000 which with the passage money from the 17 passengers very nearly reimbursed the promoters for their first cost. ENTERPRISE proved useful during the Burmese war and her speed in transmitting dispatches saved the government large sums of money. She was still in service in the 1840's having spent most of her time carrying the Indian mails to Suez to be sent overland to Alexandria.

While ENTERPRISE was being outfitted in England for her passage to India, a similar paddle steamer was under construction for the American and Colonial Steam Navigation Company of London. Built of wood by Messrs. J.H. & J. Duke at Dover, she was launched in September 1825 as CALPE but she never sailed in her intended commercial service between England, North America, and the West Indies. Purchased by the government of the Netherlands in October 1826 and renamed CURAÇAO she became the first steamship in that country's navy.

CURAÇAO's hull form was that of a typical sailing ship of the period with a short full entrance and a long run. She had but one deck which was flush except for a short

Curaçao — page 38

stepped section at the stern. Like ENTERPRISE she carried only fore-and-aft canvas being rigged as a three-masted schooner with her mizzen mast the shortest. Her single tall funnel was located just forward of the mainmast. As a naval vessel she had a row of painted ports along her sides which bore little relation to her actual armament as two ports appeared on each paddle box. At first CURAÇAO carried two 12-pounder carronades but this armament was later increased to five 36-pounders and two 6-pounders.

The engines installed in CURAÇAO were practically the same as those in ENTERPRISE and were also built by Messrs. Maudslay, Sons and Field. Rated at 100 n.h.p. with two cylinders 40 in. (1,016 m) diameter by 4 ft. (1,219 m) stroke they could develop about 150 i.h.p. One rectangular iron boiler with four furnaces generated steam at 3 p.s.i. (0,211 kg/cm²) pressure. The paddle-wheels, located well forward, were 15 ft. (4,572 m) diameter with 14 radial floats each; at 22 r.p.m. they drove the ship at about 8 knots (14,83 km/hr.). Special disconnecting cranks were fitted on the paddle shaft to allow the wheels to turn freely when the vessel was under sail with the engines stopped.

Before 1830 CURAÇAO made three voyages across the Atlantic to South America and the West Indies carrying passengers, mails, and valuable cargo. She sailed on her first voyage on 26 April 1827 from Hellevoetsluis near Rotterdam bound for Paramaribo, Surinam, with 57 passengers. She arrived after a passage of 27 days 11 hours and took five days more to go up to Curaçao, a total of 32 days 11 hours during which she employed steam power for 11 days 3 hours. On her return steam was used for 23½ days out of 29. The engines were stopped often to replace lost paddle floats and to move them out from their original positions to maintain the proper immersion as the vessel became lighter when coal was consumed. As sea water was used in the boiler, the fires had to be put out from time to time to permit the scraping out of the accumulated salt and to repair leaks.

CURAÇAO's second voyage with 68 passengers began on 1 March 1828 and her crossing to Surinam took 25 days. During her third voyage in 1829 she encountered several severe gales during which the engines worked without trouble. CURAÇAO then served in European waters until 1840 when she returned to the West Indies.

One of the important coastwise routes in Great Britain was that along the exposed eastern coast between London and Leith, the port for Edinburgh. The first steam vessel constructed specifically for a long open sea passage was CITY OF EDINBURGH. Built for the London-Leith run in 1821 by Messrs. Wigram and Green, London, she was a 401 ton wooden vessel having a length of 134 ft. 9 in., a breadth of 25 ft. 10 in. and a depth of 14 ft. 1 in. (40,867×7,784×4,292 m). She was powered by a pair of 40 n.h.p. Boulton & Watt engines. JAMES WATT, a 448 ton steamer for the same service, was built in the same year by Messrs. John Wood & Company, Glasgow. She was 141 ft. 9 in. long, 25 ft. 6 in. wide, and 16 ft. 7 in. deep. (43,204×7,772×5,055 m). Two 50 n.h.p. Boulton & Watt engines gave her a speed of 8.7 knots (16,12 km/hr.).

These were followed by other similar steam vessels and in 1826 there was constructed for this run, according to an old print, "The Largest and most superb Steam Vessel ever built in Europe". She was UNITED KINGDOM, the first steamer to be referred to by the press as a LEVIATHAN, and visitors travelled from all parts of Great Britain to view her. Her wooden hull, built by Messrs. Robert Steele and Son, Greenock, was unique in that the upper part flared out to envelope the paddle-wheels hence there were no outboard sponsons. She had one flush deck, a square stern with false quarter galleries, and a three-masted rig.

United Kingdom — page 39

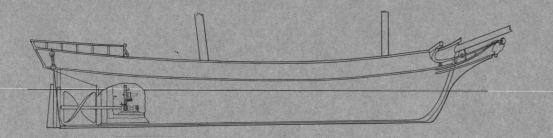

CIVETTA — 1829 — 33 T

64.47 × 12.86 × 6.89 feet
19,65 × 3,92 × 2,10 m

Joseph Ressel (1793-1857), a professional forester in Austria, sketched in 1812 an Archimedean screw propeller having two blades of half a turn each. This was about 25 years before Francis Pettit Smith in England produced the same type of propeller more or less by accident. Ressel was officially reprimanded for his early experiments but continued to work with screw propellers. After trying a small screw-propelled boat worked by two men in 1826 he obtained a patent in 1827. Later he ran some experiments on the Seine but failed to sign the necessary papers giving him operating rights. In 1829 he collaborated with Ottavio Fontana, a merchant of Trieste, in the building of CIVETTA to carry passengers between Trieste and Venice. Her fine-lined wooden hull was constructed by Vincenzo Zanon at the Panfili Yard in Trieste, and her 6 h.p. Watt-

continued

Constitutionen — page 40

continued

type engine came from Prince Schwarzenberg's Machine Works in St. Stephan, Styria. Through gearing this engine drove an 18 in. (0,457 m) diameter propeller at about 4.5 times the r.p.m. of the engine. At 11 o'clock on a July day in 1829 CIVETTA had her trial trip. It lasted five minutes. Soft solder used to connect sections of the main steam pipe from the boiler to the engine melted and allowed the steam to escape. Fearing an explosion the police forbade any further tests. There is evidence that an Englishman took CIVETTA to Sibenik on the Dalmatian coast and operated her successfully. Some connection exists between Ressel's 1812 work and the 1829 English patent issued to Charles Cummerow as the propeller and aperture drawings are the same.

UNITED KINGDOM was fitted with a pair of side-lever engines constructed by David Napier in Glasgow. With cylinders measuring about 51 in. (1,295 m) diameter by 5 ft. (1,524 m) stroke they were rated at 100 n.h.p. each; one source states that they were of 120 n.h.p. each. Rectangular iron flue boilers supplied steam at 3 p.s.i. (0,211 kg/cm²) pressure. 18 ft. (5,486 m) diameter paddle-wheels turning about 20 r.p.m. gave UNITED KINGDOM a speed of 8 knots (14,83 km/hr.). In order to eliminate the problems involved with the jet condensing of steam, Napier reportedly made an unsuccessful attempt to fit a surface condenser in UNITED KINGDOM. A successful surface condenser was finally patented by Samuel Hall in 1834 and employed on SIRIUS in 1837.

Because of geographical considerations the sea had provided for centuries the means for travel between the communities situated on the multitude of fjords that comprise the coastline of Norway. Steamship service along this coast began with the arrival of the English-built CONSTITUTIONEN in Fredricksvaern in December 1826. She was, of course, a paddle steamer and was carefully built of oak. It is possible that her hull was constructed on the Thames by William E. Evans who had established a sound reputation for well-built steamers for Thames river and Channel services. According to records at least one of his vessels went to Norway. A German traveller described her as one of the most beautiful and most comfortable vessels in Europe. Accommodations were provided aft for first-class passengers there being one saloon and two smaller cabins; second-class accommodations were forward. After the ship had been in service for a year or two the passengers' quarters were improved. As she was designed primarily for passenger service there was no cargo hold although she could carry some package freight.

It will be noted that a fairly standard arrangement is apparent in the steam vessels of the period. The boiler or boilers were located abaft the engines and the coal bunkers were on each side. This meant that as the coal was consumed the loss of weight changed the trim of the vessel but little. It also meant that with the paddle-wheels forward they were in a favorable position relative to the waves created by the vessel as it moved through the water. If further aft there was the chance that they would be working in a wave hollow without proper immersion; many early steamers failed to reach their expected speeds for this reason.

CONSTITUTIONEN was fitted with two side-lever engines constructed by Messrs. Maudslay, Sons and Field. They were rated at 30 n.h.p. each and drove her at about 7 miles (11,27 km) per hour. She was operated by a total crew of 13. Her captain and mate were both naval officers and there were six seamen to handle the sails and perform deck duties. An engineer with his assistant and three firemen operated the machinery. She carried mails and passengers along the Norwegian Coast until 1866.

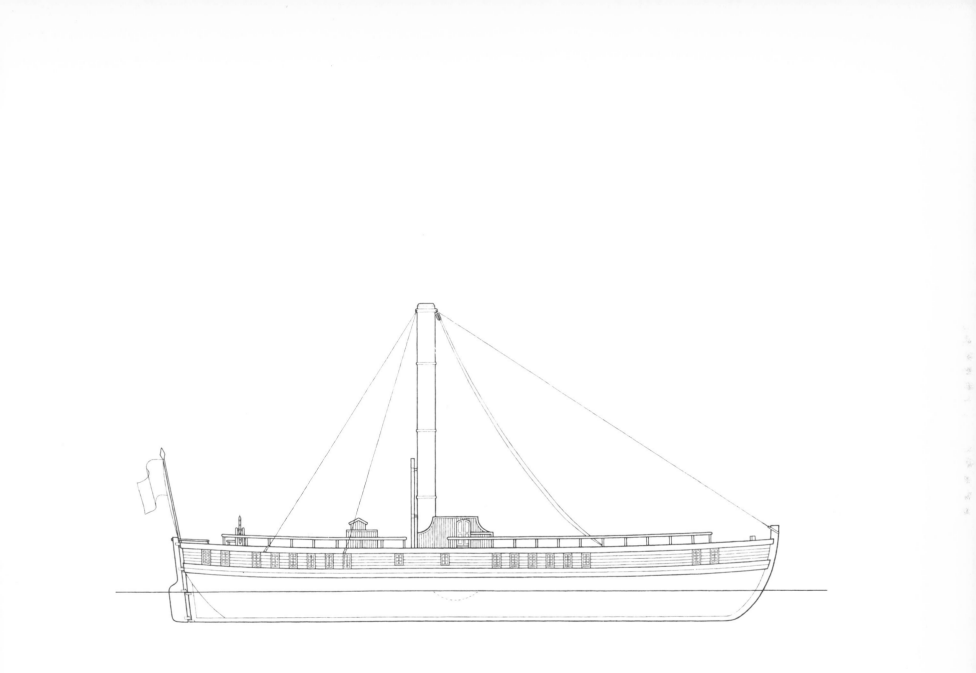

PRINZESSIN CHARLOTTE VON PREUSSEN · 1816

Patentierte Dampfschiff Gesellschaft

130.4 × 19.3 × 6 feet ◖ 236 **T** ◖ 39,745 × 5,883 × 1,829 m

STOCKHOLMSHÄXAN · 1816

Samuel Owen

31.25 × 11.5 feet ☾ 9,525 × 3,505 m

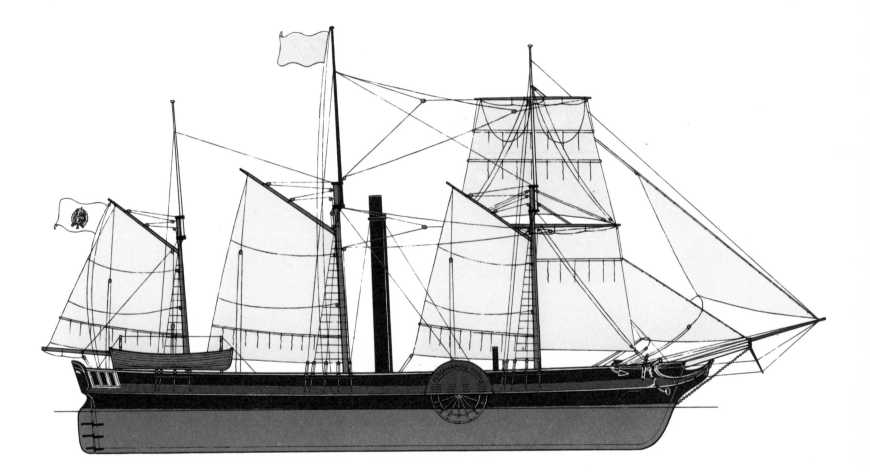

FERDINANDO PRIMO · 1818

Società Napoletana Pietro Andriel

127.3 × 20.2 × 9.5 feet ◖ 247 T ◖ 38,800 × 6,157 × 2,895 m

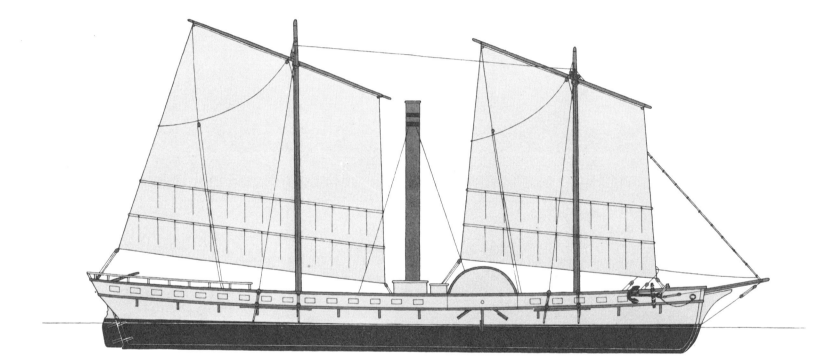

NEDERLANDER · 1823

De Nederlandsche Stoomboot Maatschappij

100.0 × 15.25 × 7.0 feet ☾ 30,479 × 4,648 × 2,134 m

ENTERPRISE · 1824

Lieut. James H. Johnston, R.N. and Associates

133.0 × 27.0 × 16.5 feet ℂ 470 T ℂ 40,537 × 8,229 × 5,029 m

CURAÇAO · 1825

Netherlands Navy

130.5 × 26.9 × 16.5 feet ◖ 438 T ◖ 39,775 × 8,199 × 5,029 m

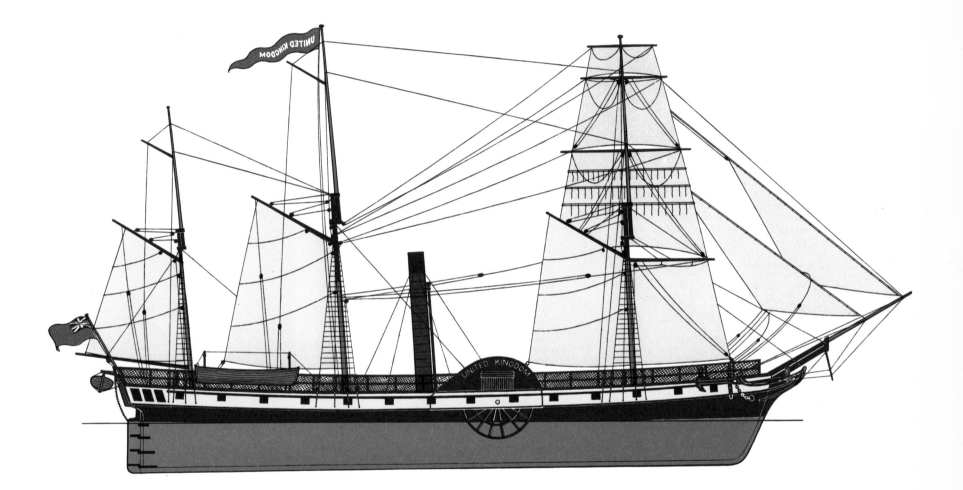

UNITED KINGDOM · 1826

160.0 × 26.5 × 17.5 feet ☾ 1000 T ☾ 48,766 × 8,077 × 5,334 m

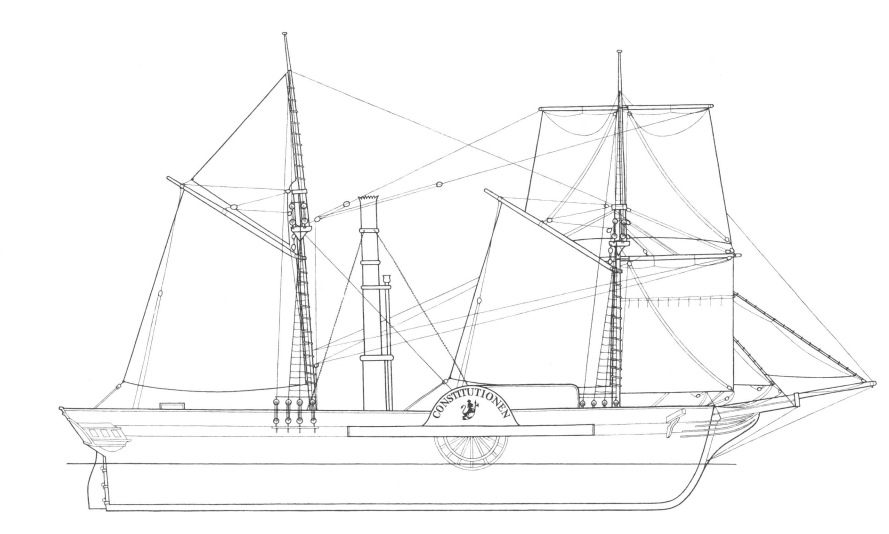

CONSTITUTIONEN · 1826

Den Norske Stat (Postvesendet)

98.917 × 17.167 feet ☾ 145 T ☾ 30,149 × 5,233 m

ARCHIMEDES — 1838 — 237 T.

106.7 × 22.5 × 13 feet
32,521 × 6,858 × 3,962 m

The successful experiments with FRANCIS SMITH led to the organization of The Ship Propeller Company to conduct further trials with a larger vessel. The company purchased Smith's patents and one of the members, Henry Wimhurst, built ARCHIMEDES in 1838. Her engines of 80 n.h.p. operating at 26 r.p.m. drove the propeller shaft through gearing at 139 r.p.m. ARCHIMEDES was rigged as a three-masted topsail schooner. The original screw had one complete turn and was located in the dead-wood 4 ft. (1.219 m) forward of the sternpost; it was 7 ft. (2,134 m) in diameter and 8 ft. (2,438 m) long. After various changes the final propeller had two blades with a diameter of 5.75 ft. (1,753 m) and a pitch of 10 ft. (3,048 m) which gave her a speed of about 9 knots (16,79 km/hr.). In 1840 ARCHIMEDES thoroughly demonstrated the practicability of screw propulsion by circumnavigating Great Britain and by making the fastest trip then on record to Oporto. She ended her career in the 1850's as a sailing vessel running between Australia and Chile.

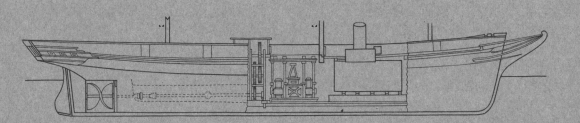

In 1837 the successes of FRANCIS SMITH and FRANCIS B. OGDEN led to the widespread use of the screw for ship propulsion. The power of a helical blade in water had been proved by the well-known screw pump invented by Archimedes hence later inventors had no claim to originalty. They could claim only the invention of methods to apply the screw to ship propulsion and there were many.

In May 1836 Francis Pettit Smith obtained a patent for an Archimedean screw having two complete turns designed to be installed at the stern of a vessel but at a considerable distance forward of a vessel's sternpost. It was successfully tried on the 6 ton launch FRANCIS SMITH on Paddington Canal in February 1837. When on one occasion about one-half of the wooden screw blade broke off the speed of the launch increased considerably. FRANCIS SMITH later had a one-turn metal screw and in September 1837 underwent extensive trials covering more than 400 miles (644 km) at an average speed of 8 miles (12,87 km) per hour.

Captain John Ericsson's propeller patent of July 1836 provided for two thin counter-rotating hoops or wheels on a common center each having eight fans or blades. The wheels were entirely submerged and located abaft the rudder. The blades on each wheel were at opposite inclinations and the after wheel turned at 1.2 times the speed of the forward one. This arrangement was intended to recover the energy normally lost in the rotation of the water as it leaves a single screw. Because of mechanical complications Ericsson later employed a single wheel.

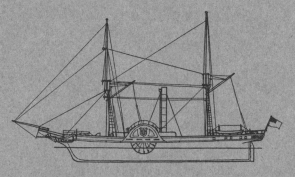

SIRIUS — 1837 — 703 T.

178.4 × 25.8 × 18.3 feet
35,173 × 7,864 × 5,579 m

SIRIUS was the first vessel to cross the Atlantic under sustained steam power. When the completion of BRITISH QUEEN was delayed her owners, seeking to forestall the commercial advantage of a prior voyage by GREAT WESTERN, chartered SIRIUS from the St. George Steam Packet Company. SIRIUS, built of wood and powered with
continued

After model experiments Ericsson built in 1837 FRANCIS B. OGDEN named for the U.S.A. consul at Liverpool who was the first to appreciate and assist him. On this vessel the propeller was 5 ft. 2 in. (1,575m) in diameter and was driven by a high pressure engine. Favorable accounts of the vessel appeared in London publications but British engineers in general were opposed to Ericsson's invention and the British Admiralty gave no encouragement.

Lieutenant Robert F. Stockton, U.S.N., in London on personal business, was impressed by the performance of Ericsson's FRANCIS B. OGDEN. Stockton ordered a small iron steamer to be propelled by an Ericsson screw; built by Messrs. Laird Brothers, Birkenhead, she was named ROBERT F. STOCKTON when launched in 1838. Her two-cylinder machinery developed 30 h.p. and on the Thames she made a speed of 13 knots (24,13 km/hr.) with the tide. She crossed the Atlantic under sail alone in the spring of 1839. Because of erratic steering during further trials in the U.S.A. one wheel was removed and the rudder placed abaft the propeller. Admitted to U.S. registry on 8 May 1840 and renamed NEW JERSEY she was put to work towing barges on the Delaware and Raritan Canal which she did successfully for about thirty years. NEW JERSEY ex ROBERT F. STOCKTON was the first iron vessel to cross the Atlantic and the first commercial vessel to be screw-propelled.

In 1816 the first privately-owned sailing packet line between North America and England was established with three ships sailing in rotation. The following years saw the introduction of other lines to England and the Continent, regular schedules, and a steady improvement in the ships employed. The sailing packet passages averaged 22 days eastbound and 34 days westbound. The importance and feasibility of regular service on these runs by steam-powered vessels was realized but slowly, yet by 1838 there were three competitors for the honor of making the first Atlantic crossing by a full-powered steamship. The first, GREAT WESTERN of the Great Western Steamship Company, was ready for sea in the spring of 1838, BRITISH QUEEN of the British and American Steam Navigation Company was being delayed by the bankruptcy of her engine builders while COLUMBUS, built by Thomas Howard to demonstrate his quicksilver boiler, suffered a boiler explosion which ended a promising experiment.

At a meeting of the directors of the Great Western Railway Company in October 1835 it was jokingly suggested that the Paddington-Bristol line be extended to New York by means of a steamship to be named GREAT WESTERN. Although many at the time believed it impossible to build a steamship with enough coal capacity for that distance the idea took hold and the Great Western Steamship Company was organized early in 1836. GREAT WESTERN was planned by the chief engineer of the railway company, I.K. Brunel, and her keel was laid in June 1836 in the yard of Patterson and Mercer, Wapping, Bristol. Launched over a year later on 19 July 1837, GREAT WESTERN was built with great care and particular attention was paid to her longitudinal strength. Her accommodations were arranged for 128 first class passengers and 20 second class, but in an emergency an additional 100 passengers could be carried; the crew consisted of 57 officers and men. The main saloon measured 82 ft. (24,993 m) long by 34 ft. (10,363 m) at its widest point and was decorated in the Louis XIV style with fifty painted panels.

GREAT WESTERN's propelling machinery, built by Messrs. Maudslay, Sons and Field, Blackwall, was installed in London. She was fitted with two side-lever engines of 225 n.h.p. each, with cylinders 73.5 in. (1,867 m) diameter by 7 ft. (2,134 m) stroke. Steam at 5 p.s.i. (0,352 kg/cm²) pressure was generated in four iron return-flue

continued
a pair of side-lever engines of 320 n.h.p., was designed for a British Isles service between Glasgow, Dublin, Cork, and London. She was equipped with a surface condenser which allowed her to use fresh water in her boilers. She left Cork for New York on 4 April 1838 with a total of 40 passengers; 450(457) tons of coal in addition to her normal stores put her very low in the water. She arrived off New York at 9:00 P.M. on 22 April where she met a firm welcome—she ran aground on the bar. Floating off at high tide with no damage SIRIUS arrived off the Battery the next morning and was greeted by a large crowd; about four hours later GREAT WESTERN steamed

continued

New Jersey — page 49   *Great Western — page 50*

continued
up the harbor. SIRIUS made a second pair of Atlantic crossings in July 1838, one trip to St. Petersburg, and then returned to her normal service in the Irish Sea. On 16 January 1847 she hit a reef in Ballycotton Bay and was a total loss.

JOHN ERICSSON — 1803-1889

Engineer and inventor. Born in Sweden he showed an early interest in the mechanical field. In army service between 1820 and 1827 he attained the rank of captain. In 1829 in England he constructed the locomotive NOVELTY for the Liverpool & Manchester railway competition. He worked on many inventions including a marine engine located entirely below a vessel's water-line. His screw propeller patented in 1836 failed to interest the British Admiralty but

continued

boilers having three furnaces each. The coal bunkers held 800 tons and were arranged to carry water ballast when the coal had been consumed. GREAT WESTERN's paddle-wheels were of the cycloidal type designed by Joshua Field in 1833; each float consisted of four separate blades arranged on cycloidal curves so that they entered the water more quietly than radial floats.

After suffering a minor fire GREAT WESTERN finally left Bristol for New York on Sunday, 8 April 1838, in a north-west gale with only seven passengers. The engines were stopped twice on the passage—once for two hours and again for twenty minutes—to tighten various bolts on the paddle-wheels.

She arrived in New York in the afternoon of 23 April only to find that she had been beaten by about four hours by little SIRIUS which had been chartered by the owners of the delayed BRITISH QUEEN. GREAT WESTERN, however, made the better passage taking 15¼ days to cover 220 miles (354 km) more than SIRIUS did in 19 days. For her return trip on 7 May GREAT WESTERN had a cargo of cotton with some silks and indigo, letters, newspapers, and 78 passengers. She continued in service between Bristol and New York until 1846. Sold in 1847 to the Royal Mail Steam Packet Company, Ltd. she ran for 10 years from Southampton to the West Indies and was considered one of their best ships. GREAT WESTERN was finally broken up at Vauxhall in 1857 being unable to compete profitably with the newer steamers.

Following the success of Smith's propeller in ARCHIMEDES, Henry Wimhurst constructed an improved vessel for further experiements. This was NOVELTY built of wood at Blackwall and launched in 1840. Unlike Smith's original long screw, that on NOVELTY was more like a fan having only two blades each of one quarter turn and it was located as close to her sternpost as possible.

NOVELTY's 25 n.h.p. propelling machinery, directly connected to the propeller shaft, had two cylinders 14.5 in. (0,368 m) diameter by 18 in. (0,457 m) stroke. Steam was supplied at the then high pressure of 60 p.s.i. (4,219 kg/cm²) by a "locomotive" or fire-tube boiler. This was the highest pressure attempted up to that time and was considered unsuitable for a steamship. After many protests new boilers and engines were installed. The latter Wimhurst referred to in 1843 as a pair of non-condensing engines having cylinders 13 in. (0,330 m) diameter by 28 in. (0,711 m) stroke in which the mean pressure was 20 p.s.i. (1,406 kg/cm²) when the steam was cut off at half stroke. With this machinery he reported that NOVELTY attained a speed of 8½ miles (13,68 km) per hour.

NOVELTY carried a barque rig with a hollow mizzen mast of iron to serve as a funnel; this was probably the first iron mast. In order to avoid the propeller's resistance when under sail, NOVELTY was provided with two wells and davits by which it could be lifted on deck. In 1841 she made the first commercial voyage by a screw-propelled vessel being chartered to carry 420 tons of cargo from Liverpool to Constantinople (Istanbul).

On 7 November 1838 the British Admiralty advertised for bids for the carriage of mails and dispatches by steam vessels between England and Halifax and New York. After lengthy negotiations the contract secured on 12 April 1839 by Samuel Cunard, a prominent business man of Halifax, was to take effect on 4 June 1840, and was to run for seven years at £60,000 per year; there were to be two sailings each month and the U.S.A. port was changed to Boston. With three Liverpool merchants Cunard organized the British and North American Royal Mail Steam Packet Company which contracted with Robert Napier of Glasgow for four ships of 1200 tons burden. To speed the work on the ships the hulls were built in different yards but Robert Napier

continued

it attracted the attention of Lieutenant R. F. Stockton, U.S.N., who ordered a small iron screw-propelled steamboat for his own account and induced Ericsson to go to the U.S.A. Ericsson did this in 1839 and became a citizen in 1848. In the U.S.A. he designed the hull and engines and superintended the construction of the U.S.S. PRINCETON launched in 1842, the first screw-propelled steam warship. Defensive armor for warships had long interested him and by 1854 he had drawn plans and built a model of a low-profile steam vessel carrying one heavy gun in a rotating turret. This design developed into the U.S.S. MONITOR of U.S. Civil War fame. In later years he worked on torpedoes and sun motors. He died in March 1889 and in 1890 in honor of his services to his adopted country the new U.S.S. BALTIMORE returned Ericsson's remains to his native Sweden.

Novelty — page 51

ISAMBARD KINGDOM BRUNEL — 1806-1859

English engineer. Born in Portsmouth, England, he showed in childhood unusual powers of mental calculation and great ability as a draftsman. At 17 after studying in Paris, he became an assistant engineer in the office of his father, Sir Marc Isambard Brunel, who was then beginning to dig the first Thames tunnel. In 1831 his design for a bridge across the Avon river at Clifton was accepted. Appointed engineer of the Great Western Railway Company in 1833

continued

continued

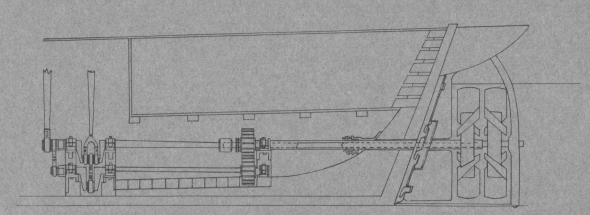

this occupied him fully for several years. His last and greatest railway work was the Royal Albert bridge over the Tamar river at Saltash. In the marine field Brunel was connected with the construction of GREAT WESTERN in 1837 and GREAT BRITAIN of 1843. In 1852 he proposed the building of a "great ship" on which construction was started in December 1853. She was finally launched as LEVIATHAN on 31 January 1858 but was registered as GREAT EASTERN. Overworked in connection with GREAT EASTERN he suffered a paralytic stroke two days before she sailed on her maiden voyage on 7 September 1859 and he died on 15 September. The best known civil engineer of his time, Brunel was commonly known as "The Little Giant". Active in other fields he was a friend of Felix Mendelssohn and a skilled water-color painter. He was elected a fellow of the Royal Society in 1830 and received the degree of D.C.L. from Oxford in 1857.

ROBERT F. STOCKTON—1838

The original propeller arrangement with two propellers abaft the rudder.

constructed the machinery for all. Named BRITANNIA, ACADIA, CALEDONIA, and COLUMBIA, the four ships were intended to be as alike as possible so that patrons could expect the same standards on all, one reason for the early success of the company.

Service was started from Liverpool, without mails, in May 1840 by the 700 ton UNICORN which was sent out to operate a feeder service on the St. Lawrence. She received an enthusiastic greeting in Halifax on 2 June and continued on to Boston for more celebrations. On 4 July 1840 the first sailing with mails was made by BRITANNIA and she arrived in Halifax on 17 July completing the trip to Boston on the following day; the total elapsed time was 14 days 8 hours.

BRITANNIA, built by Messrs. Robert Duncan and Company, Greenock, was launched on 5 February 1840. In form she was similar to the sailing packets with two decks, a square stern, and the typical head structure of the period; she carried a barque rig. Accommodations were provided for 115 cabin passengers and a crew of 89 officers and men. The officers' quarters, galley, bakery, and cow-house were located on the upper deck while on the lower deck there were two dining saloons and quarters for all the passengers and crew. The press at the time described the accommodations as "luxurious"—an overworked term that will be found in the description of almost every new passenger ship. Spaces under the accommodations could carry 225 tons of cargo.

Robert Napier's engines were of the side-lever type of 440 n.h.p. with two cylinders 72 in. (1,829 m) diameter by 82 in. (2,083 m) stroke. Four iron return-flue boilers

Britannia — page 52

having three furnaces each supplied steam at a pressure of 9 p.s.i. (0,633 kg/cm²); coal consumption was between 31 and 38 tons per day. The paddle-wheels were 28 ft. (8,534 m) in diameter and had 21 radial floats. Turning at 16 r.p.m. they gave the ships a normal speed of about 8.5 knots (15,805 km/hr.).

After making 40 Atlantic crossings for the Cunard Line BRITANNIA was sold in 1849 to the German Government for conversion to a warship. Her engines were later removed and she existed for several years as a hulk.

". . . GREAT BRITAIN is confessedly the most splendid experiment in shipbuilding ever submitted to a British public." So read in part an old illustrated broad-sheet describing the first screw-propelled steamer in Atlantic service. Having had fair success with GREAT WESTERN of 1837 the Great Western Steamship Company turned again to Brunel in 1839 for advice concerning a larger ship that might prove more profitable. He concluded that a wooden ship of the desired size would be unpractical and advised the use of iron even though there were no design precedents. Messrs. W. Patterson and Sons, Bristol, built the hull and the Great Western Company set up its own works to build the machinery estimating that it could save £15,000 by so doing although Brunel advised against it.

Brunel believed in strong ships and GREAT BRITAIN proved his point, for after years of service, lastly as a coal hulk, her hull still exists in the Falkland Islands. Five transverse bulkheads, then a novelty, gave her six watertight compartments. Accommodations for about 360 passengers were provided entirely below deck. When she first went to sea, GREAT BRITAIN carried about 1700 square yards (1421 m²) of canvas on six masts reportedly named for the days of the week beginning with Monday.

Brunel intended to employ paddle-wheels on GREAT BRITAIN, but the directors of the company, impressed by ARCHIMEDES, asked him to study the possibilities of screw-propulsion. His studies convinced him of the superiority of the screw and after seventeen months of construction, the directors voted the change. GREAT BRITAIN's engines of 1000 (1014) n.h.p. consisted of four inclined cylinders, 88 in. (2,235 m) diameter by 72 in. (1,829 m) stroke, working in pairs to drive an overhead crankshaft at 18 r.p.m. Four sets of chain-connected gearing turned the lower propeller shaft at 53 r.p.m. On her trials in 1844 with a six-bladed built-up propeller GREAT BRITAIN's speed was about 11 knots (20,39 km/hr.); later a four-bladed propeller improved her performance. Steam at 15 p.s.i. (1,055 kg/cm²) pressure was supplied by what might be called three double-ended boilers although they were three sections of one large unit. Each end of each section had four furnaces.

To eliminate launching problems GREAT BRITAIN was laid down in a dry-dock. Floated on 19 July 1843 she drew so much water that she could only move into another basin when locks into the Avon river were altered. Sent to London for exhibition in February 1845 she returned to Liverpool to load for New York in July. Leaving Liverpool on 26 July with about 60 passengers and some 806 (813) tons of cargo GREAT BRITAIN made New York in 14 days 21 hours and returned to Liverpool in about the same time. She continued her voyages until September 1846 when the ran ashore in Dundrum Bay, County Down, Ireland, when her captain was confused by a new lighthouse not shown on his charts.

GREAT BRITAIN was safely refloated in August 1847; her construction had proved itself and convinced critics as to the suitability of iron. The expense of repairs on top of salvage costs proved too much for her owners and she was sold to Messrs. Gibbs, Bright & Company who refitted her. New oscillating engines were installed, two masts

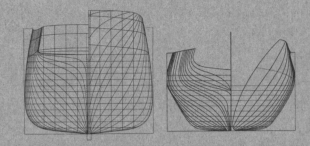

SHIP BODY SECTIONS

To the left: typical sailing vessel form normally employed for sea-going vessels propelled by paddle-wheels.
To the right: unique form of GREAT BRITAIN which gave improved stability and lower hull resistance. Its characteristics will be met again in a patented form in the 1920's.

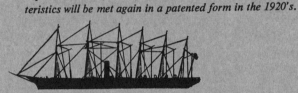

Great Britain — page 53

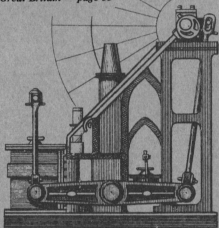

SIDE-LEVER ENGINE

The "side-lever" type of paddle-wheel engine was long a favorite with British marine engineers. It was employed in the earliest Clyde-built steamers and in its finest form as late as in the Cunard Line's SCOTIA of 1861. The overhead beam of the early Boulton & Watt land engines was replaced by two beams or levers located down near the engine's foundation plate, one on each side of the vertical cylinder. Air pumps and other auxiliaries were worked off the levers. A side-lever engine was well balanced and very economical in maintenance and repairs. Its low profile improved a vessel's stability and saved on headroom but in the case of 500 h.p. engines, for example, a side-lever engine required 20 feet (6,036 m) more length and weighed 100 tons more than the average direct-acting type.

RATTLER VERSUS ALECTO

176.5 × 32.7 × 18.5 feet
53,795 × 9,976 × 5,639 m

The successes of ARCHIMEDES and other screw-propelled vessels finally induced the British Admiralty to build a trial vessel to test the relative merits of the screw propeller and the paddle-wheel. H.M.S. RATTLER then on the stocks, a sister of H.M. paddle sloop ALECTO, was fitted with a Smith-type screw and launched in April 1843. Both vessels had engines of 200 n.h.p. So doubtful were the Lords of the Admiralty of the outcome that no broadside gun ports were cut in RATTLER in the positions normally occupied by paddle-wheels. RATTLER was subjected to various tests and it was found that her screw could be shortened by one-third without reducing its power. On sea trials RATTLER proved faster than ALECTO but the big test came on 3 April 1845. The two vessels were secured stern to stern and RATTLER towed ALECTO astern at 2.8 knots (5,19 km/hr.). Later that year the Admiralty ordered screw propulsion installed on more than twenty naval vessels.

Rigi — page 54

removed, and the original single tall funnel replaced by two shorter ones set very close together. After some further service on the Atlantic GREAT BRITAIN was put on the Australian run leaving Liverpool on her first voyage on 21 August 1852 with 600 passengers and arriving in Melbourne on 10 November.

Sold again in 1882, GREAT BRITAIN's engines were removed, her masts were altered, and she became a full-rigged ship. Heavy weather off Cape Horn in 1886 forced her into Port Stanley in the Falkland Islands where she was condemned. After serving as a coal hulk until October 1937 GREAT BRITAIN was beached at Sparrow Point, Port William, where she may still be seen.

It would be difficult to chronicle the beginning of steam navigation on every lake in Europe. The first steamboat appeared on the Lake of Constance (Bodensee) in 1817, an unsuccessful boat named STEPHANIE powered by an unused engine from a spinning mill; the first successful steamers were built in 1824. Early steamers on other lakes were L'UNION on the Lake of Neuchâtel and LEMAN on Lake Geneva both of which were launched in 1826. The oldest and finest of the Swiss lake steamers still in existence is RIGI of 1847, now preserved on the grounds of the Swiss Institute of Transport and Communications, Lucerne, where she is used as a restaurant.

RIGI's wooden hull with a single deck and cabins forward and aft was constructed in London by Messrs. Ditchburn & Mare. Probably built in sections it reportedly travelled by water to Strasbourg, from there by rail to Basel, and was drawn by horses from Basel to Lucerne. She made her maiden voyage on the Lake of Lucerne (Vierwaldstättersee) on 1 April 1848 and began regular service on 30 May; she could carry 200 passengers. In the autumn of 1952, 105 years later during which she ran every season except from 1916 to 1919, RIGI was withdrawn from service having carried more than six million passengers and travelled 777,090 miles (1,250,588 km).

As with all vessels RIGI underwent many renewals during her life. Extensive work was done on her hull and houses in 1860, 1880, and 1922; the superstructure was completely renewed during the winter of 1958-59. Details of her original machinery constructed by Messrs. John Penn & Sons Ltd., London, are lacking but her present compound oscillating engines, which for visitors can be put in motion by electric power, were built by Messrs. Escher-Wyss, Ltd. Zurich; the cylinders are 14.96 and 27.56 in. (0,380-0,700 m) diameter by 29.53 in. (0,750 m) stroke. Converted from wood to coal-burning in 1862, her present Scotch boiler supplied steam at 99.56 lbs. per sq. in. (7,000 kg/cm²) pressure. With her feathering paddlewheels turning at 46.5 r.p.m. RIGI's speed was about 11 miles (17,7 km) per hour.

157.417 × 32 × 20 feet
47,979 × 9,753 × 6,036 m

MASSACHUSETTS, built in 1845 for Captain R.B. Forbes and other merchants of Boston, was intended to be the first of a line of auxiliary steamers between that port and Liverpool. In form and rig she was a typical sailing packet and her 170 h.p. machinery was to be used only in calms or moderate head winds. She was fitted with an Ericsson screw located abaft the rudder and so arranged that it could be swung up sideways clear of the water when not in use. It was found that the Atlantic was too rough even in good weather to allow the propeller to be used advantageously and that she was too small so after two complete voyages to Liverpool she was chartered in 1846 to the U.S. War Department as a transport. Later sold to the government her machinery was removed and she became the naval storeship FARRALONES on the Pacific station. Returning to the merchant service after the Civil War as ALASKA she was wrecked on the coast of Chile in 1870.

Early steam vessels were built and operated mainly to carry passengers. Some cargo was carried but it was too expensive to carry ordinary bulky commodities in other than sailing vessels. By 1844 London had about 8000 sailing collier arrivals per year delivering 2,500,000 (2,540,000) tons of coal. In 1844 the sailing collier Q.E.D., 150 ft. (45,718 m) long by 27½ ft. (8,382 m) beam, was built of iron at Wallsend and fitted with an auxiliary steam engine of 20 n.h.p. which drove a screw propeller. She had a double bottom subdivided into tanks which were used to carry water ballast on return trips—a system that was re-invented many years later.

1852 saw the building of the first full-powered collier for the London coal trade, the screw-propelled JOHN BOWES built of iron by Messrs. Palmer Brothers & Company on the Tyne. Her machinery, located as far aft as possible, was constructed by Messrs. R. Stephenson & Company and consisted of two compact engines each of 35 n.h.p. geared to the single shaft. Her service speed was about 9 knots (16,788 km/hr.). A special feature was a 60 ft. (18,287 m) long hatch which allowed for more economical and efficient loading of coal than the usual small hatches of the sailing colliers. The total cargo and fuel capacity of JOHN BOWES was 650 (660) tons. During her life she carried various rigs starting with a three-masted one that included square sails and ending with two simple pole masts. Launched on 30 June 1852 JOHN BOWES made her first voyage about the end of July. It was found that she could make the Tyne-London round trip in 5 days delivering as much coal as two sailing colliers could in one month. She proved such a success that her design was copied widely.

John Bowes — page 55

Repowered in 1864 and again in 1883 JOHN BOWES served as a collier until 1896 when she was sold to another British firm engaged in coastwise tramping operations. She became the Norwegian SPEC in 1898, the Swedish TRANSIT in 1900, and the Spanish CAROLINA in 1908. In November 1933 as the Spanish VILLA SELGAS carrying a cargo of iron ore from Bilbao to San Esteban Pravia she sprang a serious leak in a gale and foundered almost immediately.

A paper in 1861 described the requirements for many of the steamboats employed on the rivers, bays, and sounds of the eastern seaboard of North America: "A ship in the Eastern waters is a floating American hotel. You are, therefore to conceive a double series of bedrooms, two to three hundred feet long, extending along the sides of a gigantic saloon; and that, to carry this, to furnish the passengers the luxurious accommodations of an hotel, and at the same time to accomplish 150 miles in the night, are the great objects to be obtained by the shipbuilder, the marine engineer, and the ship-owner." The crack boats were those on the important runs from New York to ports up the Hudson river and others linking New York and Boston via various ports on Long Island Sound and connecting railroads. Typical of the boats built for a long Island Sound run was COMMONWEALTH launched in 1854 from the yard of Lawrence and Foulkes at Greenpoint, Long Island. She was operated in conjunction with the Norwich, Worcester, and Boston Railroad, the connection being made at Allyn Point a few miles below Norwich on Connecticut's Thames river.

Built of wood as were many such steamers for years to come, COMMONWEALTH had the prominent "hog-frames" on each side to stiffen the relatively shallow hull. With a main hull breadth of 42 ft. (12,801 m), the breadth over her guards was 77 ft. (23,469 m). This overhanging structure was supported by iron tie-rods from the hog-frames and from king-posts. COMMONWEALTH had 120 two-berth staterooms and accommodations for about six hundred passengers in open berthing areas. She was powered by a vertical beam engine constructed by the Morgan Iron Works, New York, whose cylinder measured 76 in. (1,930 m) diameter by 12 ft. (3,658 m) stroke. Steam at 30 p.s.i. (2,109 kg/cm²) pressure was supplied by two return-flue boilers located on the guards forward of the paddle-wheels.

COMMONWEALTH began her daily service between New York and Norwich on 5 April 1855; CONNECTICUT of 1849 was her running mate. Because of a disagreement with the connecting railroad, the Norwich and New London Steamboat Company sold out in May 1860 and COMMONWEALTH was acquired by the Stonington Line which kept her in the same service. During that year the railroad from Boston to Stonington was extended to Groton on the Thames opposite New London and she began running from this terminus on 17 September 1860. On the night of 29 December 1865 the Groton wharf caught fire, the flames spread to COMMONWEALTH, which was grounded by a low tide, and she was a total loss. A much admired boat, she suffered no spectacular accidents during her years of service; the fire cut short a promising career.

Largest and finest of the Long Island Sound paddle steamers was COMMONWEALTH of the Fall River Line. Built of steel and launched in 1907 she operated regularly between Fall River and New York until service was suspended in 1937. She measured 455 ft. 8 in. (138,822 m) in length overall and had a maximum breadth of 94 ft. 7 in. (28,829 m). Double inclined compound engines developing 12,000 (12163) i.h.p. drove her at a speed of 23 miles (37,01 km) per hour. This COMMONWEALTH ended her days in a scrapper's yard in 1938.

Commonwealth — page 56

FRANCIS SKIDDY — 1852 — 1235 T

322 × 38.833 × 10.333 feet
98,143 × 11,836 × 3,143 m

FRANCIS SKIDDY was considered one of the most graceful of all Hudson River steamboats and for many years was one of the fastest.
CHANCELLOR LIVINGSTON of 1816 had a speed of 8½ miles (13,67 km) per hour while FRANCIS SKIDDY could average about 23 miles (37,01 km) per hour showing the great speed increase of U.S.A. river steamers in 36 years. FRANCIS SKIDDY normally made a round trip between New York and Albany, about 300 miles (483 km) in all, each 24 hours. She was propelled by a vertical beam engine which turned 40 ft. (12,192 m) diameter paddle-wheels having 26 radial floats. The engine's cylinder was 70 in. (1,778 m) in diameter by 14 ft. (4,267 m) stroke; the steam pressure was 40 p.s.i. (2,812 kg/cm²). In 1855 FRANCIS SKIDDY was rebuilt into a night boat which reduced her speed somewhat. She was wrecked by stranding on Van Wie's Point, a short distance below Albany, on 25 November 1864.

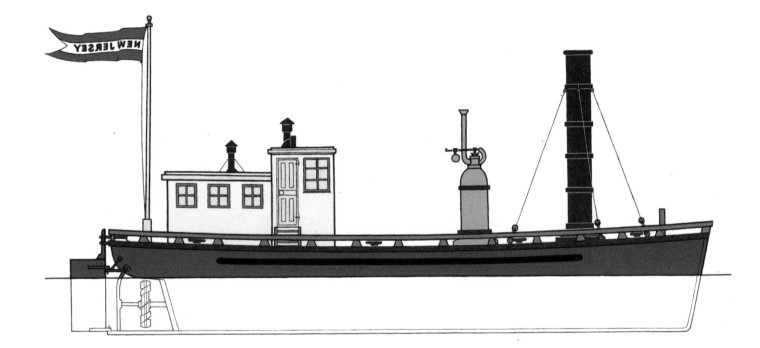

NEW JERSEY (ROBERT F. STOCKTON)

Delaware and Raritan Canal Company

63.4 × 10.0 × 7.0 feet ☾ 33 T ☾ 19,324 × 3,048 × 2,134 m

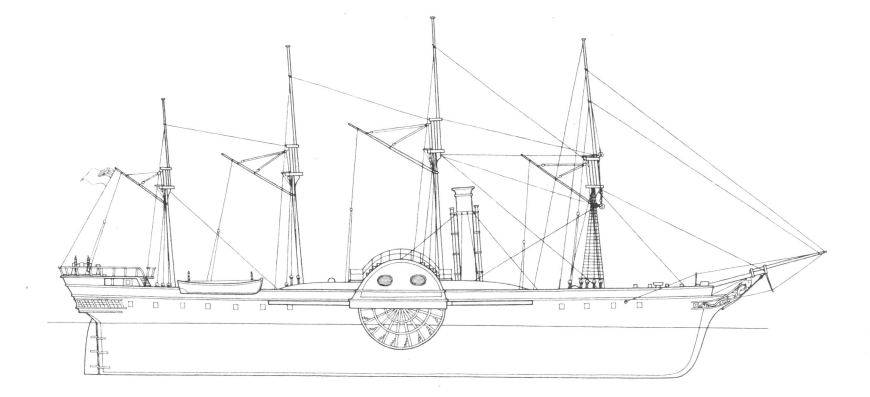

GREAT WESTERN · 1837

Great Western Steamship Company

212.0 × 34.0 × 23.2 feet ◖ 1320 T ◖ 64,616 × 10,363 × 7,071 m

NOVELTY · 1840

The Ship Propeller Company

117.0 × 24.5 × 14.5 feet ◖ 328 T ◖ 35,661 × 7,467 × 4,420 m

BRITANNIA · 1840

British and North American Royal Mail Steam Packet Company

207.0 × 34.3 × 22.5 feet ☾ 1156 T ☾ 63,092 × 10,454 × 6,858 m

GREAT BRITAIN · 1843

Great Western Steamship Company

289.0 × 50.5 × 32.5 feet ◖ 3270 T ◖ 88,084 × 15,391 × 9,905 m

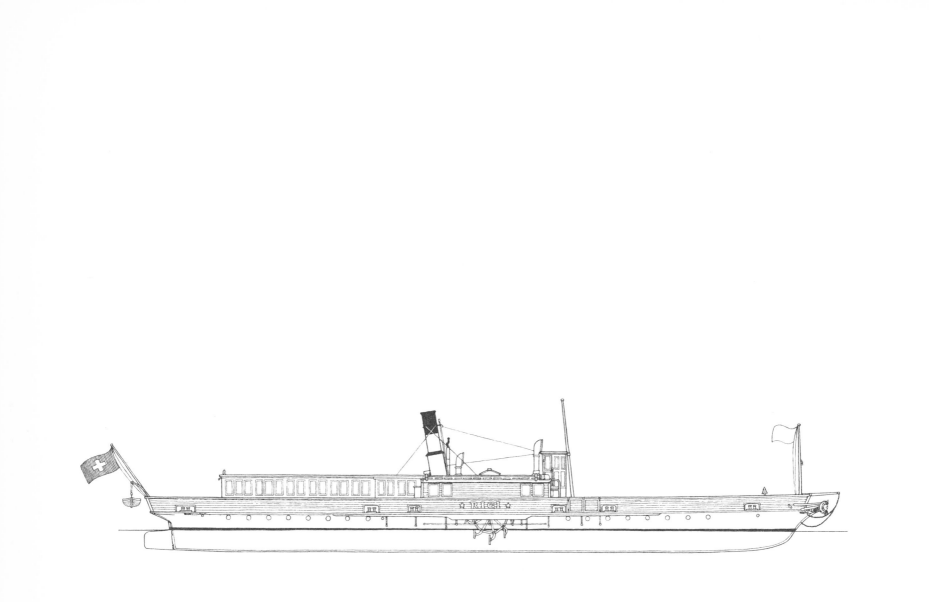

RIGI · 1847

Mail Steamship Company of the Lake of Lucerne

121.88 × 14.17 feet ◖ 90 T ◖ 37,15 × 4,32 m

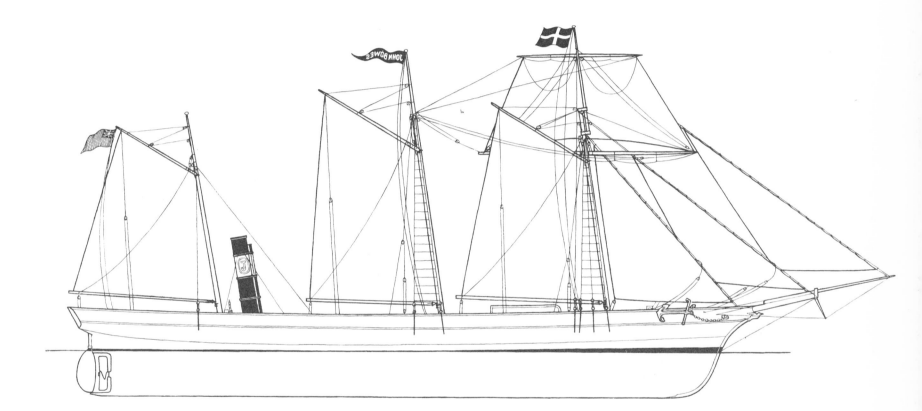

JOHN BOWES · 1852

Iron Screw Collier Company

150.0 × 25.7 × 15.6 feet ◖ 437 T ◖ 45,718 × 7,833 × 4,755 m

COMMONWEALTH · 1854

Norwich and New London Steamboat Company

300.0 × 41.5 × 13.0 feet ℂ 1739 T ℂ 91,437 × 12,598 × 3,962 m

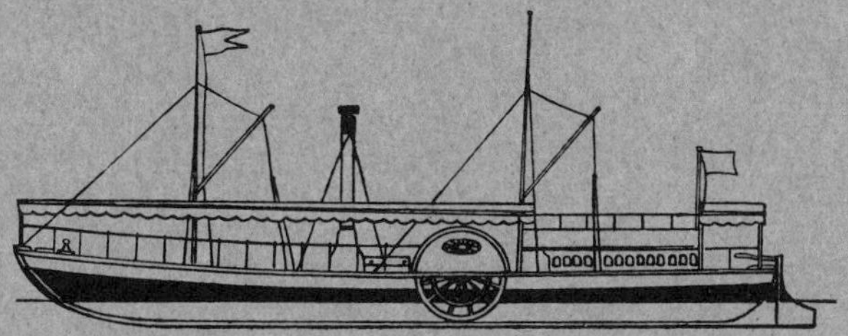

MA ROBERT — 1858

The first steamer constructed of steel was this paddle-wheel launch built for Dr. David Livingstone's Zambesi River Expedition by Messrs. Laird Brothers, Birkenhead. Named for the explorer's wife, the launch was carried to Africa in three sections and assembled on the river. Generally referred to as ASTHMATIC she was a failure as her speed of 8 knots (14,83 km/hr.) proved insufficient against the river's current and chemical action in the water soon ruined her newly patented steel plates.

Because of the high operating costs in the early days of transatlantic steamship service a regular service could only be maintained by generous government payments for carrying the mails. Such payments were made under various circumstances by Belgium, France, and Great Britain. Because of the superiority of its sailing packets, public interest in ocean-going steamships in the U.S.A. was slow to develop but in 1844 the Congress finally authorized mail contracts.

E.K. Collins, head of the Dramatic Line of sailing packets, founded in 1847 the New York and Liverpool United States Mail Steamship Company—to the public it was always the Collins Line—with the intent of establishing a U.S.A. position in steam equal to its superiority in sail. The line built in 1848 and 1849 the four finest steamships then afloat - ARCTIC, ATLANTIC, BALTIC, and PACIFIC - and they began competing among themselves for the Blue Ribbon, emblematic of speed supremacy on the Atlantic. In May 1851 PACIFIC took the eastbound record from ACADIA, one of the original Cunarders, averaging 13 knots (24,13 km/hr.); ARCTIC topped this by 1/4 knot (0,46 km/hr.) in February 1852. BALTIC set the westbound record in August 1851 averaging 13 knots (24,13 km/hr.) but PACIFIC equalled this. Their side-lever machinery of 2000 (2027) i.h.p. was too powerful for their wooden hulls and the line spent much of its money keeping the ships in repair. The loss of ARCTIC by collision in 1854 started a run of bad luck that eventually killed the line.

Adriatic — page 67

The last and finest Colllins Liner was ADRIATIC launched in April 1856. Designed and built by George Steers of yacht AMERICA fame she followed the pattern of the four earlier ships in having a wooden hull with a straight stem and a round counter stern and in being propelled by paddle-wheels. Iron hulls and screw propellers had been used in the U.S.A. for coastwise service but iron was generally too expensive and passengers did not enjoy the shaking given by a screw propeller. As a result of ARCTIC's sinking ADRIATIC had seven transverse water-tight bulkheads and carried sixteen 60-person lifeboats. She had accommodations for 316 first class and 60 second class passengers; the total crew was 170. Auxiliary sails were carried on two masts and she had two funnels; a calcium light on her foremast was the first searchlight used at sea.

ADRIATIC's 1300 (1317) n.h.p. machinery, constructed by the Novelty Iron Works of New York, consisted of two oscillating cylinders, 101 m. (2,565 m) diameter by 12 ft. (3,658 m) stroke, connected to a single crank pin. Eight tubular boilers with six furnaces each generated steam at 20 p.s.i. (1,406 kg/cm²). Coal consumption was about 145 tons per day and the bunkers carried about 1200 (1219) tons. ADRIATIC's paddle-wheels were 40 ft. (12,192 m.) diameter and each had 32 fixed radial floats; at 13 r.p.m. they drove her at a normal speed of 13 knots (24,13 km/hr.).

On 23 November 1857 ADRIATIC began her maiden voyage from New York and reached Liverpool in 10 days attaining at times a speed of 15 knots (27,80 km/hr.). After her second voyage the line failed and she was laid up in New York. She was purchased in 1861 by the Galway Line and was the only ship able to maintain the speed required by that company's mail contract. After the failure of the line in 1864 she was converted to sail and eventually became a store ship at Bonny on the west African coast where in 1885 she was beached and found to be beyond repair.

"The Floating City", "The Crystal Palace of the Sea", christened LEVIATHAN, and registered as GREAT EASTERN, this masterpiece of I.K. Brunel and J. Scott Russell was not exceeded in size for 41 years. A magnificent failure, she probably would have been a success on her intended service to India. The Eastern Steam Navigation Company organized in 1851 failed to obtain mail contracts to the east and had to abandon plans to construct several 2000 ton steamships. In their place Brunel proposed to build very large ships to run to Ceylon where their cargoes could be sent on to Indian and Australian ports in smaller steamers. Brunel also proposed to employ both paddle-wheels and a screw propeller—this alone made GREAT EASTERN unique.

The keel of the great ship was laid on 1 May 1854 in the yard of Messrs. John Scott Russell & Company, Millwall. In keeping with other unique features of the enterprise she was built for a sideways launching. Russell designed the hull upon his "wave-line" principle with a parallel middle body of 120 feet (36,515 m). Brunel devised a cellular type of structure which in effect gave the ship two hulls from the keel to the waterline. The hull was divided transversely into 12 watertight compartments with no openings in the bulkheads below the second deck. The main deck, flush from stem to stern, was also of cellular construction. There were three other decks below this.

The main deck was dotted with skylights and companionways and there were small houses for some of the officers and a smoking saloon; all passenger accommodations were below deck. The plans showed quarters for 800 first class passengers, 2000 second class, and 1200 third class but for GREAT EASTERN's first voyage in 1859 staterooms

JOHN SCOTT RUSSELL—1808-1882

British engineer. Born near Glasgow it was intended that Russell should follow his father in the Presbyterian ministry but his early leanings were towards practical science. At 16 took his degree in natural science from the University of Glasgow. He worked in shops until at 19 he started lecturing on science at Edinburgh where he had the largest classes in the University's history. In 1832-3 he held the chair for the natural philosophy course. In 1834 Russell began his famous series of observations on waves conducting experiments on a section of the Edinburgh & Glasgow Canal. They led to his "wave-line" theory for ship forms that was applied to the form of GREAT EASTERN. According to this theory a ship's entrance—the length from the bow to the maximum section —must equal the length of a solitary wave having a natural

Great Eastern — page 70

speed equal to the maximum speed proposed for the ship. The run—from the maximum section to the stern—is two-thirds of the entrance. The remainder of the ship's length is parallel body. After managing for several years a shipyard at Greenock he opened his own iron foundry and shipyard on the Thames; he designed many successful steamers. The building of GREAT EASTERN, however, cost him his yard. He was active in many engineering fields and was one of the founders in 1860 of the now Royal Institution of Naval Architects. Russell died at Ventnor, Isle of Wight, on 8 June 1882.

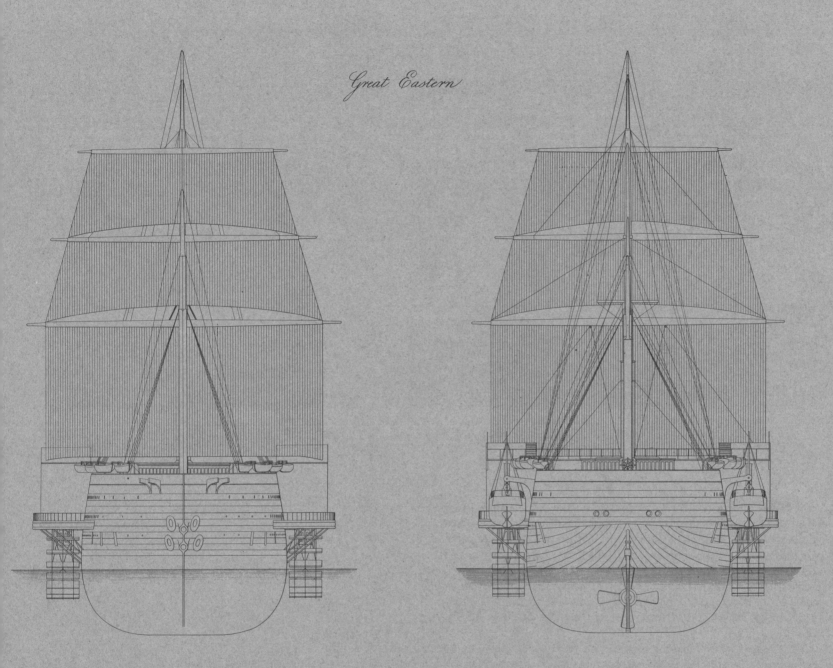

were fitted out on her second deck for only 300 first class passengers. The grand saloon, decorated in white and gilt with silver-oxidized ornamental ironwork, was 62 ft. (18,897 m) long, 36 ft. (10,972 m) wide, and 12 ft. (3,657 m) high. Her staterooms were about twice as large as the best in the Cunarders with two-high berths that folded into the bulkheads when not in use. Among the other items in each room was a settee that concealed a bath having taps for hot fresh and cold salt water. Below the accommodations were two engine rooms, five boiler rooms, bunkers for 12000 (12192) tons of coal and space for 6000 tons of cargo. Each of the five boiler rooms had its own funnel and there were six masts carrying 6500 sq. yds. (5435 m²) of auxiliary sails. GREAT EASTERN carried a total of 20 lifeboats when in service.

L'AIGLE

The French royal yacht, with Empress Eugenie on board, led the parade of 68 ships of various nationalities at the opening of the Suez Canal on 17 November 1869.

Russell's yard built GREAT EASTERN's paddle engines which were located between the second and third boiler rooms. Rated at 1000 (1014) n.h.p. there were four oscillating cylinders 74 in. (1,880 m) diameter by 14 ft. (4,267 m) stroke working in pairs, each pair having an independent air pump, condenser, and reverse gear to permit separate operation. Steam was supplied at 24 p.s.i. (1,687 kg/cm²) by four rectangular double-ended tubular boilers each having 10 furnaces. The original paddle-wheels, arranged to be disconnected in case of damage, were 56 ft. (17,068 m) in diameter with 30 radial floats; at 10.75 r.p.m. they propelled the ship at 7¼ knots (13,44 km/hr.).

The 1600 (1622) n.h.p. screw engines located aft were constructed by Messrs. James Watt & Company, Birmingham, and had four horizontal direct-acting cylinders 84 in. (2,134 m) diameter by 48 in. (1,219 m) stroke. Steam for these engines was generated at 25 p.s.i. (1,758 kg/cm²) in six rectangular double-ended tubular boilers each having 12 furnaces. The four-bladed iron screw propeller was 24 ft. (7,315 m) in diameter by 37 ft. (11,277 m) pitch. To avoid propeller drag when the ship was under way with paddles or sails, two 20 h.p. engines were fitted to keep the shaft turning. At 38.8 r.p.m. the propeller drove the ship at 9 knots (16,79 km/hr.).

GREAT EASTERN's launching was announced for 3 November 1857. On that date she was christened LEVIATHAN and started moving but as things seemed to be going wrong brakes were applied to checking winches and she came to a screeching halt. By jacking she was moved inches at a time and on 31 January 1858 she finally floated. The unforeseen launching costs and Brunel's actions caused the failure of the original company and for twenty months the ship rode at ancher in the Thames. Brunel and some of the original directors finally organized the Great Ship Company which purchased her and proceeded with the final outfitting for sea.

GREAT EASTERN, by which name she was registered, left the Thames for her trial trip on 7 September 1859 easily working up to a speed of 12 knots (22,24 km/hr.) in the Channel but an explosion in the water jacket of the forward funnel forced her into Weymouth for repairs. She continued on to Holyhead, Wales, where she was opened to sightseers. After successfully riding out a severe storm there the directors took her back to a safer berth in Southampton. In January 1859 there was another change of directors who finally got her ready for a passenger-carrying voyage.

Ignoring the fact that many of GREAT EASTERN's features made her unsuitable for short runs the new directors sent her to New York and she left Southampton on 17 June 1860 with 38 passengers, 8 company guests, and a crew of 418. She arrived in New York on 28 June after a passage of 11 days 2 hours during which she was some-what delayed by fog; her mean speed was 14 knots (25,95 km/hr.). She was greeted by enthusiastic crowds of visitors who swarmed over her. After her welcome in the U.S.A. had worn thin GREAT EASTERN returned to England on 16 August with 68 passen-gers. Several other trips across the Atlantic followed including one to Quebec in June 1861 with 40 passengers, 2500 troops, and 200 horses.

Sold in 1864 to the newly formed Great Eastern Steamship Company, Ltd., the ship was chartered for cable laying operations and between 1865 and 1874 GREAT EASTERN laid five transatlantic telegraph lines and one from Bombay to Suez. She was then laid up for eleven years. After a year as a show ship GREAT EASTERN went to the scrappers at Liverpool in 1888; it took three years to break her up.

In July 1859, a little before GREAT EASTERN left the Thames, DELTA of the Peninsular and Oriental Steam Navigation Company, Ltd. was launched. Apart from being considered the fastest English merchant ship afloat—she did 14.6 knots (27,06 km/hr.) on trials—she had a remarkable career. Designed by James Ash she was built by the Thames Iron Shipbuilding Company with engines by Messrs. John Penn & Company. As noted in connection with the original Collins Line ships, engineers were finding it as easy to over-power as to under-power a steamer. When smaller engines were installed in the P. & O. Line's iron paddler VALETTA of 1853 her original ones were too good to scrap and DELTA of about twice her tonnage was built to take them even though the P. & O. Line was then changing to screw propulsion.

Delta — page 68

DELTA followed the older type steamers in appearance having a clipper bow with bowsprit and a round counter stern with small quarter galleries. To indicate the relia-bility of her machinery she was given only a light two-masted schooner rig and she had two raking funnels, one on each side of the paddle-wheels. She had accommoda-tions for 126 first class and 50 second class passengers and there was a special room where the mails could be sorted at sea. Below the passengers' quarters was space for about 1100 (1118) tons of cargo.

The engines from VALETTA had two oscillating cylinders 72 in. (1,829 m) diameter by 7 ft. (2,134 m) stroke. Steam at 25 p.s.i. (1,758 kg/cm²) pressure was supplied by four sheet-flue boilers each having four furnaces. DELTA was fitted with feathering paddle-wheels. On such wheels the floats are arranged in pivots and so controlled that they enter and leave the water as nearly vertical as possible. Much power is lost in small diameter radial wheels by the flat angle at which the floats enter and leave the water.

DELTA first ran from Southampton to Port Said where mails and passengers were sent overland to ships waiting at Suez. At the end of 1869 she carried a special group of British guests to the opening ceremonies for the Suez Canal and was the first British ship to enter the canal. The newer screw propelled P. & O. Line ships were able to go through the canal to their eastern destinations so she was transferred to the Line's Far Eastern station.

In 1874 DELTA was sold to Japan becoming TAKASAGO MARU of the Nippon Yusen Kaisa. After four years of service her engines and boilers were removed for use ashore and she was sailed with a four-masted schooner rig back to the Clyde where a compound screw engine and new boilers were installed. Her profile then showed a three-masted schooner rig with one funnel. Returning to Japan she served on various local and inter-island runs until condemned to be scrapped in the mid 1890's. The Klondike gold rush of 1898 made anything afloat valuable and she was purchased by U.S.A. interests, renamed CENTENNIAL, and put into the Alaskan passenger service.

At the end of the gold boom CENTENNIAL was laid up in California, again apparently at the end of her life, but during the Russo-Japanese War she was sent to run the blockade of Vladivostock. Captured by a Japanese cruiser she was eventually restored to her owners for return to the U.S.A.; she was posted missing in March 1906. In 1913 a Russian expedition found her frozen fast in Arctic ice, still watertight but with no signs of the fate of the crew.

For centuries travel across the English Channel between Dover and Calais had been at the mercy of wind and tide. In good weather a fast sailing packet of the early nineteenth century made the crossing in about $3\frac{1}{2}$ hours but calms and tides often extended the time to two days. Although in 1816 the steamboat MAJESTIC crossed from Dover to Calais with 200 passengers regular service was not established until 1821 when ROB ROY, after two years in the Glasgow-Belfast trade, was put on the run. An 88 ton vessel 80.9 ft. (24,657 m) long on deck propelled by a 30 n.h.p. engine ROB ROY generally made the crossing in $2\frac{3}{4}$ hours. The French, impressed by her performance, purchased her in 1823 to carry their mails to England; they renamed her HENRI QUATRE.

In 1859 the Thames Iron Shipbuilding Company built the record-breaking JOHN PENN which made her first crossing in 1 hour 23 minutes at a mean speed of 15.2 knots. Another James Ash design she was a yachty-looking flush-deck vessel with a round counter stern and a clipper bow that had only a stub of a bowsprit. She had two well raked masts carrying trysails only and two tall thin funnels having the same rake.

JOHN PENN was named for her engine builder who installed a pair of oscillating engines rated at 150 n.h.p. With steam supplied at 22 p.s.i. (1,547 kg/cm^2) they developed 800 i.h.p. in service. The two cylinders were 46 in. (1,168 m.) diameter by 50 in. (1,270 m) stroke.

JOHN PENN was sold in 1862 to the Belgian government, renamed PERLE, and employed on the Ostende-Dover run until 1872. Purchased then by the French she kept the new name and served several years more on the Dover-Calais run.

While paddle-wheels continued as the means for propelling new cross-Channel steamers until the beginning of the twentieth century they were in 1861 nearing the end of their day on the Atlantic services. The first two screw-propelled Cunarders appeared in 1852. These were the iron screw steamers ALPS and ANDES of 1440

John Penn — page 69

HJEJLEN — 1861

82.417 × 11.646 × 5.667 feet
25,120 × 3,550 × 1,727 m

HJEJLEN, probably the oldest steel steamer in existence, has changed little since she was built by Baumgarten & Burmeister, Copenhagen, for Danish paper maker Michael Drewson. King Frederick VII was interested in her building and with his consort was aboard HJEJLEN for her maiden voyage on Silkeborgsøerne on 24 June 1861. She still carries a gilded figurehead and the Danish coat of arms on her paddle boxes but the helmsman now has a closed wheelhouse amidships and an awning shelters passengers sitting on her raised quarter deck. Instead of serving as a royal yacht she now carries up to 170 tourists and is more popular than modern motor-boats on the same route. HJEJLEN's oscillating engines have two cylinders 10 in. (0,254 m) diameter by 16 in. (0,406 m) stroke and her speed is about 8 knots (14,83 km/hr.). She has burned out two boilers and is now on her third.

tons each, primarily cargo ships intended for the West Indian service. At the height of its competition with the Collins Line, however, the Cunard Line built the iron paddle steamer PERSIA in 1855. At the time of her building she was the largest vessel on the North Atlantic run and she captured the eastbound Blue Ribbon from ARCTIC with an average speed of 13¾ knots.

Although designed to be built soon after PERSIA but not started for several years the last and finest of the Cunard Line's paddle steamers was launched at Govan, Scotland, on 25 June 1861. Her name was SCOTIA. Considering the many successful applications of the screw propeller the Cunard Line has been considered unduly conservative in using paddle wheels on SCOTIA. The line, however, was closely connected with the British government which followed the advice of older naval officers who still considered that paddle-wheels were better. The last Atlantic paddle steamers were built for the French Line in 1864.

Built of iron by Messrs. Robert Napier and Sons SCOTIA's hull had a double bottom and six transverse watertight bulkheads; she was considered to be the most strongly constructed merchant ship of her time. She was arranged to carry 300 passengers, all first class, and 1400 tons of cargo. Sail power was relatively small and with two widely spaced square-rigged masts she was nominally a brig. Two funnels completed her profile.

The Napier company also constructed SCOTIA's side-lever engines which had two cylinders 100 in. (2,540 m) diameter by 12 ft. (3,658 m) stroke. Rated at 975 n.h.p.

Scotia — page 72

these engines actually developed 4632 (4695) i.h.p. during her trials when she attained a speed of 16.5 knots (30,58 km/hr.); her mean speed in service was 13.5 knots (25,00 km/hr.). Eight tubular boilers having a total of forty furnaces supplied steam at 25 p.s.i. (1,758 kg/cm²). Fuel consumption was about 165 tons per day and the bunkers could carry 1800 (1829) tons.

Shortly after commissioning in 1862 SCOTIA captured the eastbound Blue Ribbon from PERSIA which she held until 1869. She took the westbound record from BALTIC in 1864. Although the last word in paddle-ship design and construction and the pride of the Cunard Line for many years, SCOTIA was really outdated and was withdrawn from passenger service in 1875.

A second career begain in 1879 when SCOTIA was sold to the Telegraph Construction and Maintenance Company and converted by Messrs. Laird Brothers, of Birkenhead, to a twin screw cable-laying steamer. In 1896 the bulkheads provided to keep her afloat in case of collision did keep her afloat after an explosion blew out her bow. Sold to the Commercial Pacific Cable Company in 1903 SCOTIA was wrecked on Guam in March 1904. All her people were removed safely as she hung on a reef amidships with both ends free—she broke in half during a storm about two weeks after striking the reef.

In contrast to ships designed for the North Atlantic service those intended for long distance runs offer a completely different set of requirements to their designers. The Peninsular & Oriental Line operated, in addition to the Southampton-Port Said run noted for DELTA, direct services to eastern ports via the Cape of Good Hope. CHUSAN of 1851, a 700 ton ship 190 ft. (57,910 m) long, inaugurated the Australian service in 1852.

One of the finest long distance liners of her day was POONAH, of 1862, the first of that name owned by the P. & O. Line. James Ash was her designer, too, and he received great credit for her plans. Like the other P. & O. ships of the period she had a graceful sailing-ship type hull with a clipper bow and a rounded transom stern with small quarter galleries. She carried a full barque rig and was fitted with one funnel. POONAH's iron hull was constructed by the Thames Iron Shipbuilding Company.

The P. & O. screw-propelled ships of this period were powered with a variety of engines. CHUSAN had oscillating engines, MADRAS of 1851 had beam engines with gearing, and HIMALAYA of 1852 had horizontal direct-acting trunk piston engines. By POONAH's time, a two-cylinder vertical inverted unit was the favored type. Marine engine terminology started in paddle ships where the cylinder was vertical and the piston rod came out of its top. When in screw-propelled ships the positions were reversed the term "inverted" was employed. POONAH's engines were constructed by Messrs. Humphrys and Tennant; they developed 2356 i.h.p. at 25 p.s.i. (1,758 kg/cm²) steam pressure.

In 1875 POONAH was lengthened 88 ft. (26,822 m) amidships and given compound-expansion engines of 2600 i.h.p. working at 65 p.s.i. (4,570 kg/cm²) pressure, a much more economical installation. She continued in P. & O. service until 1889 except for a period of duty as a troop transport to Egypt between 1884 and 1886. Messrs. Arbid & Co. of London purchased POONAH in 1889. They removed all of her passenger accommodations and employed her as a cargo vessel, mostly in the Mediterranean, until 1892 when she was taken to Sunderland and broken up.

OSCILLATING ENGINE

The best paddle-wheel engine under most circumstances proved to be the oscillating cylinder type in which the cylinder swings on large trunnions. It was the lightest and most compact form of paddle engine and had the fewest working parts. Steam was admitted and exhausted through the trunnions and because of leakage problems around the trunnions steam pressures employed were usually not over 30 p.s.i. (2,109 kg/cm²). The oscillating engine worked best when its mean position was vertically under the paddle shaft but the mean position could be at any angle; on some screw-propelled ships it was horizontal. The best oscillating engines were those constructed by Messrs. John Penn & Sons; the largest ever built were those in GREAT EASTERN.

Poonah — page 73

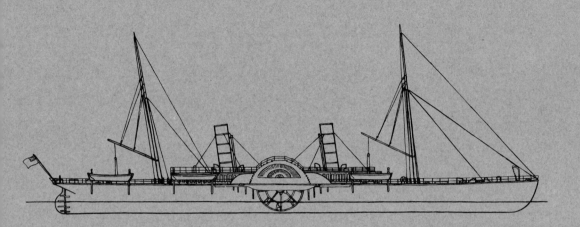

COLONEL LAMB — 1864 — 1788 T

281.0 × 34.6 × 16.7 feet
85,646 × 10,546 × 5,090 m

COLONEL LAMB was designed to run the blockade of the Southern States during the Civil War in the U.S.A. Constructed by Messrs. Jones, Quiggin & Co., Liverpool, she was the largest steel vessel yet built and one of the earliest on the Atlantic; the blockade runner HOPE by the same builders had a duplicate hull. With a light two-masted schooner rig, two large funnels, and a long slim, low-profile hull having a plumb stem and an elliptical stern she was a rakish looking vessel. COLONEL LAMB was propelled by engines of 350 n.h.p. and feathering paddle-wheels at a maximum speed of about 17 knots (31,50 km/hr.); some blockade runners made 20 knots (37,06 km/hr.) in light condition. She ran the blockade several times and successfully eluded capture; 1504 other blockade runners did not. Returning to Liverpool in 1865 she was sold to the Brazilian government and chartered to carry a cargo of explosives across the Atlantic but she blew up in the Mersey river on the night before her scheduled departure.

Among the successful steamship lines competing on the Atlantic in the 1860's was the Liverpool, New York and Philadelphia Steamship Company later known as the Inman and International Steamship Company, Ltd. Founded by William Inman the line's first sailing was made on 11 December 1850 by CITY OF GLASGOW, an iron screw-propelled steamer that had made two or three previous voyages across the Atlantic for other owners. Part of the success of the line came from Inman's interest in the comfort of the passengers particularly those in the steerage; the remainder came from the economy of the line's ships.

The Inman Line made its bid for the Blue Ribbon with the launching in December 1865 of the first CITY OF PARIS. Messrs. Tod and McGregor built both her hull and machinery at Glasgow. In keeping with Inman tradition she had a clipper bow and was subdivided by five transverse watertight bulkheads. CITY OF PARIS carried a full ship rig and had one funnel.

Orginally CITY OF PARIS was fitted with horizontal trunk engines having two cylinders 82 in. (2,083 m) diameter by 42 in. (1,067 m) stroke; rated at 500 n.h.p. they developed in service 2600 i.h.p. Eight rectangular fire-tube boilers with three furnaces each supplied steam at 30 p.s.i. (2,109 kg/cm²) pressure. With this machinery the vessel's sea speed was 13½ knots (25,05 km/hr.) and she burned 105 tons of coal per day. In 1867 CITY OF PARIS won the westbound Blue Ribbon from SCOTIA at a mean speed of 13.77 knots (25,56 km/hr.) but she was never able to take the eastbound title. Although the earlier Inman lines were by no means record breakers their long and successful operations led the Cunard Line to abandon paddle-wheel propulsion.

In 1879 while serving as a transport in the Zulu War CITY OF PARIS stranded on a rock in Simons Bay, South Africa, but was refloated and returned to service. She was repowered in 1881 and in 1883 she was sold to Abraham Hoffnung of London. Like many other liners she ended her days as a cargo vessel. As TONQUIN carrying coal from Cardiff to Marseilles in March 1885 she collided with a French steamer in fog off Malaga and sank.

City of Paris — page 74

CONNECTOR — 1863

A tug with barges is an application of the "train" concept to floating equipment—the tug is kept in constant service as the "locomotive" delivering loaded barges to various destinations and picking up the empties for a return trip. Early steamboat owners on the Clyde considered that the carriage of cargo directly on a steamer was an uneconomical use of a steam engine. CONNECTOR was constructed for the same purpose but with appropriately designed sections to give the whole a ship-shaped form. With four hinged joints which could easily be disconnected she had a sharp bow section; three cargo sections, and the stern section which contained the screw propelling machinery. It was considered that a proper connector ship should have nine cargo sections so that three with cargo could be at sea, three loading cargo, and three discharging. Thus the stern section with the machinery need never be idle. Each cargo section had one mast and sails in order that it could be operated independently if necessary. Among other advantages claimed for CONNECTOR were high speed because of the narrowness of beam, yielding joints which made it impossible for the ship to break her back in heavy seas, and the ability to detach quickly any section in case of fire or leaks. Built for the Jointed Ship Company it was intended that CONNECTOR and a fleet of similar vessels be employed in the coal trade between Newcastle and London but nothing came of the scheme. In 1963 Japanese shipbuilders proposed to construct a large tanker with a pinned joint amidships to overcome longitudinal strength problems.

ADRIATIC · 1856

New York and Liverpool United States Mail Steamship Company

343.8 × 50.0 × 32.8 feet ☾ 3670 T ☾ 104,787 × 15,239 × 9,997 m

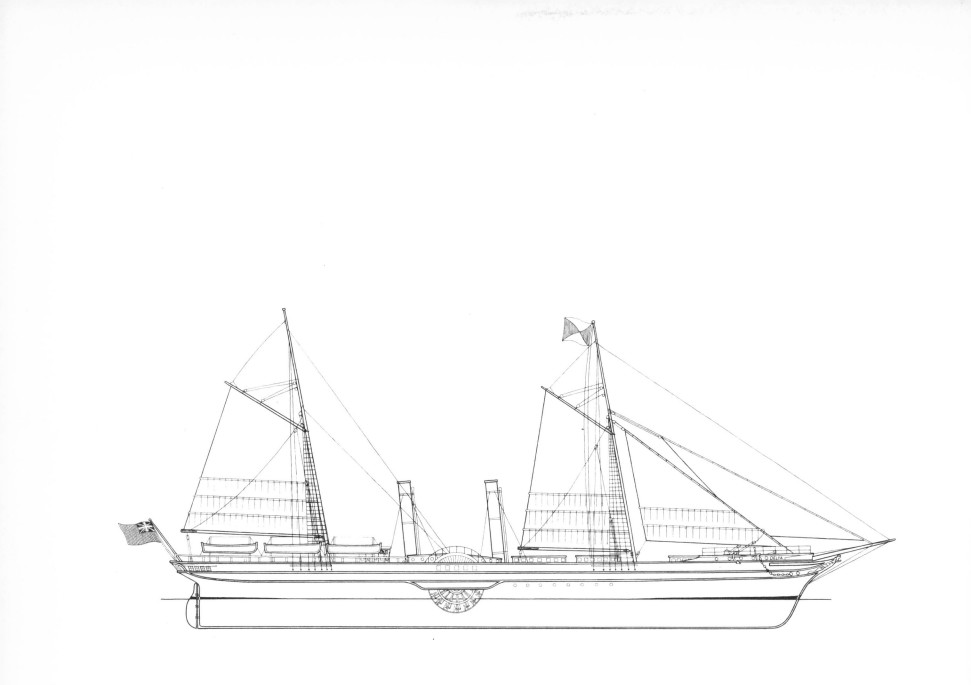

DELTA · 1859

Peninsular and Oriental Steam Navigation Company, Ltd.

310.0 × 35.25 × 22.08 feet ⟪ 1618 T ⟪ 94,485 × 10,744 × 6,730 m

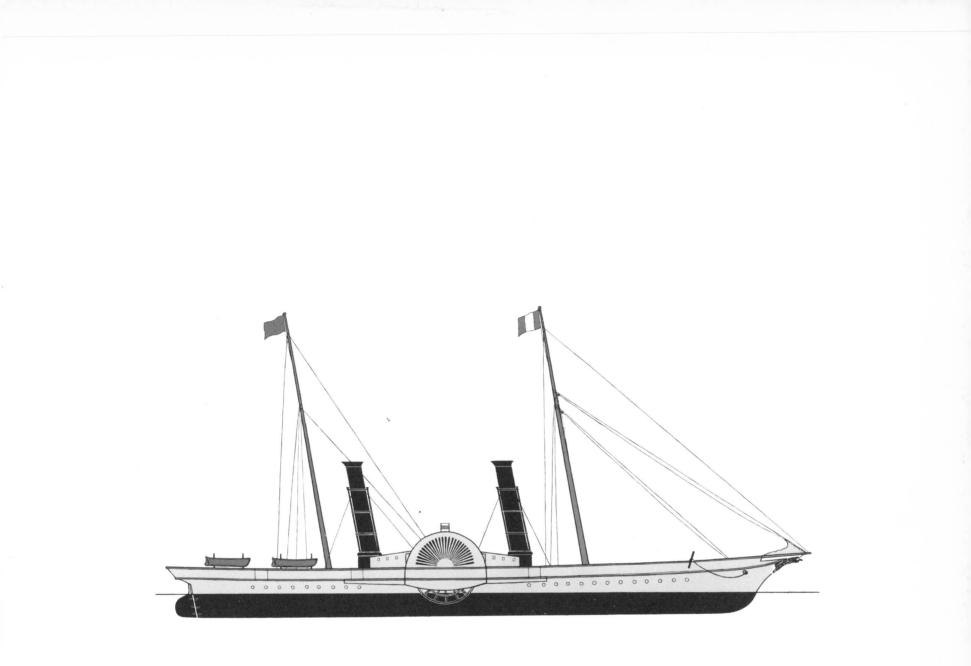

JOHN PENN · 1859

English, French, and Belgian Royal Mail Company

170.0 × 20.0 × 11.0 feet ◑ 340 T ◑ 51,814 × 6,096 × 3,353 m

GREAT EASTERN · 1858

Eastern Steam Navigation Company

680.0 × 82.7 × 48.2 feet ☾ 18915 T ☾ 207,257 × 25,206 × 14,691 m

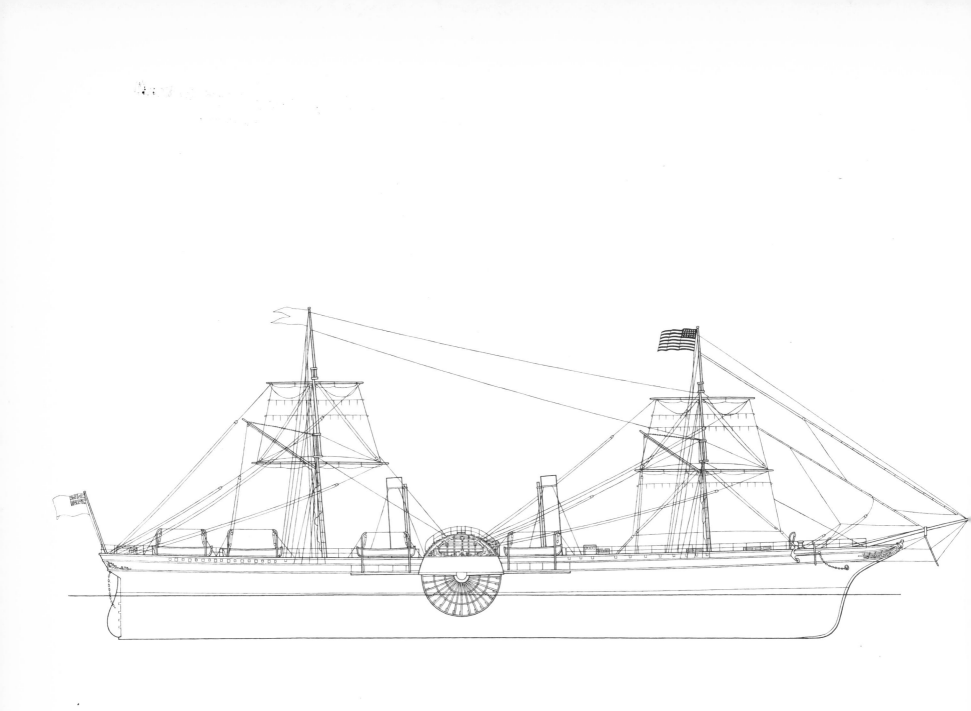

SCOTIA · 1861

The Cunard Company

379.0 × 47.8 × 30.5 feet ◖ 3871 T ◖ 115,516 × 14,569 × 9,296 m

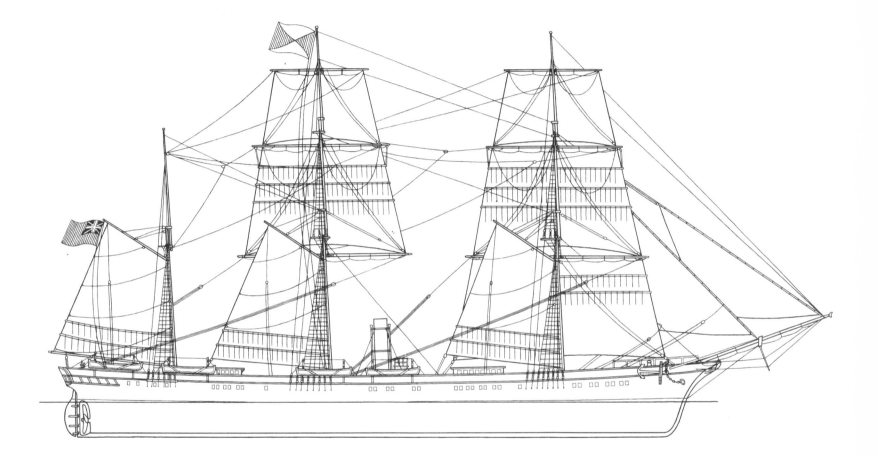

POONAH · 1862

Peninsular and Oriental Steam Navigation Company, Ltd.

315.0 × 41.6 × 27.4 feet ◖ 2152 T ◖ 96,009 × 12,679 × 8,351 m

73

CITY OF PARIS · 1865

Liverpool, New York and Philadelphia Steamship Co.

346.0 × 40.5 × 26.2 feet ❰ 2651 T ❰ 105,457 × 12,344 × 7,986 m

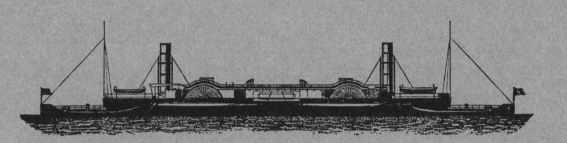

BESSEMER — 1874

This ship with a hydraulicly controlled swinging saloon was an attempt to eliminate seasickness. It was not a succes,s however. See also page 78.

The last paddle steamer constructed for the Atlantic service was the British-built iron-hulled NAPOLÉON III, 3376 tons, launched in February 1865 for the Compagnie Générale Transatlantique. Popularly known in the U.S.A. as the French Line and in France as the Transat, this line inaugurated its service between France and the U.S.A. on 15 June 1864 with the sailing of its paddle steamer WASHINGTON, 3401 tons. She was soon joined by her sistership LAFAYETTE; EUROPE of about the same dimensions was added to the run in 1866. These ships were followed by PÉREIRE, VILLE-DE-PARIS, and SAINT LAURENT, all designed as paddle steamers but, because of the success of the screw-propelled Cunarders, converted to screw propulsion while on the stocks. None were designed as record breakers but were given qualities intended to attract and hold customers—luxurious accommodations, good riding ability at sea, and, of course, a superb cuisine.

PÉREIRE, named for the president of the French Line, was built of iron by Messrs. Robert Napier and Sons, Glasgow, and launched on 4 November 1865. She had the fine-lined sailing-ship type of hull with a clipper bow then customary for paddle steamers. Her original brig rig was changed to that of a barque when she was converted to screw propulsion; she had but one funnel. Her passenger accommodations were arranged for 284 in the first class and 134 in the second.

Designed for a service speed of 13 knots (24,13 km/hr.) PÉREIRE was powered by compound engines of 800 n.h.p. having two 45 in. (1,143 m) and two 84 in. (2,134 m) diameter cylinders with a 4 ft. (1,219 m) stroke. On trial she reached a speed of 15¼ knots (28,26 km/hr.). She left Havre on her maiden voyage to New York 29 March 1866 taking ten days for the passage but later that year she reduced the time to nine days which stood as a record between those ports for some years. In 1872 she was refitted with new boilers, a set of three-cylinder compound engines that developed 1250 n.h.p., and a new propeller all of which increased her speed to 15.5 knots (28.73 km/hr.); she was also given two funnels like the newer ships in the fleet.

Outclassed and replaced on the Atlantic by newer ships PÉREIRE served on other runs maintained by the French Line. In 1881 on a passage from Marseilles to Malta machinery trouble forced her to put into the port of Goletta on the Gulf of Tunis where she caught fire. To extinguish the flames and to protect other shipping in the port she was sunk by a spar torpedo. The resulting damage was small and she was soon raised and returned to service. By 1889 she was finally considered too old for any of the French Line's services and was sold to Messrs. Kinnear & Company, London.

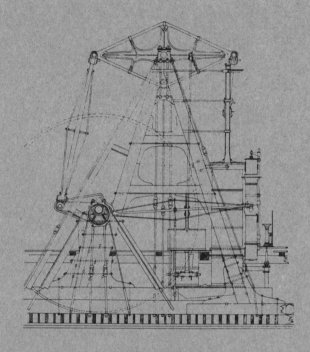

Péreire — page 85

VERTICAL BEAM ENGINE

Developed by Robert L. Stevens in the U.S.A. about 1822 from the original Boulton & Watt beam pumping engines and widely employed there for river and sound steamers and ferry boats. It never found favor in Europe. This type of engine was reliable, economical, and easy to maintain. Some were used in two and even three boats—70 to 80 years of service was not unusual.

PÉREIRE's new owners removed her engines and boilers and converted her to a four-masted full-rigged ship. She went to sea again as LANCING by which name she was known until the end of her career. Except for a few long passages such as six months from Calcutta to New York she established a good reputation for speed once averaging 18 knots (33,36 km/hr.) for 72 hours, faster than she ever went under steam. In 1893 she went under the Norwegian flag until 1896 when she was sold to a Canadian from Quebec. She went back to Norwegian owners again in 1901 and changed hands under that flag in 1918. After 24 years as a steamer and 35 years as a sailing vessel she was broken up at Genoa early in 1925 having been classed 100 A.1 by Lloyds until her end.

The Act of Congress that provided for U.S. mail contracts on the Atlantic also included a service between Panama and the Columbia River. The Oregon Boundary Treaty of 1846 made service to the settlers in this region more urgent and a contract was finally signed on 16 November 1847 which led to the founding of the Pacific Mail Steamship Company. When in 1865 bids were advertised for the establishment of a mail service between the U.S.A. and China the Pacific Mail was the only bidder and it received the contract for service from San Francisco to Hong Kong with stops at Honolulu and Yokohama.

Required to make twelve round trips per year with ships of at least 3000 tons the Pacific Mail contracted for the four largest wooden commercial steamships ever built. These were AMERICA, CHINA, GREAT REPUBLIC, and JAPAN. All except CHINA were constructed by Henry Steers at Greenpoint, Long Island,—William H. Webb built CHINA in Manhattan—and the first of the four, GREAT REPUBLIC, was launched on 8 November 1866; she was longer but not as wide or as deep as the famous clipper of the same name. These four giants had fine-lined hulls with plumb stems and round counter sterns; they were heavily constructed and were strengthened with diagonal iron strapping. Because of the heavy bottom structure the registered depth of 22.8 ft. (6,950 m) is misleading as the molded depth to the main deck was 31 ft. 4 in. (9,550 m). There were three full decks—main, berth, and cargo—with orlop decks fore and aft of the machinery spaces. A spar deck was fitted from bow to stern 8 ft. 6 in. (2,590 m) above the main deck which was closed in at the sides forward of the paddle boxes.

Accommodations were arranged on GREAT REPUBLIC's berth and main decks for 250 cabin passengers aft and 1200 steerage passengers forward. The pilot house was on the spar deck just abaft the foremast and an attached house contained the officers' cabins and a smoking room for the passengers. All four ships were fitted with small barque rigs but in service it was the practice to carry the yards on deck and to employ fore-and-aft canvas only except in emergencies. Each ship carried 12 metal lifeboats, a captain's gig, and a bellows-inflated India rubber life raft capable of holding nearly 100 persons. The holds could carry over 2000 (2032) tons of cargo, tanks held 18500 gallons (70030 liters) of fresh water, and the bunkers when full held 1500 (1524) tons of coal.

GREAT REPUBLIC was powered by a 1500 (1520) h.p. vertical beam engine built by the Novelty Iron Works; the single cylinder was 105 in. (2,667 m) diameter by 12 ft. (3,658 m) stroke. Steam at 20 p.s.i. (1,406 kg/cm²) pressure was supplied by four tubular boilers having six furnaces each; the ship had a surface condenser. In view of European progress the Pacific Mail was criticized for employing paddle-wheels on

LANCING

PÉREIRE as four-masted ship. From a model in Norsk Sjöfartsmuseum at Oslo.

Great Republic — page 86

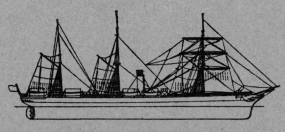

HOLLAND — 1869 — 3847 T

395.1 × 40.8 × 33.2 feet
120,423 × 12,436 × 10,119 m

During a refit in 1869 when she was lengthened about 25 ft. (7,620 m) HOLLAND was given the first inverted compound expansion engines to be employed on the North Atlantic run. From about 1850, however, compound
continued

these ships but the lag in technological development in the U.S.A. was responsible. Large iron hulls were impossible at the time and the flexibility of large wooden ships caused trouble with long propeller shafts.

There was no incentive for speed records on the Pacific—safe operation and adherence to schedules were more important. Company regulations limited the ships to a speed of 9.5 knots (17,71 km/hr.) at sea. A major reason for this was fuel economy as the 5000 mile (9266 km) passage from San Francisco to Yokohama—the Honolulu stop was never made—provided no opportunity to refuel. The average of westbound passages was 23 days 19 hours and eastbound 22 days 20 hours; the regularity of the service was the wonder of its time.

After eight years of being the only vessels on the route, these great ships were gradually replaced by iron screw-propelled steamers. GREAT REPUBLIC suffered no major mishaps. She broke her starboard paddle shaft in 1868 when 16 days out of San Francisco but continued under sail with her port wheel in operation. A partial fracture was discovered in Yokohama in 1872 but she had fine weather for the crossing and arrived in San Francisco with both wheels turning. Her last voyage to China began on 1 September 1876 and at its end she was turned over as part payment for new screw steamers being built for the Pacific Mail. In June 1878 GREAT REPUBLIC started on a coastal run between San Francisco, Astoria, and Portland and met her end on Sand Island at the mouth of the Columbia on 19 April 1879.

Two large white boats looking like frosted wedding cakes dashing through the night side by side, paddle-wheels churning foam, sparks flying from tall stacks—such were the widely sold nineteenth-century lithographs of steamboat races on the Mississippi. Perhaps the most famous of the river races was that in 1870 between the packets NATCHEZ and ROBERT E. LEE over the 1218 mile (1960 km) course from New Orleans to St. Louis. Officially it was not a race as the government disapproved of racing and both captains placed notices in the newspapers disclaiming any knowledge of a race. Most of the world, however, seemed to know about it and reportedly over $1,000,000 was wagered on its outcome.

In June 1870 NATCHEZ, sixth of that name owned by Captain Thomas P. Leathers, set a record for the course of 3 days 21 hours and 58 minutes. Captain John W. Cannon of ROBERT E. LEE was determined to better it. He stripped his boat of all unnecessary equipment, refused all cargo and passengers, and arranged that the steamer FRANK PARGOUD would supply coal for the first 100 miles (161 km); further up stream coal barges would be waiting in the river.

NATCHEZ returned to New Orleans and loaded a few hundred tons of cargo plus some passengers for a scheduled 30 June sailing. On that day ROBERT E. LEE got under way at 4:55 P.M. followed in five minutes by NATCHEZ. At 300 miles (483 km) up the river the former led by 10 minutes, mainly the result of NATCHEZ's landings for fuel; further on she adopted the barge system, too. ROBERT E. LEE arrived at St. Louis in 3 days 18 hours and 30 minutes; NATCHEZ arrived 6 hours and 36 minutes later having stopped because of fog between Memphis and Cairo. Many of the bets were cancelled as it was considered that ROBERT E. LEE had been unfairly aided by FRANK PARGOUD. The two racers were evenly matched—ROBERT E. LEE was slightly smaller than NATCHEZ but looked larger and had the larger engines. Knowledgeable river people have since considered NATCHEZ the faster boat.

continued

engines had been installed in many ships, both paddle-wheel and screw-propelled intended for long distance services. HOLLAND's inverted engines, rated at 300 n.h.p., had two 46 in. (1,168 m) diameter high pressure cylinders mounted on top of two 86 in. (2,184 m) diameter low pressure cylinders; the common stroke was 48 in. (1,219 m). Jonathan Carter Hornblower in 1781 constructed and patented a compound engine having two cylinders that worked on the same end of an overhead beam. Arthur Woolf revived the compound engine in 1804; his name is often associated with the type. Compound engines were installed in a U.S.A. river steamer in 1825 and in French vessels in 1829 and 1837.

Natchez — page 87

The great packets on the Mississippi were side-wheelers with their paddles located well aft. Dickens had few good words for the boats of his day but by Mark Twain's time their accommodations rivalled the best ashore and were far more elegant than any ocean steamship. In appearance the boats were much alike as operating conditions dictated most of their characteristics. A wide, shallow, flat-bottom, wooden hull was the work of shipwrights and on its wide overhanging main deck were located the boilers, fuel, engines, most of the cargo, and deck passengers; on a breadth of hull of 46 ft. (14,020 m) NATCHEZ had an overall breadth of 83 ft. (25,298 m) and could carry 5500 bales of cotton. Supported on pillars from 15 to 20 ft. (4,572-6,096 m) above the main deck was the work of the joiners, the hurricane or saloon deck, the promenade deck, and the "Texas" deck with the pilot house. Down the middle of the hurricane deck from the smoke pipes or chimneys—there was little seagoing language on the river—nearly to the stern was the saloon with its clerestory. It might be in length from 150-250 ft. (35,718-66,197 m) and was decorated in white and gilt with numerous glittering chandeliers. Scenes were painted on the doors of the staterooms which surrounded the saloon. There were more staterooms on the promenade deck above.

The side paddle-wheels of the big packets were operated independently by separate engines. Horse-powers were unknown on the river as the engineers rated their boats by the number of boilers and sizes of the cylinders. NATCHEZ was an eight boiler boat with cylinders 34 in. (0,864 m) diameter by 10 ft. (3,048 m) stroke; her boilers were of the flue type 42 in. (1,067 m) diameter by 36 ft. (10,972 m) long that supplied steam at about 140 p.s.i. (9,843 kg/cm²) pressure. With paddle-wheels 42 ft. (12,801 m) in diameter and 16 ft. (4,877 m) wide she could make about 18 miles (28,97 km) per hour up river while coming down river with the current 25 miles (40,23 m) per hour was often attained. Because they were built of soft woods and suffered fires, boiler explosions, snagging on sunken trees, and strandings none of the boats lasted long. This famous racing NATCHEZ was dismantled in 1879 and replaced by the seventh boat to bear that name for Captain Leathers.

In 1871 the Oceanic Steam Navigation Company, better known as the White Star Line, was founded to continue the Australian service made famous by the clipper ships of Messrs. Pilkington and Wilson and to enter the Atlantic service with new ships to be built by Messrs. Harland & Wolff, Ltd. of Belfast. The first ship of the new line, OCEANIC, left Liverpool on her maiden voyage to New York on 2 March 1871. Overheated bearings caused her to put into Holyhead for a few days but when she finally arrived in New York she attracted almost as much attention as had GREAT EASTERN eleven years earlier. After a few further adjustments based on operating experience she proved a fast and satisfactory ship although she never held the Blue Ribbon.

OCEANIC and her sisters ATLANTIC, BALTIC, and REPUBLIC, single screw ships constructed of iron, were of a type later perfected by their builder and were very narrow for their length compared with other ships of their time. With straight stems, four-masted barque rigs, and single funnels they were impressive looking ships; next to GREAT EASTERN they were the largest steamers afloat. Their design broke from the traditions inherited from the early steamships where the paddle-wheels and their machinery had forced the passenger accommodations towards the ends—first class passengers aft and second class forward. Harland & Wolff put the first class cabins and dining saloon amidships where the ship's motion would be less

CASTALIA — 1874 — 1533 T

290.0 × 60.0 × 14.2 feet
88,389 × 18,287 × 4,328 m

CASTALIA's design was intended to obviate "mal de mer" on the rough crossing from Dover to Calais. In this she was fairly successful but she had a short active life because her top speed was barely 11 knots (20,39 km/hr.). She can best be described as two halves of a longitudinally divided hull placed 26 ft. (7,925 m) apart and bound together with a strong deck. CASTALIA was propelled by two paddle-wheels placed in tandem between the hulls each worked by two direct-acting diagonal engines, one in each hull. Thus there were four combined engine and boiler rooms. She was a true double-ender with rudders at each end of each hull and duplicate controls to eliminate the need for turning in restricted ports. CALAIS-DOUVRES of 1877 was a development of CASTALIA that was faster and a better sea boat. Another attack on sea-sickness was BESSEMER of 1874, a single-hulled vessel propelled by four paddle-wheels and fitted with a swinging saloon controlled by hydraulic rams. She was not a success. See page 75.

Oceanic — page 88

ZOROASTER — 1877

The carriage of oil in bulk in wooden sailing vessels can be traced easily back to the early eighteenth century in China and Burma. In 1725 Peter the Great of Russia issued regulations for carrying oil in bulk up the Volga. The first iron sailing vessel with built-in tanks for bulk oil cargoes was probably RAMSEY of 1862 built for a Mr. Gibson of the Isle of Man and she was soon followed by
continued

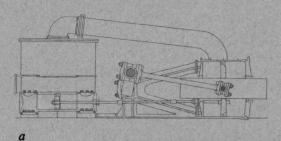

a

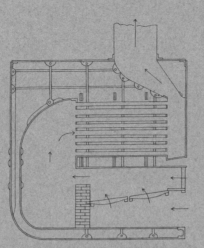

d

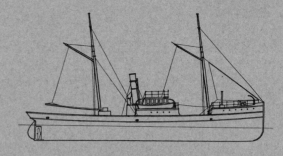

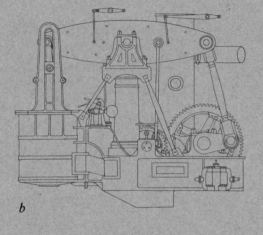

b

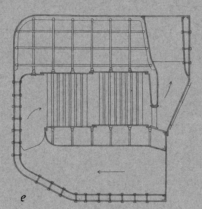

e

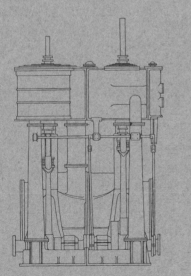

c

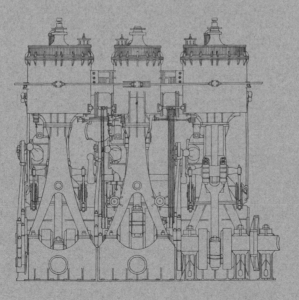

continued

others. The first steamship with oil tanks was the Belgian VADERLAND of 1872. She and two sisters were primarily passenger ships with five large oil tanks built into their lower holds. Because of certain difficulties with the Belgian government and the fact that U.S.A. law did not permit passenger ships to carry oil in bulk these ships never did load an oil cargo. ZOROASTER was the first steamship to actually carry petroleum or its products in bulk. Built of steel by the yard of Lindholmen-Motala-Norrköping in Sweden for Ludwig Nobel she had 19 independent tanks capable of carrying a cargo of 250 tons of kerosine. She was one of the earliest steamers to use oil as fuel.

TYPICAL SCREW ENGINES

a TRUNK ENGINE — *circa 1855 — For installation in a restricted space this engine has in effect a hollow piston rod in which the connecting rod is fitted.*

b GEARED BEAM ENGINE — *circa 1860 — One of many forms of geared drives used to obtain relatively high propeller revolutions from a slow moving engine.*

c INVERTED COMPOUND ENGINES — *circa 1870 — With one high-pressure and one low-pressure cylinder such units were widely employed in all sizes of vessels from launches to liners.*

TYPICAL BOILERS

d RETURN FLUE BOILER — *circa 1850-60 — Combustion gases pass from the furnaces to a chamber and back through large diameter flues to the uptake. The flues are surrounded by the water in the boiler which at steaming level is above the highest flue.*

e TUBULAR BOILER — *circa 1850-60 — In addition to heating the water in the boiler directly over the furnaces the combustion gases pass around a series of water-filled tubes.*

noticeable as well as being away from the vibration of the propeller. The saloon, extending across the ship, had large outside windows which gave it a light and airy appearance. Outside cabins were arranged fore and aft of the saloon. Accommodations were provided for 200 first class passengers and 1000 in the steerage, the latter being divided into three groups—single men forward, single women and married couples aft. A number of refinements such as electric call bells for stewards, coal-burning fireplaces in the saloon, fresh and salt running water in the staterooms, smoking room, and a ladies' boudoir made the ships outstanding.

At the time of building OCEANIC and her sisters Harland & Wolff were not able to build the required machinery so the job went to Messrs. Maudslay, Sons and Field. The ships were propelled by tandem inverted compound engines of 3000 (3041) i.h. p. arranged so that each pair of cylinders could be operated as a unit in case of accident. There were two high pressure cylinders of 41 in. (1,041 m) diameter and two low pressure of 78 in. (1,981 m) diameter; the stroke was 5 ft. (1,524 m). Twelve boilers working at 65 p.s.i. (4,570 kg/cm²) pressure and having two furnaces each were installed in each ship. The average speed was a little over 14 knots (25,95 km/hr.).

In 1875 OCEANIC went to the Pacific via the Suez Canal to start a new service for the Occidental & Oriental Line between Hong Kong, Yokohama, and San Francisco. She returned to Liverpool in 1879 for new boilers and a general modernization and sailed again to the Pacific in 1880. Another refit and a repowering was contemplated in 1895 but a survey showed her to be in poor condition. She was broken up on the Thames in 1896.

When the White Star Line was beginning its operations to New York still another company was being organized on the western side of the Atlantic. The Pennsylvania Railroad Company, interested in increasing imports that it could transport inland, had tried to form an association with the Anchor Line but negotiations collapsed and the American Steamship Company was founded by the railroad directors in 1871. Four single-screw iron steamships were ordered from The William Cramp & Sons Ship & Engine Building Company of Philadelphia. The resulting ships were nothing spectacular but became well known for their comfortable passenger accommodations and good cargo capacity. Their speeds, about 13 knots (24,13 km/hr.) on the average, compared favorably with the best at that time.

The first of the quartette, PENNSYLVANIA, was launched in August 1872 and sailed on her maiden voyage to Liverpool in May 1873. She was followed by OHIO, INDIANA, and ILLINOIS. Their hull lines were quite fine, the water-line forward being slightly hollow, and they had plumb stems and elliptical counter sterns. The arrangement of quarters on their three decks followed the accepted pattern of their time. The main deck, flush from stem to stern, was broken only by a few small houses, companionways, and skylights. Quarters for 76 first class passengers were located aft on the second deck while quarters for the officers, some special third class passengers, and the crew occupied the amidships and forward portions of this deck. The third deck was given over to the steerage passengers; the ships carried a total of 800 in third class and steerage. Below the third deck were the holds for 1740 tons of cargo. All four ships carried brig rigs and had one funnel. For some years they were the only U.S. flag ships in the transatlantic trade.

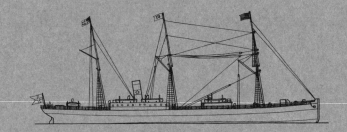

THINGVALLA — 1874 — 2436 T

300.0 × 37.0 × 21.583 feet
91,437 × 11,277 × 6,578 m

While the glamorous Atlantic Blue Ribbon liners held most of the public's attention scores of smaller steamships were plodding back and forth across the ocean carrying their passengers and cargo without notice. They made newspaper headlines only when involved in a serious accident. Such a ship was the single-screw, iron steamer THINGVALLA built by Burmeister & Wain, Copenhagen. In 1888 while operated in the immigrant trade in conjunction with GEISER and ISLAND by the Thingvalla Line (Dampskibs Selskabet "Thingvalla") THINGVALLA collided with GEISER in a fog off Sable Island. GEISER was cut practically in two just abaft the main mast and sank in a few minutes with the loss of 119 lives. THINGVALLA's collision bulkhead held and after transferring her own passengers and GEISER's survivors to the German steamer WIELAND she limped into Halifax. THINGVALLA had six watertight bulkheads and four decks, one plated with iron while the others had iron tie plates and wooden sheathing. When in the immigrant trade she had accommodations for 50 first class passengers, 50 second class, and 900 in the steerage. Her rig was that of a barquentine. She had a set of four-cylinder compound engines rated at 225 n.h.p. which developed 900 i.h.p. in service; steam was supplied by two boilers. The Thingvalla Line, the first Danish steamship line to the U.S.A., and its ships were taken over in 1898 by the Scandinavian-American Line (Det Forenede Dampskibs-Selskab) and THINGVALLA made her final run to New York in 1900.

Pennsylvania — page 89

BARON NILS ADOLF ERIK NORDENSKIÖLD — 1832-1901

Scientist and explorer. Born and educated in Helsingfors, then part of Russia, he specialized in chemistry and mineralogy. In 1858 he moved to Stockholm and after taking part in an expedition to Spitzbergen to study glaciers he was appointed Professor and Curator of the mineralogical department of the Swedish National Museum. From 1861 to 1875 he led many expeditions to Spitzbergen, Greenland, and North Russia. In 1875-76 a successful voyage east along the North Russian coast, including a boat journey up the Yenisei river, led him to attempt the long-sought North-East Passage. He believed in Barent's theory of an ice-free channel along the north Siberian coast and a strong easterly current there set up by the earth's rotation. With financial aid from Sweden's King Oscar II and others he purchased and rebuilt the German steam whaler VEGA. Starting from Karlskrona on 22 June 1878 with a crew of 18 commanded by Captain L. Palander VEGA was stopped by ice only 120 miles (193 km) from Bering Strait. She was frozen in from 28 September 1878 until 18 July 1879 and East Cape was finally passed on 20 July thus completing the first passage around the north coast of Asia. On his return to Sweden Nordenskiöld was made a baron. He is also noted for his work in the field of historical geography publishing his "Facsimile Atlas" in 1889 and "Periplus" in 1897. Nordenskiöld died in Stockholm on 12 August 1901.

PENNSYLVANIA and her sisters had compound expansion engines rated at 600 n.h.p. with cylinders of 48 and 99 in. (1,219 and 2,515 m) diameter by 4 ft. (1,219 m) stroke. With steam at 60 p.s.i. (4,219 kg/cm²) pressure these engines developed 2800 (2830) i.h.p. in service. Coal consumption was in the order of 40 tons per day.

The American Steamship Company operated without any subsidy and by 1880 it was found that most of the first class passenger trade had left the 3000 ton ships. In 1884 PENNSYLVANIA and the other three ships were taken over by the International Navigation Company (Red Star Line) which removed the first class quarters and operated the ships as emigrant and cargo carriers only, for which service they were well suited. During the 1898 gold rush the four were run between Seattle and Alaska by the Empire Transportation Company. PENNSYLVANIA was finally scrapped after the first World War.

The size of ships for all ocean routes was gradually increasing and ORIENT of 1879 was the largest yet built, excluding GREAT EASTERN, designed to operate from the Thames. Built for the Australian service of the Orient Line she was considered one of the finest liners of her day and she introduced a new standard in the Australian trade.

Messrs. John Elder & Company, Glasgow, built ORIENT's hull and engines. She was subdivided by eight transverse bulkheads and had four decks, the lower two of which were completely plated with iron; the upper decks had iron tie-plates and

Orient — page 90

wood sheathing. There was a double bottom tank aft and a deep tank amidships for the carriage of water ballast. Amidships there was a short superstructure extending from side to side and she had rather extensive deckhouses. Accommodations were provided for 120 first class, 130 second class, and 300 third class passengers. ORIENT had four masts, the two forward carrying square sails with fore-and-aft sails on the others. As built she had two funnels.

ORIENT was fitted with a set of three-cylinder inverted compound engines which had one 60 in. (1,524 m) diameter and two 85 in. (2,159 m) diameter cylinders. The stroke was 5 ft. (1,524 m) and with steam at 75 p.s.i. (5,274 kg/cm^2) pressure these engines developed 5400 (5473) i.h.p.; steam was supplied by four double-ended cylindrical boilers. As might be expected in a long distance liner her bunkers were large and could hold 3000 (3048) tons of coal. On measured mile trials ORIENT reached a speed of 17 knots (31,50 km/hr.); her speed at sea was a steady 15 (27,80).

Until ORIENT went from London to Adelaide in 37 days 22 hours on her first trip the record had been 40 days 8 hours set by CUZCO of 1871, a former Pacific Steam Navigation Company's ship purchased by the Orient Line in 1877. ORIENT proved so very popular on the run that it was decided to reconstruct and modernize her, the work being done on the Tyne in 1899. She was given new boilers, triple expansion engines, and a completely new appearance with two masts and a single funnel. Upon the completion of the work she was chartered to the Admiralty for South African trooping service until 1902 when she returned to the Australian run. ORIENT started her last voyage in October 1909 and was sold to Italian shipbreakers in the following year.

In some respects the coast of the U.S.A. state of Maine and the Swedish archipelago off Stockholm, the Skärgården, are similar. In both regions the multitude of islands, large and wooded near the mainland, small and rocky off shore, have for years attracted large numbers of summer visitors. The permanent populations depended heavily on transportation by water in the past, the daily small white steamer being the sole contact of many small communities with the outside world. The steamers have gone now from the coast of Maine but in spite of the building of bridges and roads for automobiles the "White Boats" still sail from Stockholm. They run from Stockholm out to the yachting center of Sandhamn, about 30 miles (48 km) as the crow flies, to the island of Ornö on the south, and to that of Blidö on the north, a range of about 60 miles (96,5 km). The high tide of passenger service in the Skärgården came in 1913 when the steamers carried about two million passengers.

In both regions certain steamers by their appearance, ease of handling, speed, and their captain's personality became favorites. Although older and newer boats bore the same name WAXHOLM of 1881 became almost legendary. Built by the Bergsund Engineering Works, Stockholm, she had one complete deck with a lower deck forward and aft of the machinery space on which were located the crew's quarters and two saloons. The fore deck was open, the covered space amidships held the galley, pantry, stores spaces, and cloak rooms, while the sheltered after deck could be closed in with glass panels in cold weather. On the covered promenade deck were the wheelhouse, dining saloon, and smoking room. WAXHOLM was allowed to carry 368 passengers on short runs from Stockholm but this was reduced to 266 for trips to the outer islands. Her normal crew of 14 included six waitresses.

Waxholm — page 91

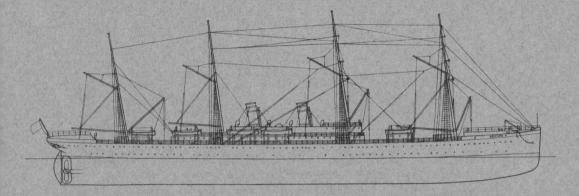

450.2 × 45.4 × 35.7 feet
137,255 × 13,838 × 10,881 m

Designed to take the Blue Ribbon the single-screw Guion liner ARIZONA was the first ship to be termed an "Atlantic Greyhound". With but limited cargo capacity she marked the beginning of the division of Atlantic liners between express steamers mainly for passengers and slower more comfortable ships capable of carrying a considerable quantity of cargo. Built of iron and engined by Messrs. John Elder & Company, Glasgow, she took the Blue Ribbon from the White Star liner BRITANNIC on her maiden voyage and held it until 1881; her mean speed across the Atlantic was 15.96 knots (27,98 km/hr.). ARIZONA had eight watertight bulkheads and four decks. The strength of her hull was demonstrated in November 1879 when she rammed an iceberg at 14 knots (25,95 km/hr.), and safely made port. She was fitted with three-cylinder compound engines and seven fire-tube boilers; on trials she reached 17.3 knots (32,06 km/hr.) with her machinery developing 6357 (6443) i.h.p. Refitted in 1898 she was given triple expansion engines of the same power, which reduced her 110 ton per day coal consumption, and sent to the Pacific for service between San Francisco and the Far East. ARIZONA later became the U.S. Navy transport HANCOCK and was finally scrapped near San Francisco in 1926.

The Bergsund Engineering Works also constructed WAXHOLM's jet-condensing compound engines which developed 280 i.h.p. at 100 r.p.m. The two cylinders were 19.61 and 34.25 in. (0,498-0,870 m) diameter by 23.35 in. (6,50 kg/cm²). WAXHOLM's service speed was 12 knots (22,24 km/hr.). She was withdrawn from service at the end of 1956 and shortly after was broken up at Hamburg.

During the early years following the beginning of the Cunard Line service in 1840 when shares had been sold to the public, the Cunard, Burns, and McIver families had quietly acquired all the shares. As the older generation died out it was eventually decided to form a joint stock company. Shares offered to the public in 1880 were quickly bought up and this naturally led to changes in management. Under family control new ships for the line had represented a careful blending of improvements with established traditions. The new Cunard Board was faced with keen competition from the White Star, Guion, and Inman Lines and with the question of steel construction. Working closely with Messrs. J. & G. Thomson of Glasgow the Board revised an 1879 contract for a 500 ft. (152,395 m) iron ship. The result was SERVIA launched on 1 March 1881, the first steel Cunarder. The use of steel instead of iron was expensive but the extra cost was soon repaid by the weight saved.

Messrs. J. & G. Thomson consulted with the Admiralty during the designing of SERVIA. With a double bottom extending nearly her full length and coal bunkers arranged to protect the boilers and engines she was considered suitable for use as an auxiliary cruiser. The hull had 12 watertight bulkheads of which eight ran up to the main deck. She had three full decks—upper, main, and lower—plus an orlop; a

Servia — page 92

560.2 × 52.3 × 37 feet
170,743 × 15,941 × 11,278 m

Faced with the competition of ARIZONA and the newly announced SERVIA the Inman Line went to the Barrow Shipbuilding & Engineering Company for a Blue Ribbon challenger. Although a beautiful ship, well patronized and well remembered, CITY OF ROME was a failure as a record breaker mainly because of interference in her design and construction. Designed to be built of steel it proved difficult to obtain and she was constructed largely of iron without the proper changes to compensate for the additional weight. Her hull had 10 bulkheads and four decks. In 1899 her clipper bow saved her when she hit an iceberg. CITY OF ROME's 24 ft. (7,315) diameter propeller was turned by three sets of two-cylinder compound engines to which steam was supplied by eight cylindrical boilers. The engines developed 11890 (12052) i.h.p. on trial when she attained a speed of 18.2 knots (33,73 km/hr.). She took nearly a day longer than ARIZONA on the Atlantic crossing. After five voyages under the Inman flag she was returned to her builders who chartered her to the Anchor Line in 1883. She served to repatriate Spanish prisoners after the Spanish-American War in 1898, was converted to a British troopship in 1900, and was finally sold to German shipbreakers in October 1902.

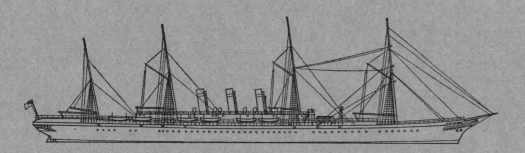

promenade deck for passengers covered a long house amidships. Normally 450 first class and 600 third class passengers were accommodated but these numbers could be increased if necessary; her crew totaled 200. SERVIA's plumb stem and elliptical counter stern were standard for the period but a prominent forecastle, two large funnels, and a three-masted rig when four were common on most ships of her size gave her a distinctive appearance.

SERVIA had a set of three-cylinder inverted compound engines which were constructed by her hull builders. There were one 72 in. (1,829 m) diameter and two 100 in. (2,540 m) diameter cylinders having a common stroke of 78 in. (1,981 m). Steam for the main engines was supplied at 90 p.s.i. (6,328 kg/cm²) pressure by six double-ended cylindrical boilers each having three corrugated furnaces in each end; one single-ended boiler furnished steam for auxiliary purposes. On trials SERVIA's engines developed 10,385 (10526) i.h.p. and she attained a speed of 17.63 knots (32,67 km/hr.). Unusual features on the ship included the first electric lighting on a Cunarder, remotely controlled watertight doors, and the provision of three methods of emergency steering.

SERVIA proved to be an excellent sea boat and even with bad weather nearly the whole way to New York on her first crossing from Liverpool in November 1881 her time was 9 days 16 hours and 30 minutes. Her normal crossings averaged about 7½ days and in spite of newer ships she retained her popularity because of her regularity and comfort. In 1893 she was put on intermediate services and in 1899 was chartered to the Admiralty for Boer War service. She did a little more Atlantic service but in 1901 after her 171st round trip to New York she was withdrawn and scrapped.

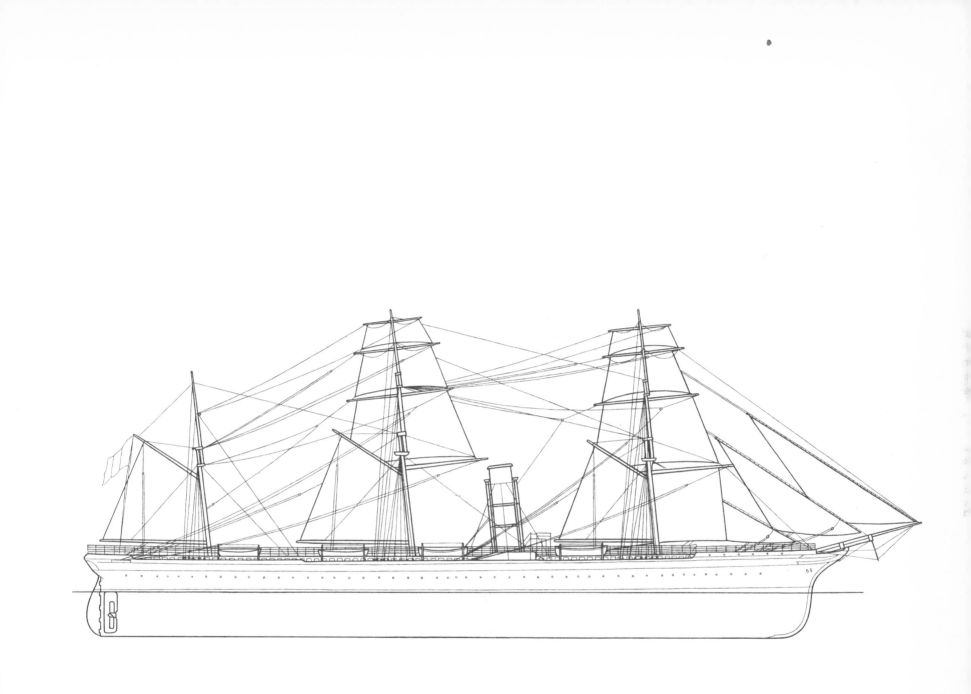

PÉREIRE · 1865

Compagnie Générale Transatlantique

345.0 × 43.5 × 29.0 feet ◖ 3150 T ◖ 105,153 × 13,258 × 8,839 m

GREAT REPUBLIC · 1866

Pacific Mail Steamship Company

360.3 × 47.4 × 22.8 feet ◗ 3881 T ◗ 109,815 × 14,447 × 6,950 m

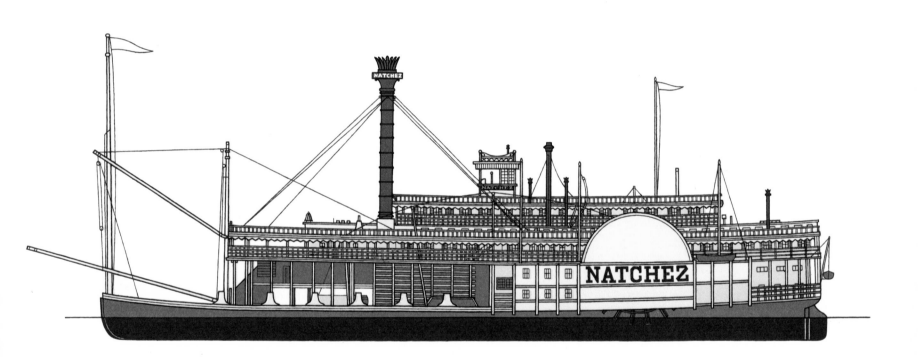

NATCHEZ · 1869

Captain Thomas P. Leathers

303.0 × 46.0 × 9.5 feet ℭ 1547 T ℭ 92,351 × 14,020 × 2,896 m

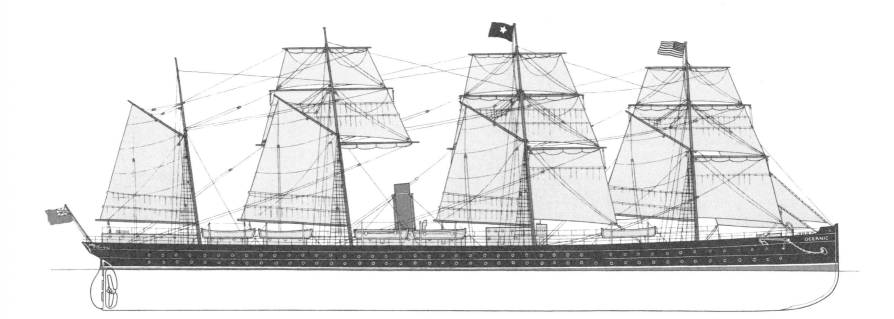

OCEANIC · 1870

White Star Line

420.0 × 41.0 × 31.0 feet ☾ 3708 T ☾ 128,051 × 12,496 × 9,449 m

PENNSYLVANIA · 1872

American Steamship Company

343.0 × 43.0 × 24.9 feet ◖ 3126 T ◖ 104,543 × 13,106 × 7,589 m

ORIENT · 1879

Orient Steam Navigation Company

445.5 × 46.3 × 35.0 feet ◖ 5386 T ◖ 135,823 × 14,111 × 10,668 m

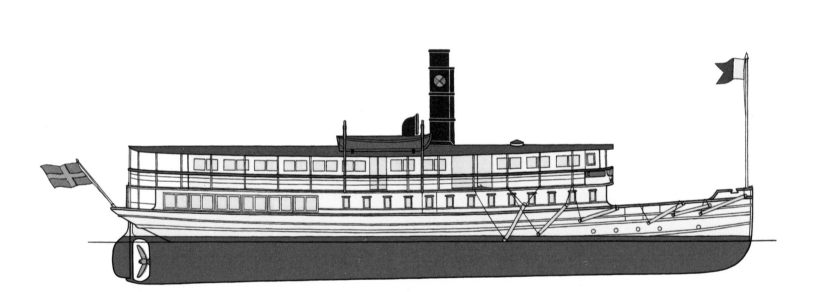

VAXHOLM · 1881

Vaxholms Ångfartygs Aktiebolag

108.27 × 19.69 feet ◖ 200 T ◖ 33,00 × 6,00 m

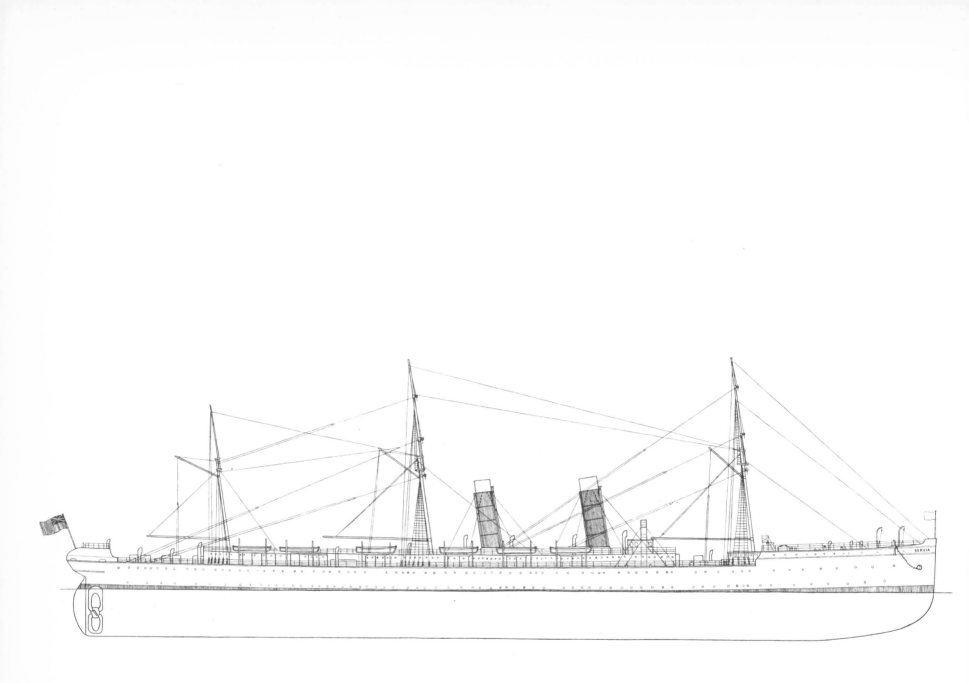

SERVIA · 1881

Cunard Steamship Company, Ltd.

515.0 × 52.1 × 37.0 feet ◖ 7392 T ◖ 156,967 × 15,880 × 11,277 m

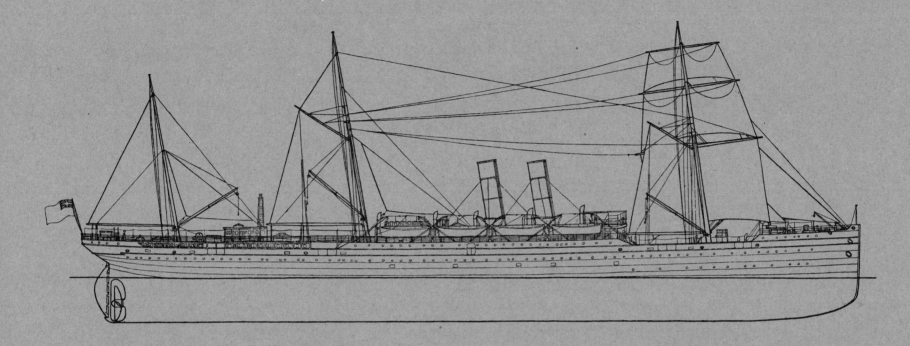

Tank vessels, more commonly called tankers, form today a very large portion of the world's merchant fleet. A tanker is specially designed and constructed to carry a bulk liquid cargo which is usually petroleum or its refined products. Some specially designed tankers carry cargoes such as molasses, hot asphalt, caustic soda, and sulphuric acid; in all about seventy chemicals are considered suitable for bulk transportation by water. The carriage of such liquid cargoes in a ship offers many problems to the designer and builder. Some and particularly petroleum vary considerably in volume with temperature changes hence provisions must be made for expansion. Deck filling lines and bottom suction piping connected to suitable pumps are required for loading and discharging cargoes. Certain types of liquid cargoes are very viscous at normal temperatures and steam heating coils must be installed to raise their temperatures before they can be handled by the pumps. Others are very volatile and special ventilating systems must be provided to remove flammable and often poisonous fumes. Above all are a multitude of provisions to guard against accidental fires.

The prototype of the modern tank ship was GLÜCKAUF constructed in 1885 by Sir W. G. Armstrong, Mitchell & Company at Newcastle-on-Tyne. Designed by Colonel Henry F. Swan she had most of the now familiar tanker features including a forecastle, a bridge amidships, a poop, and the machinery located aft. This position for the machinery reduces the possibility of cargo leakage into the boiler room. GLÜCKAUF's crew were berthed in her forecastle while the officers' quarters were at the after

DUNOTTAR CASTLE — 1890 — 5465 T

420.0 × 49.667 × 25.0 feet
128,051 × 15,138 × 7,620 m

In 1890 the Fairfield Shipbuilding & Engineering Company, Ltd., Glasgow, built this single-screw steel mail steamer for the Castle Line to South Africa. Arranged to carry 160 first-class passengers, 100 second-class, and 100 third-class she was designed in conjunction with the Admiralty and could carry 1200 troops as a transport. She was one of the last ships to have the first-class quarters
continued

Glückauf — page 103

end of the poop; she had electric lighting throughout. In company with most ships of the period she carried sails having what can best be described as the rig of a simplified barquentine.

GLÜCKAUF's transversely framed hull, constructed of both iron and steel, had two decks the lower of which formed the tops of her nine main cargo tanks. Eleven transverse bulkheads and one longitudinal bulkhead were fitted between the keel and the upper deck; the longitudinal bulkhead extended from the bow back to the boiler room bulkhead. To take care of the expansion of her petroleum cargoes a narrow fore-and-aft trunk connected to the lower tanks was built between the two decks with access hatches located on the upper deck. Lighter oil cargoes were carried in the 'tween-deck tanks to port and starboard of the trunk. The after cargo tank was separated from the boiler room by a short compartment which contained the cargo pumps.

The propelling machinery installed in GLÜCKAUF was standard for her day—a set of triple expansion engines rated at 900 (912) i.h.p. which gave her a service speed of 10 knots (18,53 km/hr.). Steam at 150 p.s.i. (10,55 kg/cm²) pressure was supplied by two cylindrical fire-tube—commonly called Scotch—boilers. GLÜCKAUF delivered her first cargo at Geestemünde in August 1886. She had a little-known sister VOR-WÄRTS which was lost at sea in 1890. Both vessels had hardly entered service before the construction of larger improved tankers was started. GLÜCKAUF was wrecked on Long Island, New York, on 24 March 1893.

During the 1880's the Canadian Pacific Railway Company spanned the North American continent and reached the western seaboard at Vancouver in 1885. With the intent of offering an alternate to the Suez route to the Far East, chartered ships were operated across the Pacific and the results encouraged the company to seek a mail contract for its route. The Russian War scare of 1885 showed the cruiser weakness of the British Navy in the Pacific and the possibility of having fast liners suitable as naval auxiliaries led the British government to grant a mail contract of £60,000 per year.

The three Canadian Pacific ships built to fulfill the terms of the contact were the first to bear the now well-known EMPRESS names—EMPRESS OF INDIA launched on 30 August 1890 and her two sisters which soon followed her into the water, EMPRESS OF JAPAN and EMPRESS OF CHINA. The second proved the flyer of the fleet holding the trans-Pacific speed record until bettered by the 1912 EMPRESS OF RUSSIA. These ships were designed in conjunction with the British Admiralty to be suitable as auxiliary cruisers or transports and were constructed of steel by the Naval Construction & Armaments Company, Ltd., Barrow-in-Furness; this company also built their propelling machinery. With white-painted, clipper-bowed hulls, light three-masted schooner rigs, and two funnels EMPRESS OF INDIA and her sisters looked more like yachts than liners intended to cover 4300 miles (7969 km) at 17½ knots (32,43 km/hr.). Their passenger accommodations were called luxurious and were arranged to carry 200 in the first-class, 60 in second-class, and 500 in the Asiatic steerage. Operating in the days before chemists supplanted silk worms their holds were specially fitted for the carriage of silk cargoes.

The three ships had twin screws driven by two sets of three-cylinder triple expansion engines of 1167 n.h.p.; the cylinder diameters were 32, 51, and 82 in. (0,813-1,295-2,083 m) and the common stroke 54 in. (1,372 m). Steam at 160 p.s.i. (11,249 kg/cm²) pressure was generated in four double-ended Scotch boilers. In their regular bunkers the ships carried 1600 (1626) tons of coal with another 400 tons in reserve. The guaranteed speed was 18 knots (33,36 km/hr.) which all attained easily; EMPRESS OF INDIA

continued

aft. Powered by a set of triple expansion engines developing 6500 (6588) i.h.p. she was designed to make 16 knots (29,65 km/hr.). On her maiden voyage to Capetown in October 1890 she made the passage in 16 days 11 hours 54 minutes breaking the previous record by nearly a day. She broke her own record three times within the following year before the larger 1891 SCOT of the Union Line beat her. Modernized with rearranged passenger quarters in 1897 she carried some troops during the Boer War and returned to commercial service until withdrawn in 1904. Laid up until 1907 she was chartered for the New York to Panama service and later did some cruising. Purchased in 1913 by the Royal Mail Steam Packet Company she was renamed CARIBBEAN and served on the New York-Bermuda and Canada-West Indies runs. During World War I she was converted to an auxiliary cruiser but proved unsuitable and in 1915 was fitted as an accommodation ship for workmen at Scapa Flow. Caught in a storm off Cape Wrath she sank on 26 September 1915.

Empress of India — page 104

MODEL TESTING

The under-water hull form of ships was for centuries shaped by tradition. Studies of floating bodies were first published in France in 1746 and model tests were conducted there between 1775 and 1785. The results of Beaufoy's tests in England between 1793 and 1798 were employed by Fulton; Chapman was working in Sweden in the same period.

The total water resistance of a ship's hull is composed of two major factors—wave-making resistance dependent upon the ship's shape and speed, and the frictional resistance of the area of immersed surface. Scott Russell's work on the first has been noted while Rankine developed theories relating to the latter but it fell to William Froude of Torquay, Devon, and his son R. E. Froude to combine the two in their proper relation. Froude began his experiments in 1856 and in 1868 he proposed to the Admiralty that a testing tank be built. In 1870 the desired funds were granted. In the Torquay tank Froude demonstrated that if the frictional resistances of surfaces having the same lengths and wetted surfaces as a series of similar ship

continued

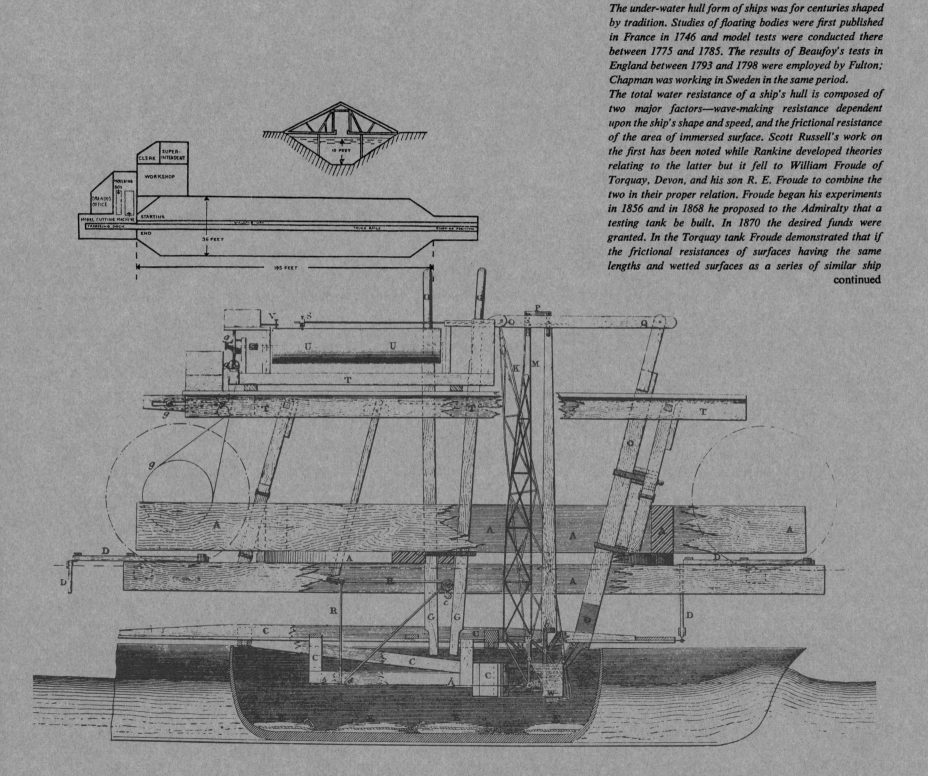

averaged 18.68 knots (34,63 km/hr.) on her trial trip. Her delivery trip to the Pacific was by way of Suez which gave a good opportunity to break-in the engines; by the time she left Yokohama everything was in top condition. The crossing to Vancouver took 10 days 13 hours and 34 minutes, a little more than two days less than the best time of the Pacific Mail steamer CHINA.

Shortly after the outbreak of the first World War EMPRESS OF INDIA was purchased by a group of Indian princes headed by the Maharajah of Gwalior and converted to a hospital ship. Given the name of LOYALTY she made 41 voyages carrying a total of 15,500 patients and in 1919 she made one voyage taking troops back to India. Purchased after her war service by the Scindia Steam Navigation Company, London, it was intended that she should become the first ship on a new service between London, Marseilles, and Bombay. New safety requirements for passenger ships, however, made it uneconomical to restore the 30 year old ship and she was laid up in Bombay at the end of 1920; she was broken up three years later.

During much of the life of the cross-Channel record breaker of 1859, the 340 ton 15 knot (27,80 km/hr.) JOHN PENN, service schedules on most of the runs depended upon the tides. Improvements in the various Channel ports eventually permitted fixed schedules and a slow increase in the size of ship employed but restricted depths of water and engineering considerations still favored paddle-wheel propulsion. By the mid-1880's 800 ton ships having service speeds of 18 to 19 knots (33,36-35,32 km/hr). were in common use.

Since 1840 the Belgian government had operated a service between Ostende and Dover with ships built for the most part by the Société Anonyme John Cockerill at Hoboken near Antwerp. Faced with a great expansion in travel between England and the Continent as were all the Channel services, the Belgian government needed larger and faster ships and in 1888 had two 1115 ton 21 knot (38,92 km/hr.) steamers built by Messrs. W. Denny & Brothers of Dumbarton. The success of these led to two even larger ships. Cockerill and Denny were each invited to build one with no restrictions as to arrangement, scantlings, machinery, or other details. The contracts did call for rejection of the ships if they failed to make 21 knots (38,92 km/hr.) with a penalty if the speed was below 21½ knots (39,85 km/hr.) and a bonus payment if above. The Denny-built LEOPOLD II was completed first and averaged 21.995 knots (40,76 km/hr.). In order to ensure a fair comparison the Cockerill MARIE HENRIETTE was sent to the Clyde in 1893 to run her trials under the same conditions. She averaged 22.2 knots (41,14 km/hr.) which made her the world's fastest paddle steamer.

MARIE HENRIETTE's steel hull had a flush weather deck and was subdivided by 12 watertight bulkheads. Considering her short run, about three hours, her passenger accommodations were considered exceptional. The main quarters were on the lower deck but there was a long deck house amidships which contained the first-class smoking room and some cabins. A shorter house further aft was used by the King and Queen of the Belgians when they went to sea. As might be expected her propelling machinery occupied a large part of her length, nearly 35 per cent. It was customary for these Channel ships to enter port stern first and to facilitate this she was fitted with a bow rudder.

In arranging the machinery the Cockerill yard followed its standard practice placing the inclined two-cylinder compound engines abaft the paddle shaft. The cylinders were 60 in. (1,524 m) and 108 in. (2,743 m) diameter by 80 in. (2,134 m) stroke. With steam

continued

forms and moving at the same speeds were deducted from the total measured resistances, the remaining resistances followed his law of Comparison. The latter is the basis of all model testing and involves the concept of "corresponding speeds", that is, models and ships of similar form may be compared at similar values of speed divided by the square root of their lengths. One great contribution of the Froudes was the so-called "constant" system of non-dimensional coefficients for recording the features of a ship and allied with this their method of comparing sectional area curves, water-lines, and midship sections. In 1871 Froude carried out the famous experiments on H.M.S. GREYHOUND to determine the total resistance of a full-sized ship, to determine the loss of power in the propeller and machinery, and to test the comparison between ships and models. There was considerable opposition to the work of the Froudes and by the end of the century there were only five testing tanks in world. H.M.S. INFLEXIBLE of 1876 was the first ship to be built from a pre-tested model but today, with model tanks in every major country, no one would think of building an important ship without first testing a model.

Marie Henriette — page 105

supplied at 117 p.s.i. (8,226 kg/cm²) by eight Scotch boilers the engines were designed to develop 8300 (8413) i.h.p. The 22 ft. 4 in. (6,807 m) diameter paddle-wheels were of the feathering type.

LEOPOLD II and MARIE HENRIETTE proved to be just about the limit in size and speed for cross-Channel paddle steamers but MARIE HENRIETTE continued a favorite long after turbine-propelled ships were put on the run. Her spacious deck and quarters below proved valuable during the first World War when she evacuated a large number of Belgian refugees from Ostende. In October 1914 when carrying wounded soldiers from the Battle of Ypres to Cherbourg her captain was misinformed concerning the lighthouse on Cape Harfleur; she ran on the rocks there and became a total loss.

The Great Lakes of the North American continent—Ontario, Erie, Huron, Michigan, and Superior—comprise about 50 per cent of the world's fresh water and large portions of the populations of Canada and the U.S.A. live in the provinces and states bordering them. The rich grain districts of both countries are close by as are large deposits of coal and ore. It was decided early to bring the ore to the coal hence the major traffic on the lakes has been the carriage of iron ore from the upper end of Lake Superior to the steel producing centers on the southern shore of Lake Erie and the lower end of Lake Huron. The ships returned with coal or in ballast. Toward the end of the navigation season of about 250 days per year grain forms a large portion of the cargoes brought eastward for trans-shipment; many ships serve as floating warehouses through the winter although the new St. Lawrence Seaway is changing many shipping practices on the lakes.

Of the vessels developed to meet the special operating conditions on the lakes the most unusual were the "whalebacks" designed by Alexander McDougall. With their decks and topsides rounded like the back of a whale, coal, grain, and ore cargoes were self stowing and there was less risk of such cargoes shifting during a storm. While water ran quickly off the rounded deck it also washed aboard easily and the deck houses were subjected to the full force of the waves. The peculiar spoon bow of the whalebacks pounded badly in head seas.

FRANK ROCKEFELLER was launched on 25 April 1896 from the yard of the American Steel Barge Company, West Superior, Wisconsin. Benefitting from experience with earlier vessels of the type her deck was given less curve. All quarters were located in the houses aft and her pilot house was separated from the main house to allow room for fueling hatches. Bulk cargoes on the lakes are loaded by spouts and FRANK ROCKEFELLER had a peculiar arrangement of cargo hatches to accommodate them. There were eleven 12 ft. by 8 ft. (3,658×2,438 m) hatches down the middle of the deck and ten 6 ft. by 4 ft. (1,829×1,219 m) hatches along the port side only thus 21 spouts could be discharging into the ship. Grab buckets on the wharves were employed for unloading. When drawing 20 ft. (6,096 m) of water FRANK ROCKEFELLER could carry 220,000 bushels (7753 m³) of wheat; her water ballast capacity was 1600 (1626) tons.

One set of triple expansion engines developing 2000 i.h.p. were installed in FRANK ROCKEFELLER the cylinders were 23, 38, and 63 in. (0,559-0,965-1,600 m) diameter by 40 in. (1,016 m) stroke. Three Scotch boilers with three furnaces each supplied steam at a pressure of 175 p.s.i. (12,304 kg/cm²). Engines and boilers were constructed by the Cleveland Ship Building Company. The ship's service speed was 14 miles (22,53 km) per hour. Although small in comparison with the lake freighters that followed FRANK ROCKEFELLER served for over 30 years.

PHOENICIAN—1888

Built in 1864 as the 272 ft. (82,903 m) ST. DAVID for the Allan Line Steamship Company, Ltd. this iron ship entered the Liverpool-Quebec-Montreal service powered by a set of simple inverted engines. The rapidly improving technology of the next few years and the demand for larger ships led many owners to lengthen and repower their ships. Thus in 1873 she was lengthened to 335 ft. (102,105 m), given a set of compound engines, and returned to the Canadian run as PHOENICIAN. Repowered again in 1888 she received the first set of quadruple expansion engines employed on the Atlantic. PHOENICIAN was operated on the company's South American runs from 1889 to 1903 and was scrapped at Genoa in 1905.

Frank Rockefeller — page 108

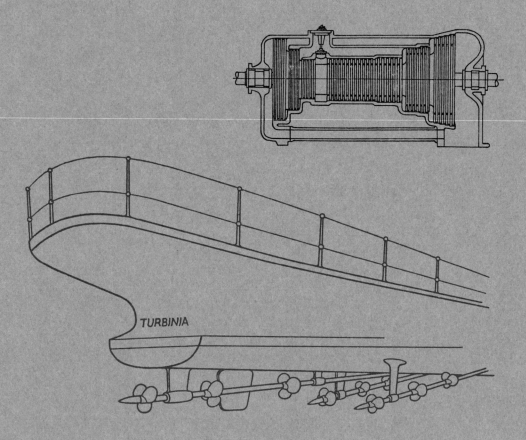

TURBINIA

SIR CHARLES A. PARSONS AND TURBINIA — 1894

100.0 × 9.0 × 7.0 feet
30,480 × 2,743 × 2,134 m

The steam yacht TURBINIA was the first vessel to be propelled by steam turbine machinery. Although relatively high speeds had been achieved by torpedo boats powered with reciprocating engines there was a limit to the speeds attainable within given weight and strength limitations. The breaking of connecting rods when operating at full power had caused severe damage. Sir Charles A. Parsons introduced in 1884 his steam turbine which had only rotating parts and in 1894 his company built TURBINIA to test a marine application of this turbine. A 6 ft.

continued

Oscar II — page 109

continued

(1,829 m) model driven by rubber bands was tested to determine the power requirements of the full-size vessel. With a single shaft arrangement the highest speed was 19.75 knots (36,71 km/hr.) and a three-shaft arrangement was finally adopted. Steam at 155 p.s.i. (10,898 kg/cm²) drove a high-pressure turbine on the starboard shaft, passed to the intermediate-pressure unit on the port shaft, and then to the low-pressure in the middle, exhausting from there to the condensers. A small reverse turbine was included on the low-pressure shaft. As these turbines were direct-drive units it was found that at high r.p.m. a

continued

The trunk ship, invented by Messrs. Ropner & Son, Ltd., Stockton-on-Tees, was an ocean-going ship type in favor at the end of the nineteenth century that was especially suitable for the carriage of bulk cargoes. Its particular feature, a trunk connecting forecastle, bridge, and poop, acted as a feeder to the main holds, provided an elevated platform on which to locate the cargo hatches, and served as a fore-and-aft access for the crew. The breadth of the trunk was about half that of the ship; the deck space outboard could be used for timber cargo. When constructed by Messrs. James Laing & Son, Ltd., Sunderland, the trunk ship OSCAR II was Sweden's largest merchant ship and one of the first ships of her size to be ordered built by a Swedish ship owner. The normal practice was to purchase second-hand tonnage.

A single-screw, single-deck ship OSCAR II had the typical plumb stem and elliptical counter stern of her day. The top of the trunk connecting her forecastle, bridge, and very short poop was parallel to her keel although on some ships it followed the sheer of the deck. Accommodations were provided in the forecastle and amidships for a total complement of 28. Below deck her full-length double bottom was fitted to carry water ballast and the capacity of her four holds was 262,273 cu. ft. (7438 m³). For handling cargo she had 16 booms mounted on eight pairs of short kingposts; the gear was worked by steam winches. Her two masts served only to support emergency sails.

The North-Eastern Marine Engineering Company, Ltd., of Sunderland furnished the triple-expansion engines and Scotch boilers installed in OSCAR II. The engines

continued

single propeller only dug a hole in the water, a phenomenon known as cavitation. The remedy—an increase in propeller area—was accomplished by fitting three propellers on each shaft. At the British Naval Review at Spithead in 1897 TURBINIA raced through the anchored fleet at 34.5 knots (63,94 km/hr.) and the best torpedo boats of the British navy could not catch her.

TRIPLE EXPANSION ENGINES

Triple expansion engines were first fitted in Boat Number 30 of the Cie. des Bateaux-Omnibus de la Seine in 1871. They became common during the 1880's and eventually were considered the standard machinery installation for ordinary merchant ships being widely employed even as late as 1930. Such engines were fitted in the thousands of Liberty ships built in the U.S.A. during World War II. They were the most economical of reciprocating engines to operate, easy to maintain, and very reliable.

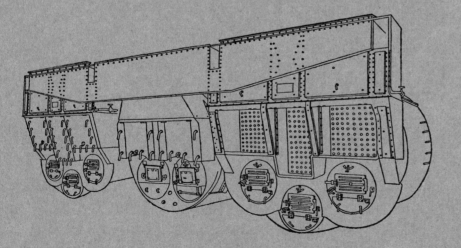

SCOTCH BOILER

For years the standard steam generator associated with reciprocating engines was the Scotch boiler, so-called because of its popularity with shipbuilders on the Clyde. It was of the cylindrical-shell, internally-fired type, fitted with corrugated furnaces, wet-back combustion chamber, and return fire tubes. The main difference between it and the earlier flue boiler was in the size of the flue or tube, the arbitrary limit being 5 in. (0,127 m). The normal working pressure of a Scotch boiler was around 175 p.s.i. (12,304 kg/cm²).

developed 1450 (1470) i.h.p. and drove her at a speed of 10 knots (18,53 km/hr.) in loaded condition. She was first employed to carry iron ore from Oxelösund on the east coast of Sweden to Rotterdam but after a year or so in this service she was sent on overseas voyages to North and South American ports. In January 1898 the British ship MUNIFICENT, having lost her propeller, was towed by OSCAR II 1200 miles (2224 km) in seven days to Horta in the Azores. On 30 June 1915 OSCAR II collided with the British auxiliary cruiser PATUCA west of Ireland and her bow and engine room were damaged. Attempts to tow her to port failed and after the crew was safely removed she sank on 3 July.

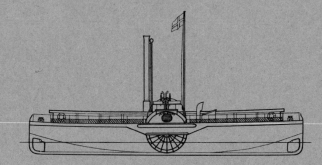

The North German Lloyd Steamship Company started an Atlantic service in 1858 and had maintained a steadily improving service but by the mid 1890's the line's express steamers were old and its business was dropping off. After careful study the company's directors decided to try for the Atlantic Blue Ribbon and ordered two ships—KAISER WILHELM DER GROSSE from the Vulcan Yard, Stettin, and KAISER FRIEDRICH from the Schichau Yard, Danzig. The financial condition of the North German Lloyd at the time was such that if the ships were failures the company would probably be ruined. To offset this risk the building contract required that the trial trip be a round-trip Atlantic voyage—if the ships failed to meet the guaranteed speed the company could return them to the builders. The shipyards were also interested in obtaining the Blue Ribbon as a boost for future business so took the risk.

Kaiser Wilhelm der Grosse — page 106

Steel was, of course, by now the accepted material for the construction of large ships. KAISER WILHELM DER GROSSE's hull had the then fashionable straight stem and elliptical counter stern; it was subdivided by 16 transverse bulkheads and had one longitudinal bulkhead in the engine room. A double bottom ran the full length of the the ship and there were four decks. Superstructures were beginning to pile up on passenger liners—on this ship were a forecastle and poop with a combination bridge and house amidships covered by an awning deck that gave the passengers a 400 ft. (121,955 m) protected promenade. With four funnels arranged in pairs and two pole masts she was a powerful looking ship. The passenger accommodations on KAISER WILHELM DER GROSSE were noted for their spaciousness and convenience. Quarters for 332 first-class passengers were located amidships, those for 343 in the second-class were abaft the engine room, while 1074 third-class passengers were berthed forward; her crew numbered 450.

A twin screw ship KAISER WILHELM DER GROSSE had two sets of four-cylinder triple expansion engines which developed a total of 28,000 (28381) i.h.p. at 77 r.p.m. with steam supplied at 185 p.s.i. (13,007 kg/cm²) pressure. The engines each had one 52 in., one 89¾ in.; and two 96½ in. (1,132-2,280-2,451 m) diameter cylinders with a common stroke of 69 in. (1,753 m). There were twelve double-ended Scotch boilers having eight furnaces each and two with four furnaces. The ship's designed speed was 22½ knots (41,696 km/hr.).

Launched on 4 March 1897, the largest ship then afloat, KAISER WILHELM DER GROSSE sailed on her maiden voyage from Bremen via Southampton to New York on 19 September 1897. Her time of 5 days 22 hours 45 minutes, an average of 21.39 knots (39,64 km/hr.), was the best yet from Southampton but not quite up to the Cunard services although her maximum day's run of 564 miles (1045 km) was a record. On her third homeward passage she met her owner's desires with an average of 22.35 knots (41,42 km/hr.) in spite of a delay in mid-Atlantic to assist a burning

FRITS JUEL — 1899 — 36.5 T

60.0 × 14.0 × 6.0 feet
18,287 × 4,267 × 1,829 m

Not all steam vessels can be the first, the largest, or the fastest. Those that just run back and forth are essential to the economies of certain regions and it seems appropriate to show the little Danish paddle-wheel ferry FRITS JUEL at the middle of her active career. Built in 1872 by Messrs. Burmeister & Wain, Copenhagen, she served regularly on the 10 minute run from Svendborg to Vindeby until replaced by a Diesel-propelled ferry in 1926 when she was held in reserve. During World War II when Diesel fuel was unobtainable and FRITS JUEL could burn peat or anything in her boiler she was recalled to service. Eventually broken up after the war her two-cylinder 10 h.p. engine is now in the Burmeister & Wain museum. Her only major repairs were a new boiler in 1891 and new plates and frames in her coal bunkers in 1916. There were hundreds like her around the world serving faithfully without fuss or notice.

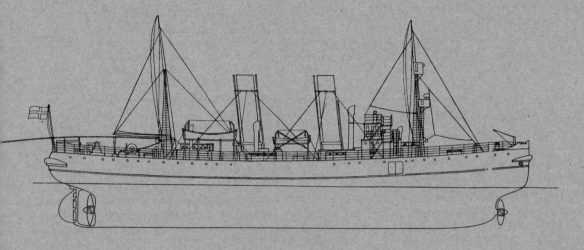

SAMPO — 1898 — 1339 T

190.0 × 43.0 × 25.2 feet
57,912 × 13,106 × 7,681 m

Picture to the left

EISBRECHER

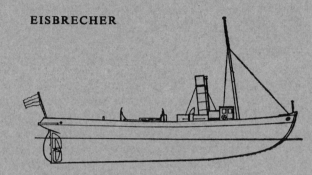

ICEBREAKERS

In the Baltic region, around the St. Lawrence region of Canada, and on the Great Lakes of North America winter operations of ships are hampered by ice and specially designed ships of large power have been built to break passages through it. Such a ship is mentioned as early as 1851 but probably the first specially built for the purpose was the one on the Elbe in Germany in 1871 appropriately named EISBRECHER. ERMACK of 1898 propelled by triple screws was a well-known powerful icebreaker. The Finnish SAMPO of 1898 was the first of the type in Europe to have a bow propeller. Many large train ferries, particularly on the Great Lakes, are given icebreaking features as schedules must be maintained throughout the winter. The Great Lakes train ferry ST. IGNACE of 1888 was one of the earliest to have a bow propeller. The hulls of all icebreaking ships taper inward and downward rather sharply from a level above the designed water-line. If caught and squeezed by ice such a hull will be lifted bodily and thus avoid destruction. Many ordinary merchant ships are given special ice strengthening around their bows to permit operations in loose ice.

ship. The glamor of having the Blue Ribbon holder brought so much business to the North German Lloyd that in 1898 the company carried 28 per cent of all the passengers landed in New York. At the outbreak of the first World War, KAISER WILHELM DER GROSSE was outfitted as a commerce raider and sent to sea. After sinking two ships and allowing two others to proceed she was caught while coaling off the Spanish colony of Rio de Oro on the west coast of Africa and sunk by the British cruiser HIGHFLYER.

After one year of service for the North German Lloyd the Schichau-built KAISER FRIEDRICH failed to meet her speed requirements and was turned back to her builders who finally chartered her to the Hamburg-American Line. Sold in 1912 to the French Compagnie de Navigation Sud-Atlantique and renamed BURDIGALA she was sunk by a submarine in the Mediterranean on 14 November 1916.

In marked contrast to these great express liners COCKERILL of 1901 was typical of the multitude of small steamers that were gradually ousting the big steel sailing vessels from the world's trade in bulk commodities even as the earlier steamers had taken the carriage of passengers from the clippers and packets. The majority of these general purpose steamers were of the three-island type so-called from the three short superstructures on their weather deck—forecastle, bridge, and poop. Technically speaking a

Cockerill — page 110

101

superstructure extends to a ship's side hence is considered to contribute to her reserve buoyancy and stability while deck houses set in from the side do not. A voyage in such a ship from Swansea in Wales to Pôrto Velho far up the Amazon near the Bolivian border was immortalized in H.M. Tomlinson's classic "The Sea and the Jungle".

Constructed of steel by the Société Anonyme John Cockerill at Hoboken for the shipping line of the same name COCKERILL had few frills. A few carved scrolls around her elliptical counter stern were her only decorations. She had one deck, four bulkheads, a 31 ft. (9,449 m) forecastle, a 25 ft. (7,620 m) bridge and a house amidships, and a short house aft. Her two masts and single funnel were "so fearful of seeming rakish that they overdo the effect of stern utility, and appear to lean ahead" to use Tomlinson's apt description. There were four cargo hatches, the two forward of the bridge being served by four cargo booms and associated steam winches while the two aft had but three booms. Sails were still carried for emergency use as such ships often travelled far from the normal sea lanes.

COCKERILL's single screw was driven by one set of triple expansion engines with cylinders 22.4, 36.6, and 60 in. (0,569-0,930-1,524 m) diameter by 41.8 in. (1,062 m) stroke. The engines were constructed by Messrs. Richardson, Westgarth & Company, Ltd., Middlesborough, England, and were rated at 233 n.h.p. She had two Scotch boilers which furnished steam at a pressure of 160 p.s.i. (1,125 kg/cm²). In good weather she could probably make 10 knots (18,53 km/hr.). Sold in 1910 to Armement Adolf Deppe of Antwerp she was transferred to British registry in 1916 when purchased by Messrs. J.W. Baird & Company, West Hartlepool, and renamed MABEL BAIRD. She was torpedoed and sunk on 22 December 1917 four miles (7,41 km) west-southwest of The Lizard.

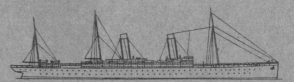

OCEANIC — 1899 — 17040 T

685.7 × 68.4 × 49 feet
208,994 × 20,848 × 14,935 m

OCEANIC, constructed of steel by Messrs. Harland & Wolff, Ltd., Belfast, for the White Star Line, was the first ship to exceed the length of GREAT EASTERN. She was also the first ship to reflect the line's new policy of large size and comfort in place of high speed. Her hull was subdivided by 13 transverse watertight bulkheads and had seven plated decks, five of them being continuous from bow to stern. She could carry 410 first-class, 300 second-class, and 1000 third-class passengers and she had a total crew of 390. Powered by two sets of four-cylinder triple expansion engines which developed 28,000 (28381) i.h.p. she made over 20 knots (37,07 km/hr.) on trial. Built to serve as an auxiliary cruiser her bunker capacity of 3700 (3759) tons of coal permitted her to steam 24,000 miles (44477 km) at 12 knots (22,24 km/hr.). In September 1914 OCEANIC was wrecked on the north coast of Scotland.

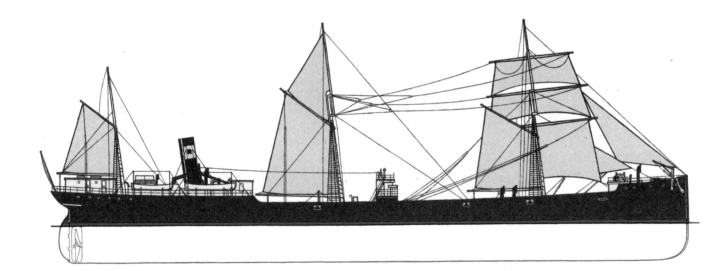

GLÜCKAUF · 1885

Deutsche Amerikanische Petroleum Gesellschaft

300.5 × 37.2 × 23.2 feet ℂ 2307 T ℂ 91,589 × 11,338 × 7,071 m

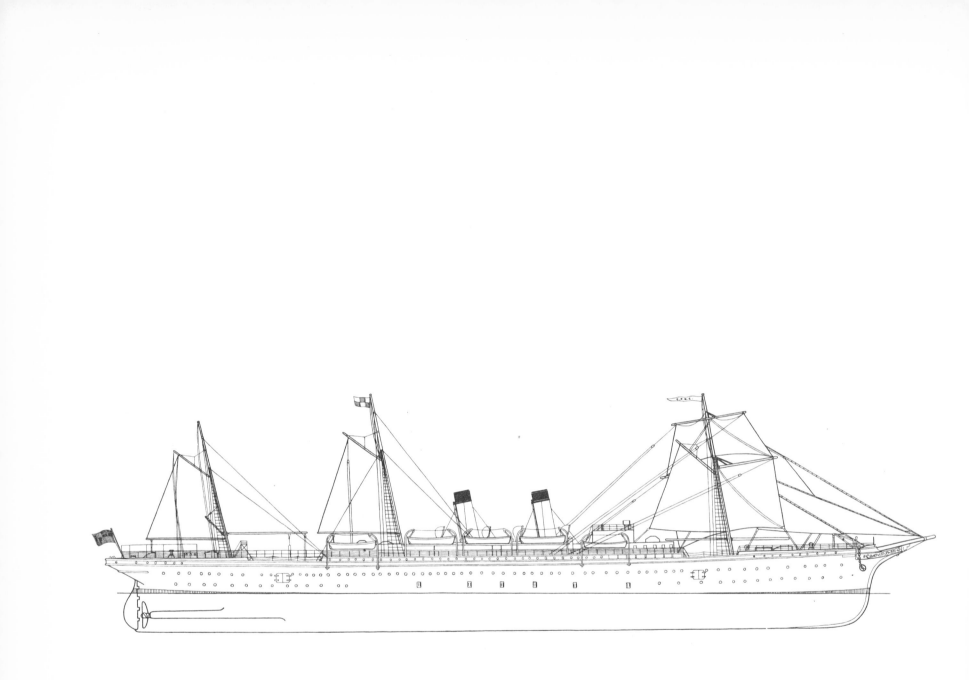

EMPRESS OF INDIA · 1890

Canadian Pacific Steamships, Ltd.

455.6 × 51.2 × 33.1 feet ◖ 5934 T ◖ 138,901 × 15,605 × 10,089 m

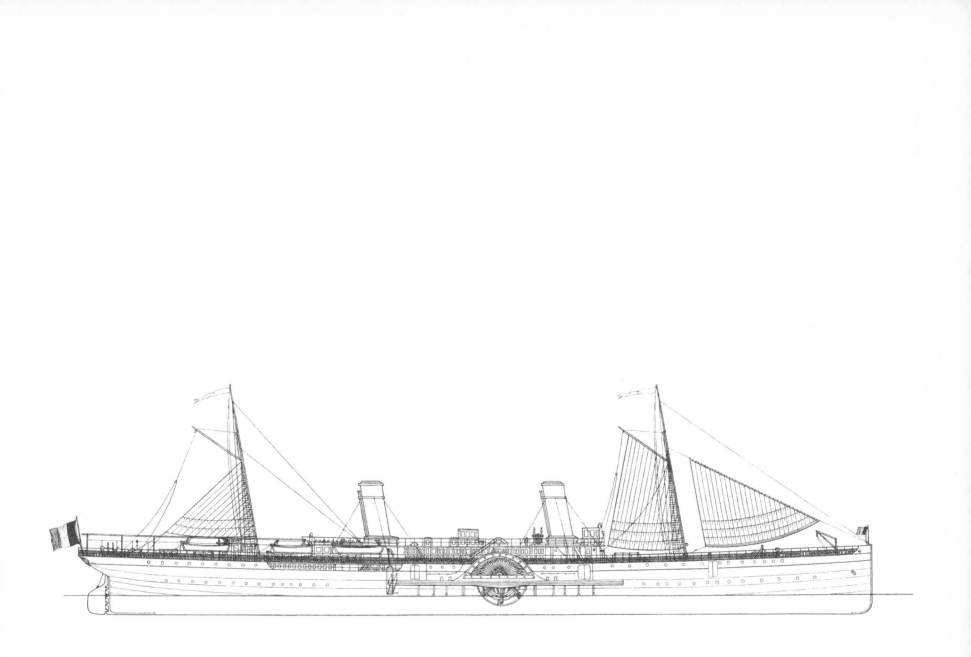

MARIE HENRIETTE · 1893

Belgian Government

340.0 × 38.0 × 15.0 feet ☽ 1525 T ☽ 103,629 × 11,582 × 4,572 m

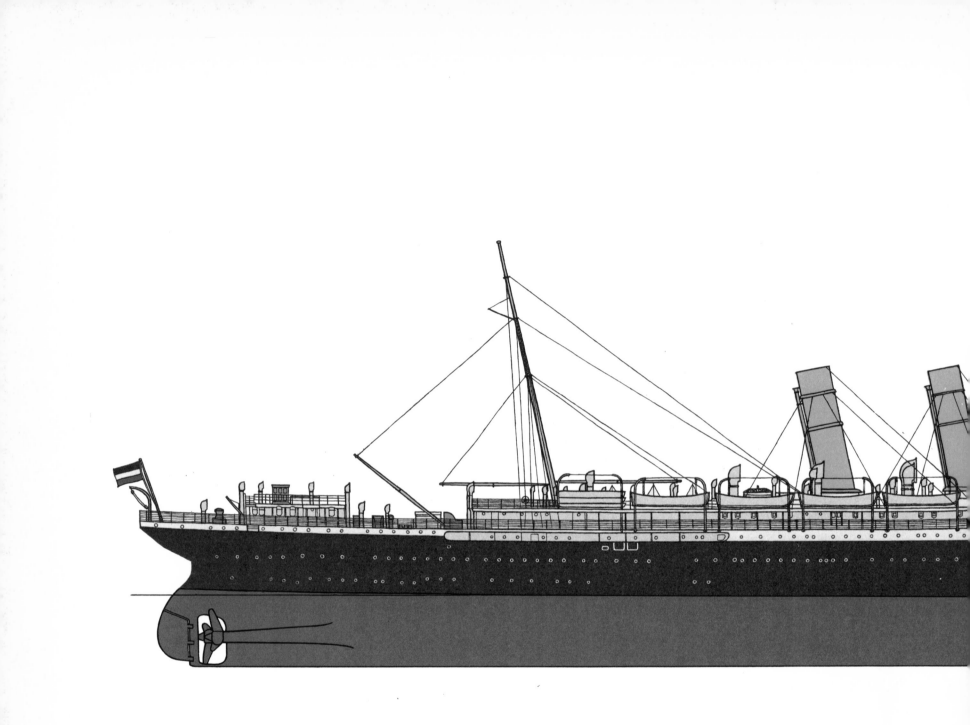

KAISER WILHELM DER GROSSE · 1897

Norddeutscher Lloyd

627.4 × 66.0 × 35.8 feet ℂ 14349 T ℂ 191,225 × 20,116 × 10,912 m

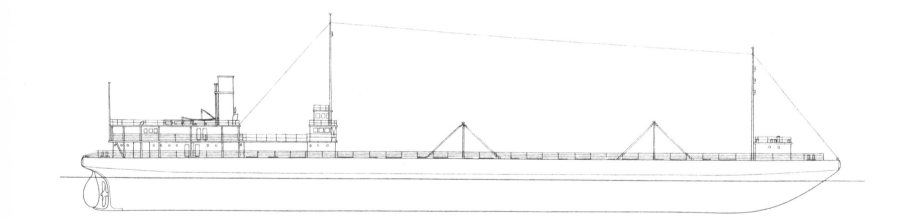

FRANK ROCKEFELLER · 1896

American Steel Barge Company

366.5 × 45.0 × 26.0 feet ◖ 2014 T ◖ 111,705 × 13,716 × 7,925 m

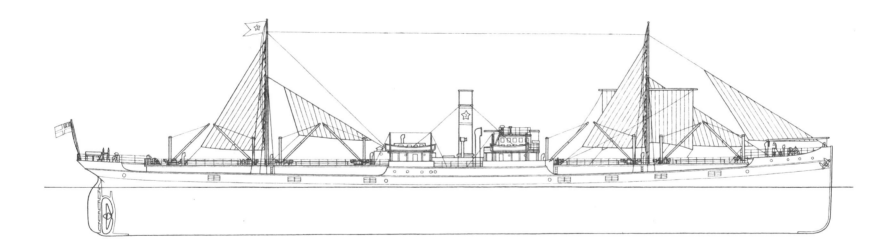

OSCAR II · 1896

Red. AB. Nordstjernan

348.5 × 48.2 × 21.6 feet ☾ 3552 T ☾ 106,222 × 14,691 × 6,584 m

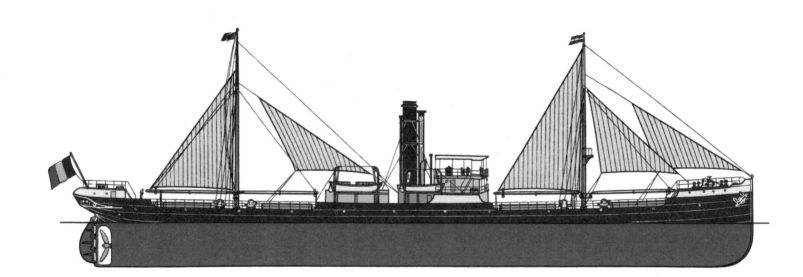

COCKERILL · 1901

Société Anonyme John Cockerill

288.4 × 45.0 × 25.0 feet ℂ 2441 T ℂ 87,902 × 13,716 × 7,620 m

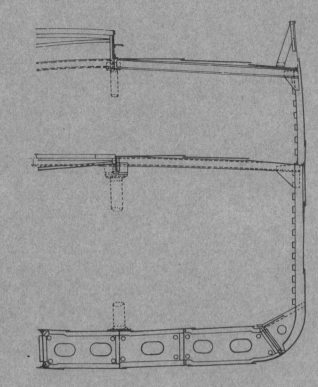

SECTION OF HOLD OF ORDINARY
TWO-DECK CARGO SHIP

King Edward — page 121

The first merchant vessel to be driven by steam turbine machinery was a joint venture of Messrs. W. Denny & Brothers of Dumbarton, Sir Charles A. Parsons, and Captain John Williamson. Denny had established a reputation for building fast packet and excursion steamers, both paddle and screw propelled, and he saw in TURBINIA's performance the possibilities of the turbine for future ships. He worked with Parsons in trying to interest various operating companies in a new turbine-driven ship but all had built new steamers only a short time before and were willing to wait for others to make the experiment. Captain Williamson, a Clyde steamship captain who had become a ship owner, offered to help and the three formed the Turbine Steamers Syndicate which was managed by Williamson.

Denny proceeded with the design and construction of the steel-hulled KING EDWARD following the general pattern of the existing Clyde steamers. She had a complete main deck, a lower deck broken by the machinery spaces, and a superstructure deck extending from the bow almost to the stern. The first-class accommodations were aft and the second-class forward with the respective dining saloons located on the lower deck. The crew's quarters were located forward on the lower deck. The superstructure deck provided a broad promenade and was obstructed only by a single mast forward, two funnels, and three small houses. For comparison Denny built at the same time the 18 knot (33,36 km/hr.) paddle steamer DUCHESS OF HAMILTON which had, considering the difference in machinery, her hull and interior arranged as nearly like KING EDWARD as possible.

KING EDWARD had three propeller shafts. Steam at 150 p.s.i. (10,546 kg/cm²) pressure from Scotch boilers entered a high-pressure turbine on the middle shaft, passed from there to low-pressure turbines on the wing shafts, and exhausted into two condensers; the total steam expansion was 125 fold. The middle shaft had a single 57 in. (1,448 m) diameter propeller while each wing shaft had two 40 in. (1,016 m) propellers spaced about 9 ft. (2,743 m) apart. At top speed the middle shaft turned at 700 r.p.m. and the wing shafts at 1000. Astern turbines were fitted on the wing shafts at the exhaust ends of the low-pressure turbines; when coming alongside piers KING EDWARD was handled with the wing shafts only like any normal twin-screw ship. The turbine machinery developed the equivalent of 3500 (3541) i.h.p. and was about 120 tons lighter than the compound diagonal paddle machinery in DUCHESS OF HAMILTON.

KING EDWARD was launched on 16 May 1901. Her hull form had been tank tested—the Denny yard had its own model tank—and Denny and Parsons hoped for a speed of 20 knots (37,06 km/hr.). On measured mile trials she averaged 20.48 knots (37,95 km/hr.). With DUCHESS OF HAMILTON she was put on the run from Fairlie across the Firth of Clyde to Campbeltown on Kintyre. KING EDWARD averaged 18½ knots (34,28 km/hr.) on this service, about two knots (3,70 km/hr.) better than the paddler. After a few years the forward propellers on the wing shafts were removed and although the turbines had performed well they did better after the change.

During World War I KING EDWARD carried troops across the Channel returning to the Campbeltown service at the war's end. After an amalgamation of services in 1927 she was placed on the Glasgow-Rothesay run. Refitted during the winter of 1936-7 she continued her normal runs during the early years of World War II but later served as a tender to troop transports coming into the Clyde. She ran again to Rothesay after the war until withdrawn in 1951 after 50 years of service.

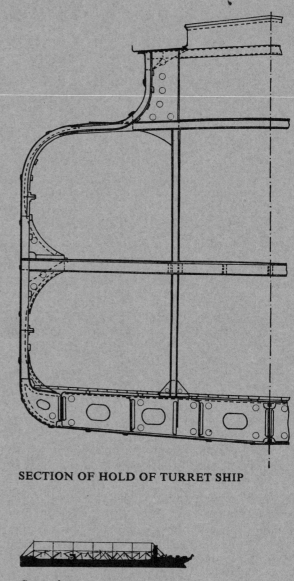

SECTION OF HOLD OF TURRET SHIP

Grängesberg — page 122

The ordinary two-deck three-island cargo ships could and did carry every conceivable type of cargo in their wanderings around the world. The arrangement of their cargo holds, however, made the carriage of ore, grain, or coal dangerous because of the possibility of cargo shifting in heavy weather and difficult to load and unload because of the 'tween deck spaces. Certain special vessels for such cargoes have been mentioned—the collier JOHN BOWES, the whaleback FRANK ROCKEFELLER, and the trunk ship OSCAR II.

GRÄNGESBERG was specially designed and built by Messrs. W. Doxford & Sons, Ltd., Sunderland, to carry iron ore from Sweden to Rotterdam. Her unique above-water hull shape had a rounded gunwale connection between her deck and sides and a continuous trunk without sheer from her 41 ft. (12,496 m) forecastle to her 51 ft. (15,544 m) poop; the connection between the deck and the trunk was also rounded. Given the name of "turret deck" this configuration was a patented development by the Doxford company of the U.S.A. whaleback steamers. This shape allowed the self stowing of dry bulk cargoes, and when the cargo was loaded up into the "turret", the breadth in which it could shift in a seaway was greatly reduced. As the tonnage measurement rules were then worded the trunk was not considered a part of the main hull and for a period turret-deck ships had lower tonnages and consequently paid lower port dues than normal ships carrying the same amounts of cargo. Turret-deck ships were considered to be especially sea-kindly as when loaded deeply the normal deck was alternately in and out of the water thus serving to reduce rolling.

The propelling machinery in GRÄNGESBERG was located aft thus giving a long unobstructed cargo hold. For handling cargo as quickly as possible out of the hatches on the turret deck she was equipped with 14 masts and 24 cargo booms whose gear was worked with steam winches. The masts were arranged in pairs—"goal post" masts so-called from their resemblance to the posts set up at each end of a football field. It was said that an ore cargo unloaded from her in 30 hours would have required 14 days from an ordinary ship. GRÄNGESBERG had Doxford-built three-cylinder triple expansion engines with cylinders 26, 43, and 72 in. (0,660-1,092-1,829 m) diameter by 51 in. (1,295 m) stroke. Rated by Lloyds Register of Shipping at 370 n.h.p. they developed 2400 (2433) i.h.p. and gave her a service speed of 10 knots (18,53 km/hr.). Later renamed BEUKELSDIJK she ran aground and broke in two in 1923.

Although Diesel-electric and turbo-electric ship propulsion systems are generally thought of as fairly modern developments the Diesel-electric system is the older. It actually preceded the direct-drive Diesel engine in ships and was installed in the world's first Diesel-propelled vessel, the triple-screw river tanker VANDAL. The reason for this was that the early Diesel engines could not be reversed and the use of electric propulsion motors provided a means for reversing the screws to go astern. At a technical meeting in Kassel, Germany, in June 1897 Dr. Rudolf Diesel reported on his new engine and Marcus Wallenberg of Sweden immediately saw the advantages of the new prime mover. He worked with Dr. Diesel and set up licensing arrangements with the Nya AB Atlas at Sickla, Sweden—now the AB Atlas Copco, Messrs. Burmeister & Wain in Copenhagen, and Emanuel Nobel whose Swedish company controlled most of the petroleum production in Russia and had its shops in St. Petersburg. K.W. Hagelin, an engineer with the Nobel firm, had set up the firm's petroleum transporting operations by canal and river tankers from the fields in Baku to St. Petersburg. In 1902 he planned a new tanker to be propelled by Diesel engines that was constructed during the winter of 1903/4.

VANDAL was a typical shallow-draft river vessel that drew only 6 ft. (1,83 m) in loaded condition. A full deck-height trunk connected short raised decks at the bow and stern; the breadth of the trunk was about three-fifths of that of the main hull. She was transversely framed and was subdivided into 11 main compartments. There were two main cargo tanks forward and two aft of her main engine room amidships; the electric propelling motors were aft. The crew were berthed under the raised deck forward, in the forward end of the trunk over a deep tank, and in the after end of the trunk over the motor room. Even for such a vessel sails were then considered necessary and she had two hinged masts on each of which could be set a trysail and a staysail.

Three three-cylinder, four-cycle, single-acting Diesel engines were installed in VANDAL each driving one 85 KW generator which in turn drove one propulsion motor. The engines, the largest constructed at the time by the Nya AB Atlas and normally rated at 120 b.h.p. each at 250 r.p.m., were capable of developing a maximum of 150 b.h.p.; the cylinders were 11.77 in. (0,299 m) diameter by 16.93 in. (0,430 m) stroke. Following the practice on early steam engines flywheels weighing about 7720 lbs. (3500 kg) were fitted on these engines. An auxiliary generator provided power for the steering gear which operated two large rudders, a fire pump, the anchor windlass, a searchlight, and the general lighting of the accommodations. For unloading her 700 ton cargo in between 5 and 6 hours VANDAL had two electric rotary pumps that were

Vandal — page 123

driven by one of the main generators. Her speed in loaded condition was 7 knots (21,97 km/hr.) and as is now the modern fashion her engines were directly controlled from the bridge.

The Canadian Pacific Railway, operators of the successful EMPRESSES on the Pacific, entered the Atlantic trade in 1903 with the purchase of Elder Dempster's Beaver Line from England to Canada which had started as a sailing ship line in 1867 and turned to steam in 1874. The well-established Allan Line—it had sent sailing vessels to Canada as early as 1819—had ordered two new ships to compete with the newest Beaver Line ships but this turn of events required a special effort. The ordered ships were to have been ordinary twin-screw steamers with reciprocating engines but larger and faster than any previously considered for the Canadian run. Impressed by the success of KING EDWARD the Allan Line directors contracted with Sir Charles A. Parsons for triple-screw turbine machinery for their new ships. Many shipping people at the time questioned the wisdom of installing the relatively unproved turbines in such large ships.

Victorian — page 126

The two ships became VICTORIAN constructed by Messrs. Workman, Clark & Company, Ltd. Belfast, and VIRGINIAN built in the Clyde by Messrs. Alexander Stephen & Sons, Glasgow. Although the machinery change required a complete reconstruction of her stern VICTORIAN was launched in April 1901, only ten months after keel laying, thus becoming the first turbine-propelled Atlantic liner. Outwardly she was simply a larger version of the typical combination passenger and cargo liner of her day for intermediate services. With three full decks in her hull as well as orlops forward and aft, she had a forecastle, bridge, and poop with extensive houses amidships and aft. She had a single oval funnel and two masts. VICTORIAN had accommodations for 470 first-class passengers on her bridge and promenade decks amidships, for 240 second-class on the main and upper decks, and for 940 third-class in 'tween-deck spaces. She could carry about 8000 tons of cargo and had refrigerated compartments for fruit and dairy products from Canada. While VICTORIAN and VIRGINIAN were considered sister-ships there were minor differences in their appearance and passenger accommodations.

VICTORIAN's machinery was arranged like that in KING EDWARD—a high-pressure turbine on the middle shaft and low-pressure turbines with reversing sections on the wing shafts—but from the beginning her shafts had but one propeller each. Nine single-ended Scotch boilers supplied steam at a pressure of 180 p.s.i. (12,655 kg/cm²). Designed for a sea speed of about 17 knots (31,50 km/hr.) she made a trial speed of 19½ knots (36,25 km/hr.) with the turbines developing 12,000 (12163) s.h.p. at 260 r.p.m. On her maiden voyage to Canada in April 1905 she was not pushed and it took several voyages to correct minor problems in the turbine machinery. In June 1906 she made a passage from Rimouski on the St. Lawrence to Moville in Ireland of 5 days 5 hours which stood as an eastbound record for a considerable period. At the end of 1906 she was overhauled at Liverpool and some changes were made in the turbines. Returning to the Canadian service she ran very successfully until the outbreak of World War I.

On 14 August 1914 VICTORIAN was commissioned as an auxiliary cruiser and did extensive service with the British Ninth and Tenth Cruiser Squadrons. As the need for food and troops became of importance she was put on escort duty and carried cargo and troops as well. By the war's end the Canadian Pacific had taken over the Allan Line and after refitting VICTORIAN commenced operations for that company in the

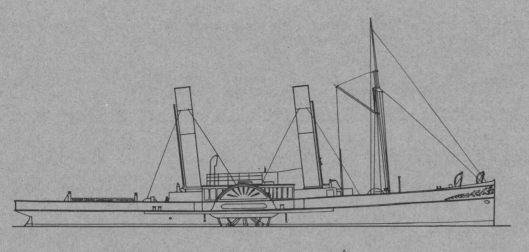

TUGS — CIRCA 1900

It has been noted that some of the earliest steamboats were built specifically for towing operations on canals. Others were pressed into service from time to time to tow wind-bound sailing vessels. The tug INDUSTRY of 1814 was designed to tow barges from Greenock up the Clyde to Glasgow before the dredging of a channel. Towing operations in connection with the collier fleet began on the Tyne in 1822. Steam tugs did not appear on the Thames until 1832; the first ones were unwanted boats from the Tyne which often could not stem the tide in the Thames. The tug HERCULES was built in the Netherlands in 1825. In the U.S.A. the towing of cargo barges on the Hudson started in 1826 and for years many of the tugs were old passenger steamers with their superstructures cut down. The famous NORWICH of 1836 was broken up in 1923 after 80 years as a tug; her original engine was used until her end.

Although NEW JERSEY ex ROBERT F. STOCKTON demonstrated the suitability of the screw for tug propulsion, paddle-wheels were favored until the 1860's after which screw tugs were more generally employed. They are now constructed in a variety of sizes from the large and powerful for long distance towing and salvage work down to launch sizes for restricted waters. Paddle tugs continued to be built for years, however, for several reasons among them being the fact that full power could be applied in either direction and a separate engine on each wheel made them very handy. For such reasons the British Admiralty constructed in the 1950's a class of paddle tugs having Diesel-electric machinery which were specially designed to handle aircraft carriers.

While European tugs usually had their towing hooks located nearly amidships to allow more freedom to turn, the U.S.A. tugs were built with long deckhouses so that the towing bitts were located well aft. Many tug operations in the U.S.A. involved the movement of barges lashed alongside as well as long-distance coastwise tows where the position of the towing point was not important.

丸

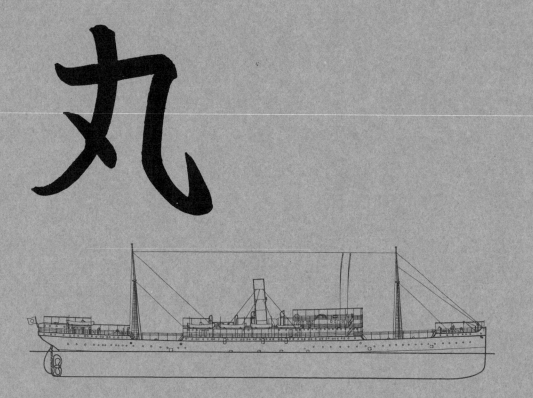

420.0 × 50.0 × 30.5 feet
128,016 × 15,239 × 9,296 m

While the great engineering advances were being made in the European-built express steamers well designed ships were being constructed in other parts of the world. The hull and engines of NIKKO MARU, a cargo and passenger ship designed for the Australian service of the Nippon Yusen Kaisha, were built by the Mitsu Bishi Dockyard & Engine Works, Nagasaki. Launched in October 1903 her steel hull had eight transverse watertight bulkheads and two complete decks. She had the usual three super-structures—forecastle, bridge, and poop—with houses amidships and aft. Accommodations were provided for 60 first-class passengers, 28 second-class, 24 intermediate, and 108 in the steerage. The first-class quarters were elaborately decorated by famous Japanese artists of the time. The social hall at the forward end of the first-class saloon had been shown at a trade exhibition in Osaka and used as a retiring room by the Emperor and Empress of Japan during their visit. NIKKO MARU was propelled by one set of three-cylinder triple expansion engines which developed 6694 (6785) i.h.p. on trials when she attained an average speed of 17.75 knots (32,90 km/hr.). As she was intended to operate in tropical waters she was fitted throughout with awnings and among her engineering features was a special ventilating system for the first-class accommodations that could deliver heated or cooled air. Considered the Japanese super-liner of her day she had a long life and was sunk on 9 April 1945.

MARU

Japanese ships receive at their christening a sort of family name, "Maru", which, however, does not mean ship. The term is derived from the Japanese national flag which, as we know, symbolizes the red sunrise. The flag is called "Hino Maru" meaning the roundness of the sun. The Japanese consider the circle to be the perfect geometrical shape. A ship at sea with its human and mechanical resources and functions is felt to be a complete organism worthy of honorary title of "Maru". Young men well developed from a body and soul point of view were formerly allowed to add "Maru" to their family names. During the age of chivalry castles were also granted the right to use the title. The Emperor's palace "Gohom Maru" is an example.

Vermont — page 127

spring of 1920. At the end of 1921 her original direct drive turbines were replaced by geared units after which she ran as a cabin class liner; her name was soon changed to MARLOCH. From 1925 on she served as a reserve ship but saw considerable service until sold to shipbreakers in 1929.

VIRGINIAN was sold in 1918 to the Swedish American Line, repowered with de Laval geared turbines, and renamed DROTTNINGHOLM. She saw considerable service during World War II and was eventually scrapped in Italy in 1955.

For nearly two centuries in North America the Richelieu, Lake Champlain, and the Hudson provided a relatively easy route for explorers, settlers, and invading and defending armies. After the country settled down the same route logically served for commercial communications between the cities of New York, Montreal, and Quebec. Lake Champlain followed the Hudson as the second body of water to have regular steamboat service, the first steamer on the lake being VERMONT of 1808. She ran from Whitehall at the lower end of the lake to St. Jean on the Richelieu in Canada until 1815. Canals were built in the 1820's connecting Whitehall with the Hudson and the upper end via the Richelieu with the St. Lawrence. They were never big enough to take the steamers which provided commercial service up and down Lake Champlain until the New York & Canada Railroad was completed up the western shore of the lake in 1875. The steamboats then served the continually expanding summer tourist trade.

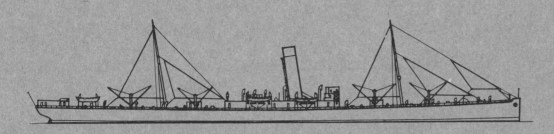

512.0 × 62.3 × 34.5 feet
156,058 × 18,988 × 10,515 m

Constructed for the Anglo-American Oil Company, London, by Scott's Shipbuilding & Engineering Company, Ltd. of Greenock, NARRAGANSETT is now considered to have been before her time. She was about twice the size of any previous tanker, was the largest in the world until the beginning of World War I, and was the largest to have transverse framing. From considerations of strength she had her machinery amidships with eight main cargo tanks forward and eight aft. With four pumps divided between two pump rooms her 11,000 (11 176) ton cargo could be discharged in 12 hours. A single-screw ship NARRAGANSETT had one set of three-cylinder triple expansion engines which developed 5500 (5575) i.h.p.; six single-ended Scotch boilers supplied 200 p.s.i. (14,062 kg/cm²) steam. On trial she attained a speed of nearly 13 knots (24,13 km/hr.). Designed primarily for the oil trade from the U.S.A. to Europe she also complied with the Suez Canal regulations. Because of her unusual size and structural features she suffered many cracked plates and required much local patching during her life. NARRAGANSETT was sunk off the Scilly Isles on 16 March 1917.

Largest and next to the last of the 29 steamboats built on Lake Champlain was VERMONT of 1903, the third to bear the name. Designed by J. W. Millard of New York, the contract for her hull and engine was awarded to Messrs. W. A. Fletcher Company, Hoboken, New Jersey, and she was assembled at Shelburne, Vermont, under the direction of L.F. Barrett. In general arrangement she followed the practice of U.S.A. river and sound steamboats established in the five previous decades, some had more and some had fewer than her 90 berths for passengers. Her steel hull was carefully designed to obtain the greatest strength from the lightest scantlings, based on experience gained in building light, shallow hulls rather than the rules of a classification society. On her lower deck which was broken by the machinery space were, from forward to aft, crew's quarters, a bar and lunch room, the galleys and pantries, officers' dining room, and stewards' quarters. Aft on the main deck was the dining saloon seating 150 which had plate glass windows all around to permit a good view of the lake scenery. Fifteen of her staterooms were on the main deck forward of the paddle-wheels while the remaining thirty were at the sides of the main saloon on the deck above. The wheelhouse and six staterooms for officers were located at the forward end of the hurricane deck; the remainder of that deck was open for passengers.

VERMONT was propelled by a jet-condensing vertical beam engine; its single cylinder was 55 in. (1,397 m) diameter by 10 ft. (3,045 m) stroke and it developed 1800 (1824) i.h.p. There were two return tubular boilers which generated steam at 50 p.s.i. (3,515 kg/cm²). Her feathering paddle-wheels drove her at about 21 miles (33,80 km) per hour. Laid up in 1932, her engine was sold for scrap a few years later and at the end of World War II her superstructure was removed and her steel hull towed down the Hudson for conversion to a Diesel-propelled freight boat.

When the Champlain Transportation Company, still under its original charter, ceased operations in 1948 it was the oldest steamboat company in the world. Its last boat, TICONDEROGA of 1906, similar to but smaller than VERMONT, is now preserved on land at the Shelburne Museum.

The nineteenth-century fruit trade on both sides of the Atlantic developed some very fast brigs and schooners but they were eventually displaced by the more reliable steamers. A few days of calm weather might mean that a brig's cargo of oranges would have to be pitched overboard. In 1870 Captain Lorenzo D. Baker conceived the idea of carrying bananas from Jamaica to Boston and started his venture with the schooner TELEGRAPH. Auxiliary steamers were placed in the trade in the early 1880's and specially built steamers soon followed. By the turn of the century Captain Baker's venture, which had become the United Fruit Company, owned or had under charter 75 steamers employed in carrying bananas from its own plantations in the Caribbean region to various U.S.A. ports.

SAN JOSE, one of three single-screw steamers constructed by Messrs. Workman, Clark & Company, Ltd., Belfast, was the first vessel equipped with refrigerating machinery to deliver a cargo of bananas to Boston. She had three full steel decks in her hull and a wooden orlop deck forward of the boiler room. Her only superstructure was a forecastle and there was a long house amidships. Each hold and 'tween-deck space was fully insulated and fitted with ducts through which air chilled by Linde refrigerating machinery was forced. Side ports in the upper 'tween-deck spaces as well as hatches were provided for loading and unloading cargo. In addition to the usual cargo booms and steam winches there were appliances specially designed to handle bunches of bananas of which SAN JOSE could carry 45,000.

San José — page 128

Messrs. Workman, Clark & Company, Ltd. also constructed the machinery for SAN JOSE which consisted of one set of three-cylinder triple expansion engines with cylinders 25, 41, and 68 in. (0,635-1,041-1,727 m) diameter by 48 in. (1,219 m) stroke. With steam supplied by three Scotch boilers at 190 p.s.i. (13,359 kg/cm²) the engines developed 2750 (2787) i.h.p. at 80 r.p.m.

The Cunard Line approached the steam turbine problem, as it had many others, by careful experimentation. Two ships were built at the Clydebank yard of Messrs. John Brown & Company, Ltd., sisters except for their machinery. CARONIA of 1904 was a twin-screw ship fitted with quadruple expansion engines while CARMANIA, launched early in 1905, had Parsons triple-screw turbine machinery. They were large ships, 650 ft. (198,119 m) long, and CARONIA's reciprocating engines developed 22,000 (22300) i.h.p. On trials for which her underwater hull had been scraped and painted CARONIA averaged 19.7 knots (36,63 km/hr.) but with a dirty bottom CARMANIA managed to make 20.4 (37,80 km/hr.).

In 1903 the British government had made an agreement with the Cunard Line for two ships capable of maintaining 24 to 25 knots (44,48-46,33 km/hr.) in the mail and passenger service across the Atlantic which were to be available to the Admiralty in time of war. When the two ships were ordered in May 1905 there was no question concerning the propelling machinery to be installed—it would be steam turbines driving four shafts. The first to be launched was LUSITANIA in June 1906 from the yard of Messrs. John Brown & Company, Ltd. MAURETANIA was constructed by Messrs. Swan, Hunter & Wigham Richardson, Ltd. of Wallsend-on-Tyne and launched in September 1906. Although constructed to the same basic design the builders were given a free hand and the ships differed in many respects particularly in their passenger accommodations and interior decorations; there were also differences in the turbine blading, condensers, and boilers and MAURETANIA proved the more successful ship.

Mauretania — page 124

LUSITANIA and MAURETANIA represented a considerable jump in size and their structure required careful study. The flat keel was composed of three thicknesses of plating and special high-strength steel was employed in their topside structure. There was of course a full-length double bottom and there were two orlops forward and aft of the machinery spaces; there were four continuous decks in the main hull. Extending aft from a combined forecastle and bridge was a nearly full length promenade deck above which were two long houses. There were 15 watertight transverse bulkheads and all watertight doors in them were hydraulically operated, 38 of them by remote control from the navigating bridge. MAURETANIA had accommodations for 563 first-class, 464 second-class, and 1138 third-class passengers; her total crew consisted of 812 officers and men. She could carry only 1500 (1524) tons of cargo which was composed largely of mail and her passengers' baggage.

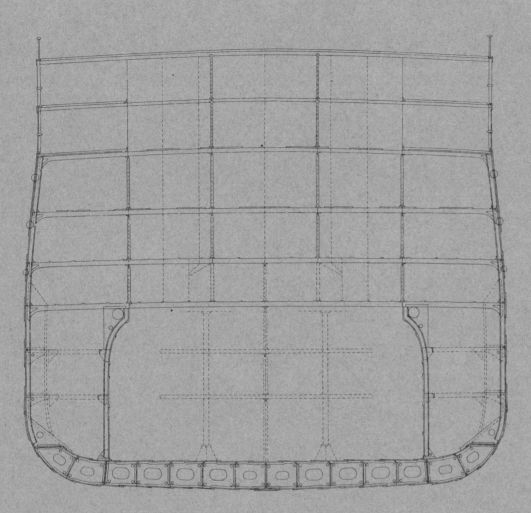

The turbines for MAURETANIA were direct-drive units constructed by the Wallsend Slipway & Engineering Company, Ltd. which developed a total of 70,000 (70952) s.h.p. High-pressure turbines drove the two outboard shafts and low-pressure turbines the inboard shafts. There were in all 25 Scotch boilers, 23 double-ended and 2 single-ended, which supplied steam at a pressure of 195 p.s.i. (13,710 kg/cm²). The ship's bunkers carried more than 6000 (6096) tons of coal. Each of the four shafts had a single four-bladed propeller 16.75 ft. (5,105 m) in diameter which normally operated at 180 r.p.m. MAURETANIA averaged 27.4 knots (50,78 km/hr.) on her trials.

LUSITANIA sailed on her maiden voyage from Liverpool to New York on 7 September 1907 and MAURETANIA started her first passage on 16 November. Following KAISER WILHELM DER GROSSE the Atlantic Blue Ribbon had been held by various German ships but on her second westbound passage LUSITANIA set a new record. MAURETANIA soon set a new eastbound record and the two ships alternated the Blue Ribbon between themselves until LUSITANIA's ill-fated end in 1915. MAURETANIA then held the Atlantic speed records until BREMEN came out in 1929.

During World War I MAURETANIA served first as an auxiliary cruiser and later as a hospital ship for which duty she was invaluable. Both the British and the Germans found that the money spent in subsidizing express liners with the view of employing them as auxiliary cruisers was a mistake. The high speeds of such ships came only at the expense of coal consumption and it proved impossible to keep them fueled when serving as cruisers. Refitted after the war MAURETANIA went back on her normal run and in 1922 was converted from coal to oil fuel. With her original direct-drive turbines she still managed to lower her own records and lost the Blue Ribbon to BREMEN in 1929 by very small margins—8 hours 52 minutes westbound and 7 hours 27 minutes eastbound. In 1931 by crossing the Atlantic four times in a month MAURETANIA set another sort of record. She was withdrawn in October 1934 and broken up at Rosyth in 1935.

KING EDWARD · 1901

Turbine Steamers Syndicate

250.5 × 30.1 × 10.0 feet ☾ 551 T ☾ 76,350 × 9,175 × 3,048 m

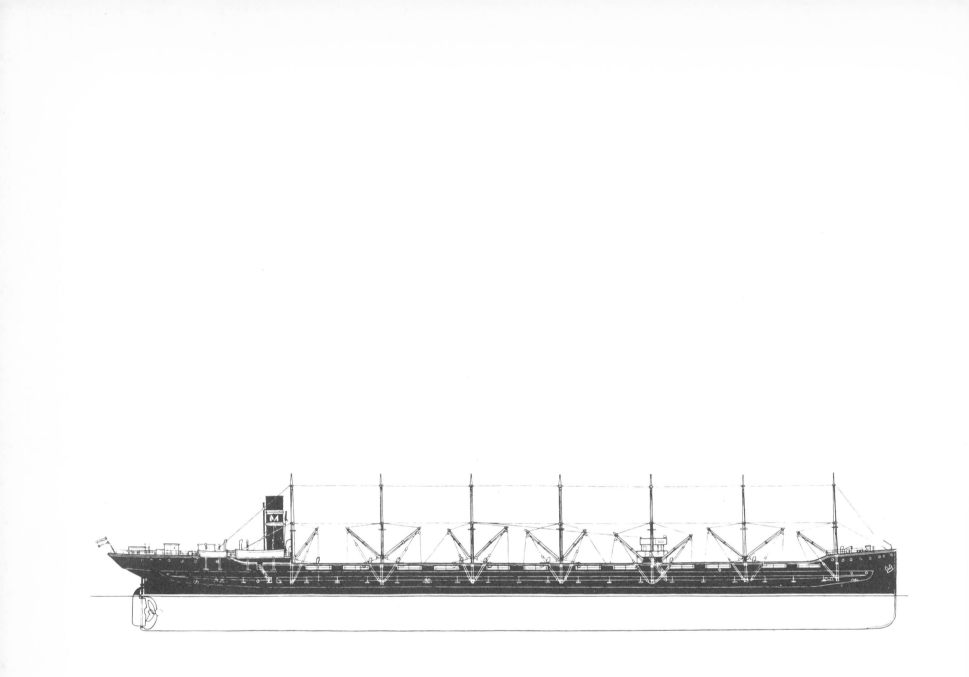

GRÄNGESBERG · 1903

Algemeene Scheepvaart Maatschappij (W.H. Muller & Company)

440.2 × 62.0 × 26.0 feet ℂ 6749 T ℂ 134,209 × 18,898 × 7,925 m

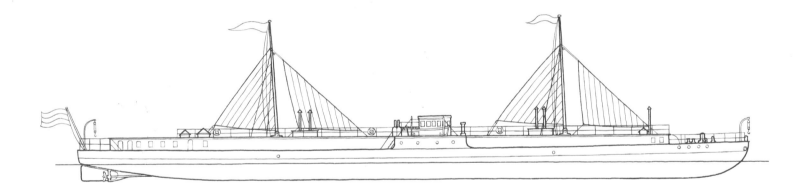

VANDAL · 1903

Naphtaproduktions-Gesellschaft Gebrüder Nobel

244.4 × 31.8 × 8.0 feet ◖ 1000 T ◖ 74,5 × 9,68 × 2,44 m

MAURETANIA · 1906

Cunard Steamship Company, Ltd.

762.2 × 88.0 × 57.1 feet ℂ 31938 T ℂ 232,318 × 26,822 × 17,404 m

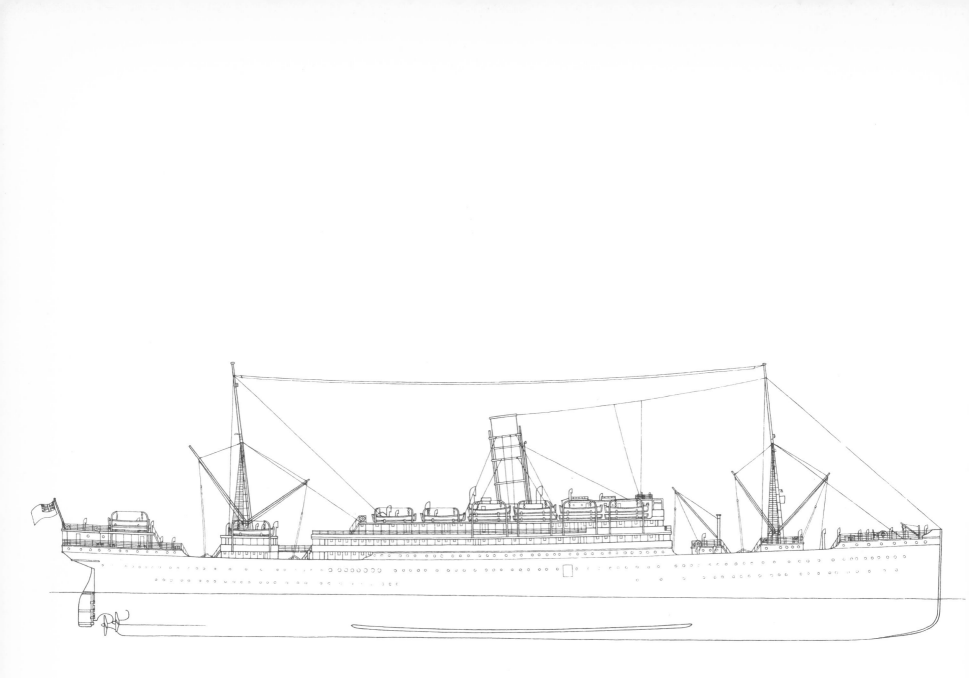

VICTORIAN · 1904

Allan Line Steamship Company, Ltd.

520.0 × 60.0 × 38.0 feet ◖ 10629 T ◖ 158,492 × 18,287 × 11,582 m

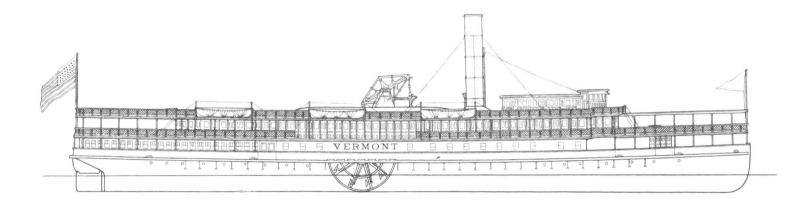

VERMONT · 1903

Champlain Transportation Company

251.5 × 34.9 × 10.6 feet ◖ 1195 T ◖ 76,655 × 10,637 × 3,231 m

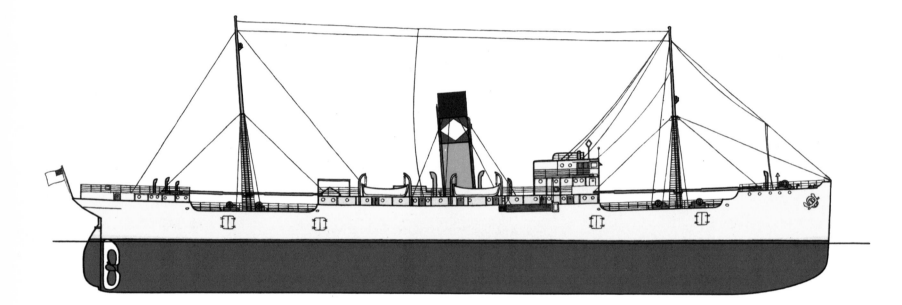

SAN JOSÉ · 1904

Tropical Fruit Steamship Company, Ltd.

330.0 × 44.6 × 31.6 feet ❲ 3296 T ❲ 100,581 × 13,594 × 9,632 m

SKETCH OF STEAM SCHOONER LOADING

"Naval architects have for so long recognized the great increase in strength obtained by framing a vessel longitudinally, that it is a matter for wonder that some practicable system of longitudinal framing has not been arrived at, or hitherto suggested, the advantage being so clear and so desirable." So wrote Joseph W. Isherwood, later Sir Joseph, in a paper read before the Institution of Naval Architects in London in April 1908 describing his newly patented system of longitudinal framing. In an ordinary transversely framed ship the deck beams and shell frames support local loads but contribute nothing to the longitudinal strength to resist bending. On the other hand, longitudinal beams and frames can do both at the same time which results in lighter structure for the same strength. To support such longitudinals, however, widely spaced deep transverse plate or web frames are required.

In spite of the above quotation, however, Scott Russell had constructed a ship without transverse frames as early as 1834. He built many others with partial longitudinal framing including GREAT EASTERN. Among others who developed systems of longitudinal framing were Messrs. Randolph Elder & Company, J. E. Scott, and J. Bruhn in England and F. M. Lilliehöök in Sweden. It can be appreciated that the deep transverse web frames could offer serious obstacles to the stowage of general cargoes. Isherwood proposed and exploited his system primarily for tankers for which it proved ideal and the system has since been employed for other bulk cargo carriers. Longitudinal framing is still not favored for general cargo ships.

The ship that introduced the Isherwood system was the single-screw steel tanker PAUL PAIX constructed by Messrs. R. Craggs & Sons, Ltd., of Middlesborough, England. Built as a single-deck three-island ship she had an expansion trunk, whose width was about half her breadth, extending from forecastle to poop right through the bridge in order to maintain continuity of structure. There were in all eight pairs of cargo tanks evenly divided by the machinery space. Six pairs of tanks were 30 ft. (9,144 m) long and were employed when the ship was carrying heavy oil cargoes; shorter tanks at the ends of the ship were about 12 ft. (3,658 m) in length. All eight tanks were employed when light refined petroleum products were carried. There was a double bottom under the machinery space only which could be used for oil fuel or salt water ballast.

Paul Paix — page 140

PAUL PAIX was propelled by one set of quadruple expansion engines constructed by the North-Eastern Marine Engineering Company, Ltd. of Newcastle. The cylinders were 21½, 30, 44, and 64 in. (0,546-0,762-1,118-1,626 m) diameter by 45 in. (1,143 m) stroke; Lloyd's rated the engines at 376 n.h.p. Three single-ended Scotch boilers supplied steam at 220 p.s.i. (15,468 kg/cm²). The ship's normal fuel was coal, there being an athwartships bunker forward of the boiler room; reserve bunkers were located in the bridge space outboard of the trunk. PAUL PAIX had a long and useful life not being broken up until 1935.

Early voyagers venturing along the inhospitable coast of northern California glimpsed through the heavy fogs great trees on cliffs rising from the sea. These were the primeval stands of the coastal redwood, the Sequoia sempervirens, which grew in an area that stretched north from San Francisco for about 400 miles (644 km) and reached in from the sea about 30 miles (48 km). Cutting operations started in the early 1850's when the gold rush caused a population explosion in California. Because of the mountainous country all transportation of the lumber had to be by sea but there were no ports, only "dog-holes". A slight headland or a clump of offshore rocks was the only protection against strong northwest winds and heavy seas sweeping in from the Pacific—that name hardly applies north of San Francisco.

Small sailing schooners were first employed to carry the lumber from the mills south to San Francisco. As they rode at anchor in the dog holes with their sterns only a few feet from boiling reefs and ledges, the lumber slid from the cliffs down wooden chutes to their decks; in later days wire cables were employed. About 1880 a small steam engine was installed well aft in one of these schooners; various authorities claim the honor for five different vessels. NEWSBOY of 1888 was the first steam schooner to be launched with engines installed and it was not many years before sails were entirely discarded. Although the type retained the name of steam schooner, the sailing vessel form was also abandoned. In its place there developed an easily driven hull, fine below the light water-line to keep the propeller under water when going north in light condition, and full above to provide good carrying capacity. Stability with large loads was also important.

WILLAPA, constructed entirely of Douglas fir by Messrs. John W. Dickie & Son, Inc. at Raymond, Washington, was a typical single-ended steam schooner as developed from the first steam conversions. The first of the so-called "double-enders" with machinery amidships was constructed in 1905 but they were not commonly built until 1916. Designed to carry a large deck load of lumber, WILLAPA had a forecastle and poop to protect the ends of the load; the poop was particularly important when run-

PAUL PAIX — MIDSHIP SECTION

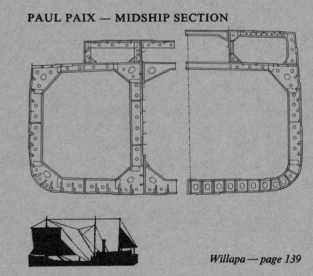

Willapa — page 139

ning heavily laden before the wind and sea down to San Francisco. Many of the lumber schooners had accommodations for passengers as for a long period there was no other means of transportation along the coast.

WILLAPA was propelled by a set of three-cylinder triple expansion engines having cylinders 11½, 19, and 32 in. (0,292-0,483-0,813 m) diameter by 24 in. (0,610 m) stroke; they developed 475 i.h.p. Steam was supplied by one oil-fired single-ended Scotch boiler. Oil fuel was introduced in the steam schooner fleet in 1893; WILLAPA carried her oil in steel tanks located in the poop to port and starboard of the machinery casing. Fires and reefs ended the careers of many of the steam schooners. WILLAPA foundered on Vivorilla Cays, Honduras, on 29 October 1916.

Ships constructed for the various cross-Channel services from England to the Continent always have called for considerable ingenuity in connection with their designs. The available depths of water have required light-weight ships in order to carry the necessary loads and the arrangements of piers have limited ship lengths. By 1910 the best of the Channel steamers were, in relation to their lengths, about 30 per cent faster than the Atlantic greyhounds and were only exceeded in speed by the naval torpedo boats and destroyers.

While the Dover-Calais run was made in a little over an hour, many of the services offered overnight accommodations. Founded in 1877 the Stoomvaart Maatschappij Zeeland of Vlissingen (Flushing) had operated such a night service from Vlissingen to Queensborough on the Medway employing fast paddle steamers. All of the company's ships had been constructed by the Fairfield Shipbuilding & Engineering Company, Ltd., Glasgow, and when increasing traffic required new ships the Fairfield designers were consulted as to the best means of propulsion. Reciprocating screw engines were finally chosen as best meeting the requirements of the run. It was the practice of the operator to employ three ships on the run, each serving two weeks and then having one off for maintenance; the three new ships were ORANJE NASSAU, PRINSES JULIANA, and MECKLENBURG.

In contrast to the paddle steamers such as MARIE HENRIETTE which had relatively unobstructed weather decks, the newer steamers with extensive deckhouses were looking more and more like miniature versions of Atlantic liners. ORANJE NASSAU and her sisters were constructed of steel with two complete decks and a lower deck forward and aft of the machinery spaces. On the upper deck was a forecastle and several long houses over which was a 195 ft. (59,436 m) long covered promenade deck. The ships had ten watertight bulkheads. Sleeping accommodations were provided for a total of 244 first-class passengers and 110 second-class; in view of the increasing demand there were 64 single-berth first-class staterooms. Space was provided in the forecastle for a post office and mail room; limited quantities of cargo, much of it perishable in nature, could be carried in the lower holds and the forecastle.

The main propulsion machinery in ORANJE NASSAU consisted of two sets of four-cylinder triple expansion engines developing a total of 10,000 (10 136) i.h.p.; each engine had one 28 in., one 43½ in., and two 49 in. (0,711-1,105-1,245 m) diameter cylinders with a common stroke of 33 in. (0,838 m). Steam at 190 p.s.i. (13,359 kg/cm²) pressure was generated by four coal-fired double-ended Scotch boilers. For general lighting, submarine signalling, and other uses ORANJE NASSAU had three steam-driven electric generators. On measured mile trials all three ships easily attained a speed of 22½ knots (41,70 km/hr.) and on service runs maintained 22 knots (40,77

Oranje Nassau — page 141

195.7 × 37.7 × 12.3 feet
59,648 × 11,490 × 3,749 m

The first sea-going vessel to be propelled by a Diesel engine was VULCANUS, a tanker constructed by the Nederlandsche Scheepsbouw Maatschappij, Amsterdam, for the Nederlandsche-Indische Tank Stoomboot Maatschappij. She was intended for service in the Netherlands East Indies distributing petroleum products from the wells and refineries on Borneo. Built on the turret deck principle with forecastle and poop, her turret served as an expansion trunk for her three main cargo tanks which were so arranged that three grades of petroleum could be carried simultaneously without contamination. Case-oil could be carried in a dry cargo hold forward. She was propelled by a Werkspoor 6-cylinder, 4-cycle, single-acting Diesel engine constructed by the Nederlandsche Fabriek, Amsterdam. All cylinders were 15.75 in. (0,410 m) diameter by 23.63 in. (0,600 m) stroke. At 165 r.p.m. the engine developed 500 b.h.p. and drove her at about 8 knots (14,83 km/hr.) loaded. Her deck machinery was driven by compressed air. VULCANUS served until December 1931 when she was broken up; her engine was still in perfect running condition.

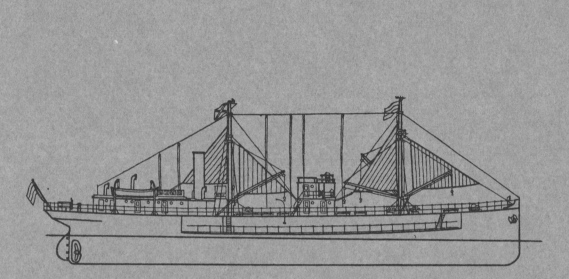

km/hr.) which was one knot (1,85 km/hr.) over the guaranteed speed. Except for a period during World War I ORANJE NASSAU was in night service until 1 January 1927 when she opened a day run from Flushing to Folkstone. From 1940 to 1945 she served the British Navy as a depôt ship returning to cross-Channel night runs in 1946. She was sold for scrap in 1954.

To many in the maritime world the appearance of a ship is important and the positions of the masts and funnels are carefully studied. False funnels have often been fitted to give the proper balance to a ship's profile and on occasion the position of a funnel has dictated the location of the propelling machinery to the detriment of other qualities of the ship. When SELANDIA entered service in 1912 she created quite a stir as she had three masts but no funnel. It was purposely omitted by her designers and owners so that she would be recognized immediately as a motorship. Although there were earlier motorships the twin-screw SELANDIA, because of her size, is generally considered the first ocean-going vessel propelled by Diesel engines.

Actually three motorships were constructed at about the same time. SELANDIA and her sister FIONIA, sold to the Hamburg American Line immediately after completion, were built by Messrs. Burmeister & Wain, Copenhagen, while Messrs. Barclay, Curle & Company, Ltd., Glasgow, built JUTLANDIA. Constructed of steel, with a full-length double bottom, two continuous decks, and six transverse bulkheads SELANDIA can best be described as a four-island ship as she had a forecastle, two

Selandia — page 142

bridges, and a poop, Her propelling machinery was located under the second bridge which arrangement permitted three holds forward and one aft capable of carrying a total of 7410 (7529) tons of cargo. The weather deck between the forecastle and first bridge was arranged to carry special timber which the company imported to Denmark in large quantities. In the forward bridge were a large dining saloon, lounge, and cabins for 26 passengers all equipped to a high standard of comfort, the public rooms being particularly high and airy to suit the conditions met on the route from Copenhagen to Bangkok.

SELANDIA's two main engines were constructed by Messrs. Burmeister & Wain to Dr. Diesel's principles but had many improvements developed by their builder. They were eight-cylinder, four-cycle, single-acting engines developing 1250 (1267) i.h.p. each at 140 r.p.m.; all cylinders were 20^7/$_8$ (0,530 m) diameter by 28$\frac{3}{4}$ (0,730 m) stroke. There were two auxiliary Diesel engines developing 250 i.h.p. at 230 r.p.m., one to supply the compressed air needed to reverse the main engines and the other to drive an electric generator. One small oil-fired boiler provided steam for heating the passenger's and crew's quarters. The mizzen mast served as a funnel to carry off the exhaust gases from engines and boiler. SELANDIA's double bottom carried enough Diesel fuel to permit her to cover 30,000 miles (55600 km) at her sea speed of 11 knots (20,39 km/hr.).

Running on the Copenhagen-Bangkok route until the outbreak of World War I SELANDIA was then sent out of the European danger zone and operated in the Pacific until the end of the war. Returning to the same service she continued to run without incident except for a brief lay up in 1931 until sold to Norwegian owners in 1936 and renamed NORSEMAN. Severely damaged in 1938 she was laid up because of the expense of repairs but in 1940 she was sold to the Finland-America Line who made the necessary extensive repairs to the hull. Renamed TORNATOR she was chartered to the Japanese; stranding in Omaisaki Bay she became a total loss in January 1942.

The major steamship services between North America and Great Britain, France, and Germany were the only ones on which large high-speed express steamers were profitable or indeed because of fueling problems could be operated at all. The intermediate services and long distance routes required comfortable and economical ships capable of carrying substantial amounts of cargo and relatively large numbers of passengers. Intended for a route roughly parallel to SELANDIA's; a large part of which was in tropical waters, JAN PIETERSZOON COEN, when launched in 1915, was the largest ship yet constructed in any Netherlands shipyard.

JAN PIETERSZOON COEN, built of steel by the Nederlandsche Scheepsbouw Maatschappij, Amsterdam, had three continuous decks in her hull. The uppermost had teak planking with steel tie plates on steel beams while the lower two were of full steel construction. She had eight watertight transverse bulkheads and the ten watertight doors in them could be closed from the navigating bridge in case of emergency. On her uppermost continuous deck she had a forecastle and a long combined house, bridge, and poop; above this were two levels of houses for passengers' quarters. Accommodations were provided for 202 first-class passengers, 129 second-class, 46 third-class, and 42 fourth-class; the total crew was 261. The first-class public spaces were luxuriously equipped and decorated with much carved wood work. They included a deck saloon, smoking room, dining saloon, and a verandah cafe. Unlike TITANIC she was equipped with enough lifeboats to take all persons on board.

RUDOLF DIESEL — 1858-1913

German engineer. As an assistant to the thermodynamic scientist G. von Linde he came into contact with technical heat problems quite early. In trying to improve the overall efficiency of steam machinery from fuel burning to power delivery he proposed to eliminate the boiler and to burn pulverized coal directly in the engine's cylinders. Working with the M.A.N. and Krupp companies he produced a successful engine. Unlike a petrol engine where a mixture of petrol and air is exploded by a spark-producing apparatus, in Diesel's engine the heat of air compressed in the cylinder ignites the fuel upon injection where it burns at constant pressure. Although developed to utilize powdered coal a change was soon made to heavy petroleum products as fuel. Diesel's principles have been employed in the development of many varieties of engines—two-stroke and four-stroke cycles, single and double acting, and opposed-piston types. Dr. Diesel vanished under mysterious circumstances on a journey between Antwerp and Harwich.

Jan Pieterszoon Coen — page 143

133

Except in way of the foremast JAN PIETERSZOON COEN's cargo hatches had to be trunked up through her houses. She carried extensive cargo handling gear for a ship of her type. On the foremast were four 6-ton booms for handling ordinary cargo and one 25-ton boom for special loads. On kingposts on the bridge deck were two 3-ton booms. The gear for all of these was worked by steam winches. There were in addition eight hydraulically operated cranes.

The propelling machinery consisted of two sets of three-cylinder triple expansion engines built by the Nederlandsche Fabrick van Werktuigen en Spoorwegmaterieel having cylinders 27, 44 and 75 in. (0,680-1,120-1,900 m) diameter by 49¼ in. (1,250 m) stroke. Each set developed 3000 (3041) i.h.p. at 85 r.p.m. Steam was delivered at 213 p.s.i. (15,000 kg/cm²) pressure by eight coal-burning single-ended Scotch boilers. JAN PIETERSZOON COEN's service speed was 15 knots (27,80 km/hr.). She operated between Amsterdam and the Netherlands East Indies via the Suez Canal until 1940. On 14 May 1940 she was scuttled at IJmuiden to block the entrance of the North Sea Canal.

In spite of certain advantages demonstrated by FRANK ROCKEFELLER the faults of the whaleback design were such that bulk cargo ships on the Great Lakes of North America developed along more normal lines, but in many respects they are hardly more than huge self-propelled barges. Their lengths and proportions are determined by the limited depths of water, loading and unloading facilities, lock sizes, loads to be carried, and lake wave characteristics. For years the standard length over all was 600 ft. 0 in. (182,880 m). While each owner had his particular requirements the limits were such that ships from different building yards varied only in minor details.

D.G. KERR, constructed of steel with longitudinal framing in the yard of the American Shipbuilding Company, Lorain, Ohio, is typical of this class. At the bow her stem is vertical, her sections have no flare, and her anchors are stowed in pockets so that they cannot catch on anything when the ship is passing through locks. The propelling machinery is pushed as far toward her stern as possible and she has a short elliptical counter. Her cargo space is essentially a parallel-sided box which has a slight sheer to its single deck. In lake terminology this is the spar deck. The main deck on modern lakers exists only at the ends; through the cargo space it is an horizontal girder port and starboard that forms the top of a wing ballast tank. Under the cargo hold is a deep double bottom with a specially strengthened tank top to withstand the impact of falling ore from the loading spouts and the abrasive effects of the mechanical grab buckets used for unloading.

The accommodations in D. G. KERR and similar ships are at the bow and stern. Forward there is a forecastle with two houses above. Here are located the navigating spaces, captain's and deck officers' quarters, and spaces for wheelmen and deck watchmen. In houses aft are the accommodations for the engineering officers, oilers, cooks, seamen, firemen, and coal passers. D.G. KERR is propelled by one set of three-cylinder triple expansion engines having cylinders 24¼, 41 and 65 in. (0,622-1,041-1,651 m) diameter by 42 in. (1,067 m) stroke which develop 1800 (1824) i.h.p. Three coal-burning Scotch boilers furnish steam at 180 p.s.i. (12,655 kg/cm²) pressure. In addition to the normal auxiliaries there is a large capacity ballast system to handle water ballast in and out of the double bottom and wing ballast tanks.

In 1921 D.G. KERR participated in some special loading experiments. On 7 September 1921 at Two Harbors, Minnesota, 12,508 (12708) tons of iron ore were loaded from spouts in 16½ minutes. Five days later this cargo was unloaded at Conneaut,

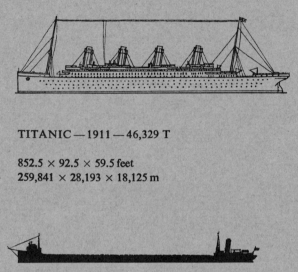

TITANIC — 1911 — 46,329 T

852.5 × 92.5 × 59.5 feet
259,841 × 28,193 × 18,125 m

D. G. Kerr — page 144

The sinking of the White Star liner TITANIC on 14 April 1912 on her maiden voyage with the loss of 1503 lives was one of the worst sea disasters of all time. No ship then afloat and few today could have survived her raking collision with an iceberg but the major reason for the great loss of life was the lack of sufficient life-boat capacity for all on board. Like her earlier sister ship OLYMPIC the triple-screw TITANIC was constructed by Messrs. Harland & Wolff, Ltd., Belfast. She had 15 transverse watertight bulkheads and, including all her midship superstructures, she had eight steel decks. Accommodations were provided for a total of 3300 persons—735 first-class, 675 second-class, and 1030 third-class passengers with a crew of 860. Built to the medium-speed high-comfort standard of the White Star Line TITANIC was propelled by a combination of reciprocating and turbine engines. Her two wing propellers were driven by four-cylinder triple expansion engines developing 15,000 (15204) i.h.p. each which exhausted to a direct-drive 16,000 (16218) s.h.p. Parsons turbine on the middle shaft. TITANIC's service speed was 21 knots (38,92 km/hr.).

IROQUOIS — 1907 — 9202 T
476.3 × 60.3 × 33.5 feet
145,175 × 18,378 × 10,210 m

NAVAHOE — 1908 — 7718 T
450.2 × 58.3 × 31.2 feet
137,220 × 17,769 × 9,510 m

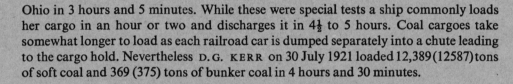

Ohio in 3 hours and 5 minutes. While these were special tests a ship commonly loads her cargo in an hour or two and discharges it in 4½ to 5 hours. Coal cargoes take somewhat longer to load as each railroad car is dumped separately into a chute leading to the cargo hold. Nevertheless D.G. KERR on 30 July 1921 loaded 12,389 (12587) tons of soft coal and 369 (375) tons of bunker coal in 4 hours and 30 minutes.

As may be seen from NARRAGANSETT and PAUL PAIX it was some years before the now familiar pattern set by GLÜCKAUF became the accepted arrangement for tankers. Typical of the many bulk oil carriers constructed during the second decade of the twentieth century was S.V. HARKNESS launched in 1917 by the Skinner & Eddy Corporation, Seattle Washington. Built of steel on the Isherwood longitudinal system she had one complete deck, 18 transverse bulkheads, and one longitudinal bulkhead through the cargo tanks. There were nine pairs of main cargo tanks and six pairs of summer tanks in the wing spaces abreast the expansion trunk. The total cargo capacity was 76,400 barrels (2151 m³) and three grades of refined petroleum products could be carried at the same time without contamination. Between the aftermost cargo tanks and the boiler room, separated from each by cofferdams, was a short compartment that could be used as a coal bunker or for oil fuel. Additional oil fuel could be carried in a deep tank under a dry cargo hold forward; the total fuel oil was 1050 (1067) tons.

The bridge and midship houses accommodated the captain, the deck officers, the petty officers, and the navigating spaces. The seamen and firemen were berthed in the poop while the engineering officers had their quarters in a house on the poop.

The original propelling machinery in S.V. HARKNESS consisted of geared turbines manufactured by the General Electric Company that developed 2500 (2534) s.h.p. and drove her at 11 knots (20,39 km/hr.). Steam at 210 p.s.i. (14,765 kg/cm²) pressure was furnished by three single-ended Scotch boilers. A donkey boiler located in the machinery casing on the main deck supplied steam for the cargo pumps when in port. In the middle 1920's S.V. HARKNESS was repowered with a 6-cylinder, single-acting Diesel engine of 2400 (2433) b.h.p. which gave her a speed of 10.1 knots (18,72 km/hr.).

SW Harkness — page 145

THE HORSE AND CART OF THE ATLANTIC

Here again is the "train" concept. IROQUOIS, the first twin-screw tanker to be built with propelling machinery aft, was designed to tow the six-masted schooner-rigged barge NAVAHOE. Constructed by Messrs. Harland & Wolff, Ltd., Belfast, for the Anglo-American Oil Company, Ltd., the "horse and cart" were a familiar sight on the Atlantic from 1908 to 1931. Quadruple expansion engines in IROQUOIS drove the pair at 10.1 knots (18,72 km/hr.) and between them they could deliver 18,000 (18,288 tons of cargo. NAVAHOE set her sails when the wind was fair and once, when forced to slip her tow line in a gale, she reportedly arrived at the unloading port ahead of IROQUOIS. NAVAHOE served as a storage barge in Venezuela from 1931 until she was towed to sea and scuttled in 1936. IROQUOIS went to the shipbreakers in 1947.

PERALTA — 1920 — 6149 T

420.0 × 54.0 × 35.0 feet
128,016 × 16,459 × 10,668 m

Nearly 100 years after sceptics predicted that the first iron ship would sink the first practical seagoing vessel of man-made stone—concrete—was launched. She was the 84 ft. (26,6 m) motorship NAMSENFJORD designed and built in Norway in 1917 by N. K. Fougner. Although requiring about half the steel of an ordinary ship of the same size concrete ships are heavier when completed and have less resistance to impact. As the steel is in the form of reinforcing rods not employed for ordinary ships concrete vessels have been built in many countries under emergency conditions when ships of every type were needed. The single-screw tanker PERALTA, built in San Francisco and one of eight such vessels ordered by the U.S. Shipping Board in 1918, had two longitudinal bulkheads and 13 transverse bulkheads. There were 18 tanks for cargo oil and two holds for dry cargo. She was fitted with three water-tube boilers and 2800 i.h.p. triple expansion engines but because of building delays she never carried a cargo. PERALTA's engines were removed in 1925 after which she served as a fish reduction plant until 1945. Still afloat in 1960 she has since been sold to serve as a breakwater in British Columbia.

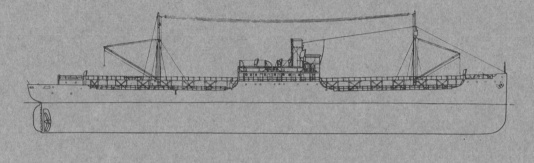

Although built for the Standard Oil Company of New Jersey S.V. HARKNESS was operated by the company only until 1925 after which she was owned and operated by a series of Standard Oil Company affiliates including the Baltisch-Amerikanische Petroleum Import G.m.b.H., Danzig, the Rederi A/B Höggarn, Stockholm, and the Panama Transport Company. Her last registered owner in 1949 was "La Columbia" Società Marittima per Azioni. Renamed SVITHIOD in 1926 she bore this name until the end of her career. In 1934 her cargo tank section was renewed, a common experience for tankers, which increased her length 6.9 ft. (2,103 m) and her depth 1.9 ft. (0,579 m). She saw considerable service during World War II mostly in South American waters but with special voyages to Italy, the Canary Islands, and Iceland. In September 1939 her German crew was replaced by a Norwegian one and at relatively short intervals she was manned by crews from Denmark and the U.S.A. Her last wartime crew change was made in August 1942 when Danes again came aboard.

Generally speaking there are two classes of dry cargo—deadweight and cubic. In relation to a ship's displacement a deadweight cargo such as iron ore needs only a small hold capacity while a cubic cargo, say baled cotton, requires a large amount of space. One method of increasing cubic capacity without an appreciable increase in the measured tonnage of a cargo ship was to build a substantial complete superstructure from bow to stern. The superstructure deck, hereafter called the shelter deck, was continuous and unbroken at the ship's side and had one or more openings at the middle line in accordance with tonnage regulations; certain openings were also required in the 'tween-deck bulkheads. These openings could have temporary non-watertight closing plates and because of these the 'tween-deck space was considered legally open to the sea hence not measured for tonnage. Shelter deck ships are not as safe as those in which the transverse bulkheads extend watertight to the weather deck and new tonnage measurement regulations are now being considered which will maintain the shelter deck benefits without the dangerous openings in deck and bulkheads.

Saint Dunstan — page 146

SAINT DUNSTAN, constructed by the Northumberland Shipbuilding Company, Ltd., Howdon-on-Tyne, was typical of the many shelter deck ships designed and built just after the first World War to carry general cargo. With her propelling machinery amidships and six transverse watertight bulkheads she had four main holds. The after part of number 2 hold was divided by a wooden bulkhead forming a short compartment which was usually employed for cargo but it could serve as a reserve coal bunker. While normally a coal-burner SAINT DUNSTAN's full-length double bottom was constructed to carry oil fuel under the cargo holds in case a change became desirable; the double bottom under the machinery space carried reserve feed water.

Unlike earlier ships all of SAINT DUNSTAN's seamen and firemen were berthed aft over the propeller and under the steering engine. The accommodations for the captain and deck officers were in the navigating bridge house while the engineering officers had their quarters on the shelter deck abreast the engine room casing. SAINT DUNSTAN's cargo was handled in and out of her main holds by 5-ton cargo booms; two lighter booms on short kingposts amidships served the reserve bunker space. All the cargo gear was worked by steam winches.

Triple expansion engines with Scotch boilers formed the standard propelling machinery for steamers such as SAINT DUNSTAN. Her three-cylinder engines, constructed by the North-Eastern Marine Engineering Company, Ltd., Wallsend, had cylinders 27, 44 and 73 in. (0,686-1,118-1,854 m) diameter by 48 in. (1,219 m) stroke which were supplied with 180 p.s.i. (12,655 kg/cm²) pressure steam by three single-ended boilers. The engines developed 3400 (3446) i.h.p. and drove her at 11½ knots (21,31 km/hr.) on loaded trials.

TONNAGE MEASUREMENT

In discussing ships few things are more confusing than the subject of their tonnage measurements on which port dues and other charges are based. The subject may be considered in two periods—before and after the passage of the British Merchant Shipping Act of 1854. Originally in English the word "ton" was not a unit of weight but one of space derived from the wine "tun". Vessels were taxed on the number of tuns of wine that they could carry. Experience showed that a formula based on length of keel, breadth, and depth—$K \times B \times D/94$—gave approximately the number of wine tuns that could be carried. Because of difficulties in measuring a ship afloat a basic measurement became the length on deck and the depth was assumed to be one-half the breadth, thus tonnage equalled $(L-\frac{3}{5}B) \times B \times \frac{1}{2}B/94$. With the introduction of steam propulsion L was further reduced by the length of the machinery space. France employed a similar formula while the Baltic countries used various systems based on the weights of certain volumes of grain.

The 1854 Act prescribed a system, named after its originator George Moorsom, whose principles are still in use although modified by a multitude of interpretations and regulations. In tons of 100 cu. ft. (in English units) gross tonnage represents the actual internal capacity of a ship. Its net tonnage or earning capacity is determined by deducting from the gross the volumes occupied by the propelling machinery, crew's quarters, and certain stores spaces. All maritime nations now employ the basic Moorsom system with their own modifications. The tonnages given in this book are the national gross tonnages for modern vessels and what was recorded at the time of registration for early steamers.

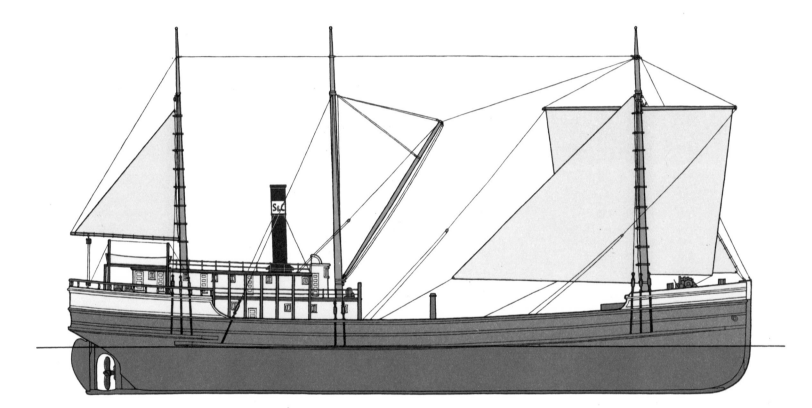

WILLAPA · 1908

Sudden & Christensen Company

178.5 × 40.0 × 13.3 feet ☾ 752 T ☾ 54,406 × 12,192 × 4,054 m

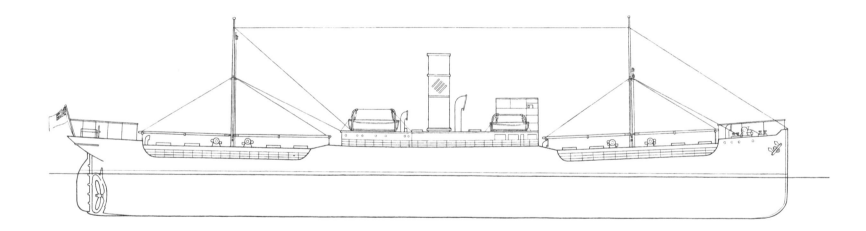

PAUL PAIX · 1908

Lennard's Carrying Company, Ltd.

355.2 × 49.4 × 25.7 feet ℂ 4196 T ℂ 108,264 × 15,057 × 7,833 m

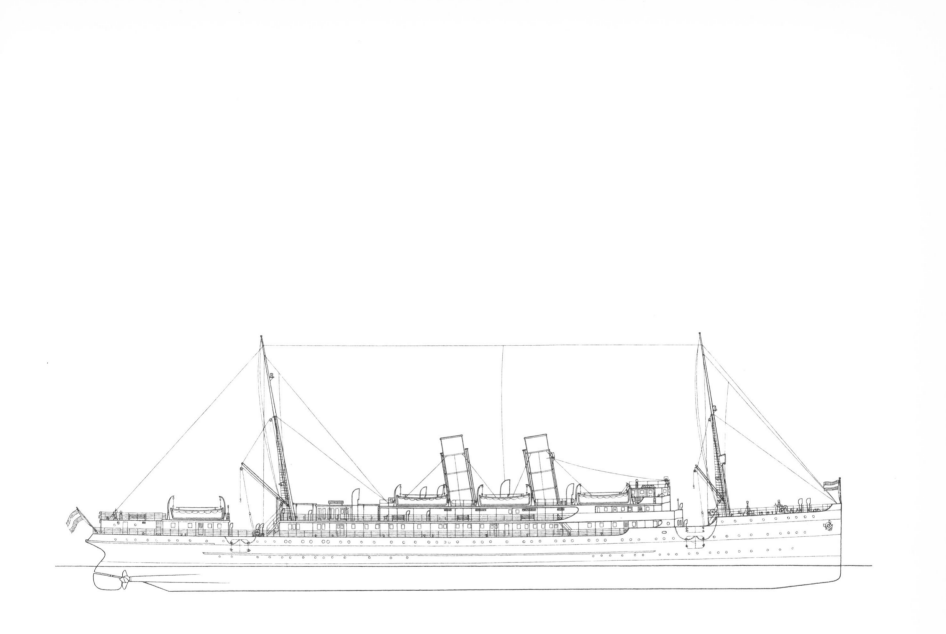

ORANJE NASSAU · 1909

Stoomvaart Maatschappij Zeeland

350.0 × 42.7 × 16.4 feet ◖ 2885 T ◖ 106,679 × 13,014 × 5,000 m

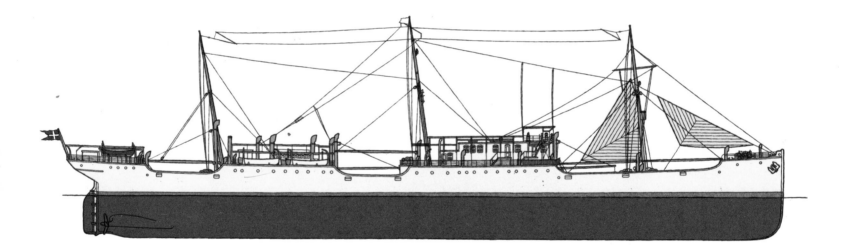

SELANDIA · 1911

Aktieselskab det Östasiatiske Kompagni

370.4 × 53.2 × 27.1 feet ◖ 4950 T ◖ 112,897 × 16,215 × 8,260 m

JAN PIETERSZOON COEN · 1915

Nederlandsche Stoomvaart Maatschappij

503.5 × 60.6 × 35.8 feet ☾ 11140 T ☾ 153,467 × 18,470 × 10,912 m

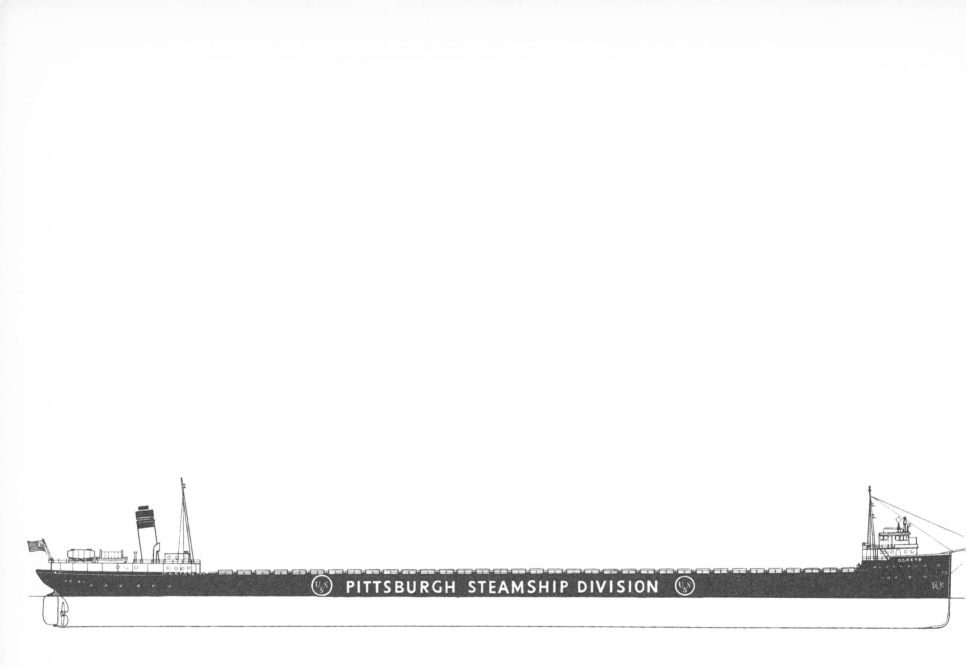

D. G. KERR · 1916

Pittsburgh Steamship Company, Inc.

580.0 × 60.0 × 32.0 feet ℂ 7758 T ℂ 176,783 × 18,287 × 9,753 m

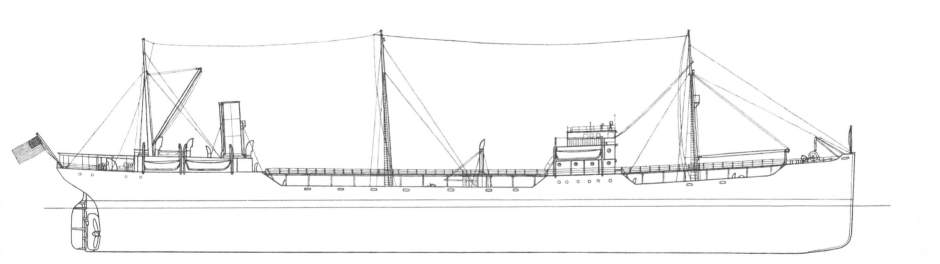

S. V. HARKNESS · 1917

Standard Oil Company (New Jersey)

419.4 × 57.2 × 29.8 feet ₵ 5293 T ₵ 127,833 × 17,434 × 9,083 m

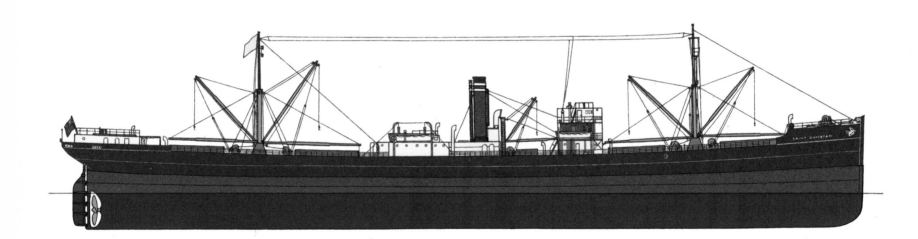

SAINT DUNSTAN · 1919

Rankin, Gilmour & Company

400.0 × 53.0 × 32.8 feet ℂ 5661 T ℂ 121,920 × 16,154 × 9,997 m

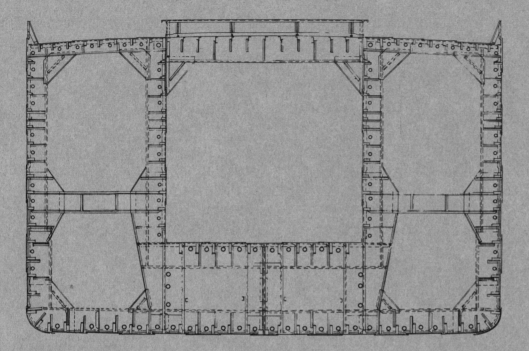

MIDSHIP SECTION—G. HARRISON SMITH

From a shipowner's point of view it would be ideal if his ships could operate at all times with full cargoes on outbound and return trips. Some general cargo ships do manage to operate with nearly full cargoes on voyages involving many ports where portions of their cargoes are unloaded and loaded at each port. Many specialized bulk cargo ships such as tankers and ore carriers, however, carry a paying cargo in one direction only and make the return passage in ballast. Occasionally it is possible for a ship to make triangular voyages carrying different cargoes on two legs and ballast on the third. G. HARRISON SMITH was designed and built for such a service. Her main trade was transporting heavy iron ore from Cruz Grande, Chile, to the Bethlehem Steel Corporation's plant at Sparrows Point, Maryland. Sailing from there in ballast she picked up oil in Mexico for delivery to ports on the west coast of South America.

Any discussion of the features of a heavy-ore carrier must mention the general subject of stability. A ship is said to be stable if she returns to her upright position after being heeled over by the external forces of wind and waves. Whether or not a large ship is stable depends on the hydrostatical qualities of her form and the disposition of internal weights such as cargo, fuel, stores, and water ballast. A ship is said to be "tender" if she heels easily—"stiff" if she does not. It is easily recognized that a tender ship, while comfortable in a seaway, can be dangerous. A stiff ship can also be dangerous as she rolls quickly thus making it difficult or impossible for the crew to move around safely; masts, booms, and other topside equipment may be carried away.

G. Harrison Smith — page 157

A small quantity of heavy ore piled on the double bottom of an ordinary cargo ship would load her down to her marks but she would be unreasonably stiff. In G. HARRISON SMITH the bottom of the ore holds was about one-third of her depth up from the keel. The two longitudinal bulkheads forming the sides were 30 ft. (9,144 m) apart thus the cross section of her ore holds was only about 29 per cent of her total cross-sectional area. There were three ore holds each 120 ft. (36,576 m) long. The surrounding U-shaped portion was employed to carry oil in bulk being divided longitudinally and transversely into 11 pairs of tanks for cargo oil and 2 pairs for fuel oil. G. HARRISON SMITH was framed longitudinally and the arrangement of her ore holds made it possible for all of their framing to be in the wing tanks. Thus they were smooth on the inside which made them easy to unload with grab buckets.

G. HARRISON SMITH and her sister BETHORE, owned by the Ore Steamship Company, were constructed in the Sparrows Point shipyard of the Bethlehem Steel Corporation. With a plumb stem, elliptical counter stern, forecastle, short bridge, and poop she looked from a distance like an ordinary tanker. On closer examination one would notice her two goal-post masts and three pairs of king posts all fitted with cargo booms. These served her nine cargo hatches which were closed by patented corrugated steel covers. The pump room for her cargo oil pumps was located under her bridge. The capacity of her ore holds was 367,120 cu. ft. (10396 m³) and the cargo oil tanks could carry 128,059 barrels. (20361 m³). The accommodations for the captain and deck officers were located in the bridge houses while the remainder of the crew were quartered aft.

A twin-screw ship G. HARRISON SMITH was propelled by two sets of three-cylinder triple expansion engines having cylinders 25, 41, and 68 in. (0,635-1,041-1,727 m) diameter by 48 in. (1,219 m) stroke. They developed a total of 5000 i.h.p. at 80 r.p.m. Three oil-fired single-ended Scotch boilers generated steam at a pressure of 200 p.s.i. (14,062 kg/cm²). Her normal service speed was 11½ knots (21,31 km/hr.).

Following World War I there was no rush to build challengers for the Atlantic Blue Ribbon held by MAURETANIA but a considerable number of fine ships were constructed for various intermediate services. GRIPSHOLM, built by Messrs. Sir W.G. Armstrong, Whitworth & Company, Ltd. at Newcastle for the Swedish American Line's service between Gothenburg and New York, was the first North Atlantic liner to be propelled by Diesel engines. Named for Sweden's historic Gripsholm Castle, once the home of the Swedish kings, her interior decorations and furniture were designed to conform to the general style and periods of the famous halls of the castle.

GRIPSHOLM was constructed in the normal fashion with transverse framing. In the main hull were three steel decks with an orlop deck in the three forward cargo holds but her superstructure was arranged so that for half her length amidships there were two additional strength decks. She was subdivided by ten watertight transverse bulkheads; the ten watertight doors in them could be operated from the navigating bridge as well as at each individual door. She had a normal elliptical counter stern but her straight stem raked slightly forward. Accommodations were normally provided for 91 first-class passengers and 355 second-class but by the use of Pullman berths in some of the staterooms these numbers could be raised to 129 and 482 respectively. Quarters were arranged for a total of 1006 third-class passengers. With a crew of 320 officers and men the total on board was 1937. The first- and second-class accommodations were

Gripsholm — page 158

FULLAGAR — 1920 — 398 T

150.0 × 23.7 × 10.1 feet
45,719 × 7,224 × 3,078 m

The ancient method of joining two pieces of like metal by heating and pounding them into one mass with a hammer is still employed but to most people today the term "welding" means the use of an electric arc to melt the edges of the pieces being joined and to deposit new joining
continued

amidships while the third-class rooms were on the lower decks both forward and aft. All were provided with mechanical ventilation, heated or cooled air directly to each berth in the first- and second-class staterooms but heated air only to each room in the third-class.

In her six cargo holds GRIPSHOLM had 284,000 cu. ft. (8042 m³) of space for carrying general cargo. A special insulated compartment in number 3 hold provided space for 13,200 cu.ft. (374 m³) of refrigerated cargo. For voyage use her refrigerated compartments held 11,000 cu. ft. (311 m³) of meat, fish, fruit, and vegetables while 16,000 cu. ft. (453 m³) of space were provided from dry stores. Three-ton booms on her two masts and kingposts forward and aft served the cargo holds and storerooms; number 3 hold also had a 20-ton boom for special loads. All the cargo winches, ten 3-ton and two 5-ton, were electrically driven as were the anchor windlass and mooring winches.

GRIPSHOLM had two machinery spaces amidships, the forward one containing her auxiliary engines and the after one the two main engines that drove her twin screws. Two Scotch boilers were installed in the compartment just forward of the auxiliary engine room to provide steam for heating and for a fresh water distilling unit. Messrs. Burmeister & Wain, Copenhagen, constructed all of GRIPSHOLM's Diesel engines. The two main engines were six-cylinder, four-cycle, double-acting engines which developed a total of 13,500 (13684) b.h.p. at 125 r.p.m. and drove the ship at 17 knots (31,50 km/hr.). All cylinders were $33^1/_{16}$ in. (0,840 m) diameter by $59^1/_{16}$ in. (1,500 m) stroke. While some main engines drive their own air compressors GRIPSHOLM's did not and in the auxiliary engine room were three three-stage compressors driven by 700 (710) b.h.p. four-cylinder Diesels. Also located there were three Diesel-driven 220-volt electric generators. It will be noted that two funnels were provided to take care of the engine exhaust gases.

GRIPSHOLM sailed on her maiden voyage from Gothenburg to New York on 21 November 1925 and settled down to steady service. During World War II she became famous as a repatriation ship. In March 1946 she returned to the Atlantic run after changes in her passenger accommodations that increased her gross tonnage to 19,105 and provided for 210 first-class and 710 tourist-class passengers. Sold in 1954 to the North German Lloyd and renamed BERLIN she made her first voyage from Bremen to New York on 8 January 1955. Her passenger quarters had again been changed to accommodate 98 in the first-class and 725 in the tourist.

Such were the demands for iron ore at the Sparrows Point Plant of the Bethlehem Steel Corporation that company-owned ships were insufficient and many vessels were operated under long term charters. AMERIKALAND and her sistership SVEALAND, constructed in 1925 by the Deutsche Werft A.G., Hamburg, and owned by Messrs. Axel Broström & Son. Gothenburg, were two of the ships employed in the trade. At Cruz Grande the loading basin had been blasted out of solid rock to a depth of 40 ft. (12,192 m) and the loading facilities consisted of a series of spouts, sixteen in all, similar to those employed on the Great Lakes. The port restrictions did not permit much variation in ship dimensions or arrangement hence at first glance AMERIKA-LAND might easily be mistaken for G. HARRISON SMITH. A closer look, however, would pick out the superficial differences—the line of plating at the breaks of the forecastle and poop, the absence of three pairs of kingposts, a shorter funnel, houses at the sides of the poop, and the position of the life boats. Built to exactly the same

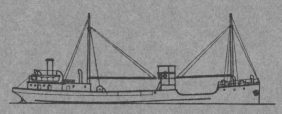

continued

metal. Nicholas de Barnados obtained in St. Petersburg in 1885 a patent for a method of electric welding employing a carbon arc. It proved difficult to regulate the heat of the arc and to exclude the atmosphere to avoid oxidation in the weld. This led to the development of steel electrodes with various coatings that melted and protected the new weld until cool. By the second decade of the twentieth century electric welding was widely employed for ship and engine repairs and for certain details in new construction. The first all-welded vessel was FULLAGAR constructed on speculation by Messrs. Cammell Laird & Company, Ltd., Birkenhead. Launched on 5 February 1920 she was sold after completion to Messrs. T. & J. Brocklebank, Ltd. A coasting vessel of the well-deck type she was originally propelled by a Cammellaird-Fullagar 4-cylinder, opposed-piston, 2-cycle Diesel engine that developed 500 (507) b.h.p. at 105 r.p.m. and drove her at 10 knots (18,53 km/hr.) on trials. About 1923 she was repowered with an ordinary 2-cycle Diesel.

In 1924 FULLAGAR ran aground and had a portion of her bottom set in 11 in. (0,279 m). The bent plates were forced back to their original shapes without fractures in the plates or welds. She served three other owners and was renamed successively CARIA, SHEAN, and CEDROS, the latter being under the Mexican flag. She sank after a collision in 1937.

Amerikaland — page 160

149

designer's length, breadth, and depth and with the same ore hold arrangement as G. HARRISON SMITH she is a good example for pointing out some of the confusions that arise from various records and the effect of things not readily discernible from the exterior of a ship.

In the triangular operation of G. HARRISON SMITH it was soon found that the income derived from the carriage of oil from Mexico to South America did not offset the Panama Canal tolls on the tanks and the extra time involved in loading and discharging the oil. The wing tanks for oil cargoes were changed to ballast tanks. Two new ships were constructed by the Sparrows Point Yard, MARORE and STEELORE, without the tanker features and propelled by single-reduction geared turbines in place of the triple expansion engines. The weight saved by these changes enabled them to carry 625 (635) tons more iron ore than G. HARRISON SMITH.

When Messrs. Axel Broström & Son arranged to build ore ships for charter it was natural that they follow the design of a ship that had proved satisfactory. Such are the differences, however, in national regulations concerning measurement points that AMERIKALAND was recorded as being 11 ft. (3,353 m) longer and 0.4 ft (0,122 m) deeper. Although built without the tanker features like MARORE the different national tonnage rules made AMERIKALAND's gross tonnage 7417 tons higher. It is because of such differences that both the Panama Canal and Suez Canal authorities each have their own tonnage rules under which ships using these canals must be measured.

The main difference between AMERIKALAND and the U.S.A. built ships was that she had Diesel engines. Her two main engines were eight-cylinder, four-cycle, single-acting, Burmeister & Wain Diesels that developed 3200 (3244) All cylinders were 29.13 in. (0,740 m) diameter by 47.42. (1,200 m) stroke. It is interesting to compare the propeller sizes required to properly utilize the power developed by the three types of propelling machinery installed in these ore carriers. The propellers for G. HARRISON SMITH's triple expansion reciprocating steam engines were 17.5 ft. (5,334 m) diameter by 16.75 ft. (5,105 m) pitch. MARORE's steam turbines drove propellers of 15.67 (4,775 m) diameter by 12.5 ft. (3,810 m) pitch. On AMERIKALAND the propellers were still smaller — 14.11 ft. (4,300 m) diameter by 11.29 ft. (3,440 m) pitch.

When ready for sea AMERIKALAND weighed 284 (289) tons less than G. HARRISON SMITH but 343 (348) tons more than MARORE. She left on her maiden voyage to Cruz Grande on 10 April 1925 and served steadily in the unglamorous but necessary ore trade. She was sunk off the coast of the U.S.A. in 1942.

After World War I the Norddeutscher Lloyd resumed service with COLUMBUS, completed in 1922 but started as HINDENBURG in 1914. The winning of the Atlantic Blue Ribbon by KAISER WILHELM DER GROSSE in 1897 had so improved the financial position of the company that in 1926 a new project was started to retrieve the Blue Ribbon from MAURETANIA. Two ships of about 50,000 gross tons were planned, one to be built in Bremen and the other in Hamburg. No direct subsidies were received as was the case with earlier express liners but much indirect assistance was given by the German government. The ships were built in great secrecy probably as much to whet public interest as to conceal engineering details. While the 1897 record breaker was a careful development of previous liners the new ships—BREMEN and EUROPA—introduced many revolutionary features.

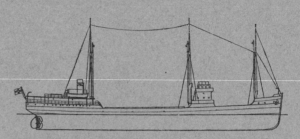

BELDIS — 1924 — 2406 T

294.1 × 45.3 × 19.1 feet
89,642 × 13,807 × 5,822 m

The motor vessel BELDIS was especially designed to carry such diverse cargoes as timber and locomotives. She was built and engined by Sir W. G. Armstrong, Whitworth & Company, Ltd., Newcastle, for Skibs A/S Christen Smith's Rederi, Oslo. A single-deck vessel with forecastle, bridge, and poop she had her propelling machinery aft. Her two long holds were arranged to be as clear of obstructions as possible and her deck was strengthened to carry heavy loads; each hold was served by one long hatch. The full-length double bottom was arranged to carry fuel oil or water ballast, the fore and after peak tanks carried water ballast only, and there was a ballast tank between her upper and bridge decks. The navigating spaces and accommodations for the owner and captain were in the bridge houses while the remainder of the crew were berthed aft. For handling cargo BELDIS had six 3-ton booms operated by steam winches. Her single screw was driven by an Armstrong-Sulzer Diesel rated at 1350 (1368) b.h.p. at 100 r.p.m.; all her auxiliary machinery was steam-driven with steam being supplied by two oil-fired Cochran boilers.

Bremen — page 162

In the 1830's the construction of a steamship capable of crossing the Atlantic was widely believed to be impossible. Fuel consumption in relation to delivered power was so high that no ship could ever carry enough fuel for the passage. The use of steam vessels would be limited to rivers and short overseas runs where ample fuel supplies were available. Sail would be supreme on the oceans. About one hundred years later it was believed that high-speed express steamers would always be required on the North Atlantic as the establishment of an air ferry between Europe and North America was economically out of the question. Steamship records across the Atlantic were set between recognized offshore marks—lighthouses and lightships, not pier to pier. Several hours could elapse after passing such a point before a ship was berthed and unloading started. To speed her top priority mails to their destinations from even further off shore BREMEN *was equipped with a catapult-launched seaplane.*

A quick glance at the profiles of MAURETANIA and BREMEN will show how complete was the break with the past. Gone were the long standard vertical stem and counter stern—they were replaced by a raking rolled-plate stem and a cruiser stern. On BREMEN's topsides everything was shaped as far as possible to reduce wind resistance even to the two squat funnels. These, however, were found to cover the after decks with soot and fumes and EUROPA's funnels were of a more normal shape; BREMEN's were later raised 15 ft. (4,572 m). Unseen below the water at the bow was a large bulb similar to the ram bow seen on old warships. BREMEN's hull form was the result of many tank tests and by reducing the size of the bow wave the bulb served to reduce wave resistance. To further minimize resistance bilge keels to reduce rolling were omitted but she was equipped with Frahm anti-rolling tanks.

BREMEN was constructed in the city after which she was named by the Deutsche Schiff- und Maschinenbau A.-G. Werk. Her keel was laid on 18 June 1927 and she was launched on 16 August 1928, being sponsored by President Hindenburg. She had a complete double bottom and four decks continuous from bow to stern; three orlops below and four levels of superstructure and houses gave her a total of 11 decks amidships. There were 14 main transverse watertight bulkheads which were fitted where required with hydraulically-operated watertight doors.

In laying out the passenger accommodations it was necessary to study what was being offered by the ships then operating on the North Atlantic and by the newest hotels ashore. Travel patterns had changed and there had been an increasing demand for comfort in all classes since World War I. On BREMEN there were no provisions for a steerage class and the third-class staterooms were equal to second-class quarters in older ships. Naturally the first-class accommodations were the most important and they were arranged in a three-storied block amidships. To simplify food service problems all dining saloons, galleys, and associated spaces were arranged on one deck; the first-class dining saloon could seat more than 600 persons. BREMEN was arranged to carry 615 first-class passengers which could be increased to 811 by the use of Pullman berths, 300 second-class which could be increased to 500 by reducing the number of first-class cabins, 496 tourist-class, and 617 third-class. With a normal crew of 990 the total persons on board could have been 3214.

Great advances had been made in marine engineering since MAURETANIA won the Atlantic record and BREMEN's four 4-bladed 16.4 ft (5,00 m) diameter propellers were driven at 180 r.p.m. by single-reduction geared turbines which developed a total of 123,300 (125000) s.h.p., nearly twice the power of the older ship. Instead of Scotch boilers BREMEN had 20 oil-fired water-tube boilers which supplied steam at a pressure of 330 p.s.i. (23,202 kg/cm²) superheated to 700° F. Her total electric generating capacity was 2440 KW at 220 volts. BREMEN sailed on her maiden voyage to New York via Southampton on 16 July 1929 and set a record for the crossing from the latter port of 4 days 17 hours 42 minutes. In 1934 she reduced this to 4 days 14 hours 27 minutes at a mean speed of 28 knots (51,89 km/hr.). At the outbreak of World War II BREMEN was in New York and made a dash for Germany to avoid seizure. By passing north of Iceland and approaching Germany along the coast of Norway she eluded British warships and arrived safely. She was burned out during an air raid on Bremerhaven on 18 February 1941 and was eventually cut up for scrap.

The ship-model testing work started by the Froudes was taken up by other experimenters as the years passed. This led to gradual improvements in the hull forms of ships which meant lower power requirements for a given speed or conversely higher speeds for a given power. Certain low-resistance hull forms have been patented, one of the best-known being that invented by F.F. Maier of Germany. One authority has noted, however, that it is difficult to determine the dividing line between the ability of an inventor as a naval architect and the qualities of his patent as equally good results have been obtained from the resistance point of view without the use of patented forms.

In the course of experience since the building of the first Maier-form vessel, the German fishing trawler WEISSENFELS in 1928, it has been shown that Maier's conclusions regarding his invention were only partly correct. For moderate and high speed cargo and passenger ships the original Maier form has been so changed that few of the original features remain. Because of poor propulsion results on single-screw ships the first modification was to employ a normal stern with a Maier bow but by the late 1940's the entire underbody was of normal form with Maier characteristics above water only to improve seaworthiness. It has been shown that the Maier form is good for ships operating in waves of about their own lengths but that in ships having lengths considerably greater than the waves encountered a normal ship form will lose less speed. This explains the early success of the Maier form on 160-170 ft.

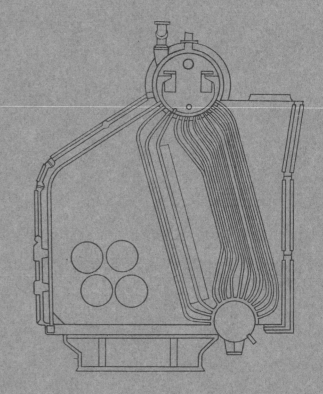

WATER-TUBE BOILER

The reliable but heavy Scotch boiler with its great mass of contained water was seldom built for working pressures over 250 p.s.i. (17,577 kg/cm²). To avoid undue strains about 12 hours were required to raise steam from cold water and such a boiler could not be forced with safety. While satisfactory for merchant service such restrictions made the Scotch boiler unsuitable for naval vessels where weight was at a premium and delays could not be tolerated. Water-tube boilers having a small steam drum, one or more water drums, and banks of tubes through which the hot combustion gases passed were developed for naval use by Belleville of France in 1879, in England by Thornycroft in 1885 and Yarrow in 1889, and in 1889 by Messrs. Babcock & Wilcox in the U.S.A. Although Scotch boilers may still be seen they are rarely installed in new ships today. Pressures of 1200 p.s.i. (84,370 kg/cm²) are common for naval water-tube boilers while half that is normal on merchant ships. This may be compared to the 2 p.s.i. (0,141 kg/cm²) employed on early steamboats.

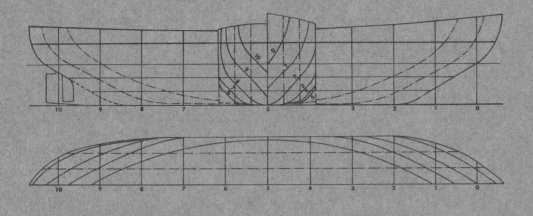

MAIER-FORM HULL

One of the best known of patented hull forms which was developed in Germany during the 1920's by F. F. Maier. As can be seen from the drawing the sections forward and aft approach the triangle in shape. They were so shaped that their centroids lay on as straight a line as possible and these lines for the forward and after bodies projected to the midsection were to coincide. The bilge of the midsection was cut off parallel to the end sections. The inventor claimed that his form produced a very even flow of water along the shortest paths which resulted in lower frictional resistance than for normal forms. The cut-away at the bow and stern tended to reduce wave resistance. It will be noted that the diagonal bilge is similar to that of GREAT BRITAIN *of 1843.*

(48,767-51,815 m) long trawlers operating in the North Sea where the waves have lengths of about 130 ft. (39,624 m). It has been written that Maier's chief contribution was to interest other experimenters in developing good normal ship forms.

Cyrnos — page 161

The first French-owned ship to have the Maier form and to have double-acting Diesel engines was the twin-screw CYRNOS built to the order of the French government in 1929 by the Weser Yard of the Deutsche Schiff- und Maschinenbau A.-G. She was operated by the Compagnie Fraissinet in the passenger and cargo service between Marseilles and Corcica. With a full-length double bottom and two complete decks in the hull she was subdivided by seven transverse watertight bulkheads; there were two cargo holds forward and one aft of her midships machinery spaces. For superstructures she had a forecastle and poop; the deck over a long house amidships joined the poop deck to form a long promenade.

Although CYRNOS was small she was arranged to accommodate four classes of passengers. These were two de luxe first-class cabins on the promenade deck and cabins for 60 on the lower deck amidships. Quarters for 60 second-class passengers were arranged in the poop and on the lower deck aft. The third-class accommodations forward consisted of two large spaces with berths, one for 16 men and the other for 8 women. On the lower deck just abaft the machinery casing was an open space of about 900 sq. ft. (83,61 m²) area without any fittings that was allotted to fourth-class passengers. In her three holds CYRNOS could carry about 885 (900) tons of cargo and motor cars were carried on the open upper deck forward of the main house. Cargo was handled by 3- and 5-ton booms worked by electric winches.

The two main engines in CYRNOS were six-cylinder, two-cycle, double-acting M.A.N. Diesels with attached air compressors; all cylinders were 17.32 in. (0,440 m) diameter by 24.41 in. (0,620 m) stroke. Three 3-cylinder Diesels drove 75 KW electric generators to furnish power for cargo handling and other ship's services. The main engines developed a total of 3650 (3700) b.h.p. and drove CYRNOS at 16 knots (29,65 km/hr.).

CUTTY SARK and other clipper ships made reputations carrying wool from Australia to England but the steamship with insulated holds and refrigerating machinery made it possible to transport meat, dairy products, and fruit from the countries "down under". The New Zealand Shipping Company, Ltd., which operates passenger ships from England to New Zealand and Australia via the Panama Canal also has a number of refrigerated cargo ships on the run. A good example of the company's pre-World War II tonnage was the twin-screw motorship OTAIO. Designed by Messrs William Esplen, Son & Swainston, Ltd., London, to carry both refrigerated and general cargo, she was constructed in 1930 by Vickers-Armstrongs, Ltd., Barrow-in-Furness. Two sister-ships, ORARI and OPAWA, were constructed at the same time by Messrs. Alexander Stephen & Sons, Ltd., Glasgow.

Otaio — page 164

OTAIO had a full-length double bottom, two continuous decks, and an orlop forward of her midship machinery space; she was subdivided by eight transverse watertight bulkheads forming three holds forward and three aft. All of her three superstructures were long. By employing most of the forecastle, bridge, poop, and number 2 upper 'tween deck for general cargo, all insulated spaces except number 5 'tween deck were protected from the direct rays of the sun. This was an important consideration in calculating the load on the refrigerating machinery when travelling in tropical waters. OTAIO had 410,000 cu. ft. (11610 m³) of space for refrigerated cargoes and 230,000 cu. ft. (6513 m³) for general cargo.

One feature of OTAIO's design was that all of her crew were accommodated amidships. Her seamen and greasers were berthed in the bridge abreast the engine casing the cooks, stewards, and petty officers on the bridge deck, while the captain and radio operator had their quarters on the boat deck. The officers' dining saloon, crew's mess rooms, galley, and associated spaces were all on the bridge deck. For handling cargo OTAIO had twenty 10-ton booms so arranged that four could work each hatch except numbers 1 and 6. The foremast was fitted with one 50-ton boom. One electric winch was provided for each 10-ton boom, those at hatches numbers 1 and 6 being equipped with warping heads to aid in mooring.

OTAIO's two main engines were of the four-cylinder, opposed-piston type constructed by Messrs. William Doxford & Sons, Ltd., Sunderland. Unlike normal Diesel engines in which the fuel is burned between the piston and the cylinder head, combustion in the Doxford engine takes place between two pistons. The lower piston has the longer stroke and has a single connecting rod while the shorter-stroke upper piston transmits its power through a crosshead and two connecting rods to the crankshaft. In OTAIO's engines the cylinder diameters were 27.56 in. (0,700 m), the stroke of the upper piston 34.65 in (0,880 m), and that of the lower piston 48.03 in. (1,220 m). Her two engines developed a total of 9450 (9579) b.h.p. at 120 r.p.m. and gave her a trial speed of 15¾ knots (29,20 km/hr.). Two boilers, which at sea were heated by the exhaust gases from the main engines but which could be oil-fired in port, furnished enough steam for heating and for most of the electrical power when the refrigerating machinery was not in operation. OTAIO had three 306 KW, 220-volt generators each driven by a five-cylinder, four-cycle Diesel. Her refrigerating plant consisted of carbon dioxide units which cooled brine that could be circulated at three different temperatures to the insulated compartments.

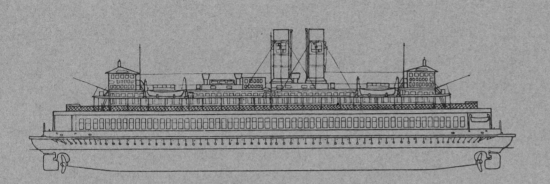

During World War II OTAIO, lying in the Victoria Docks, London, with other ships of the New Zealand Company's fleet, was struck by a bomb on the night of 7 September 1940. It pierced two decks in way of number 4 hatch but fortunately did not explode and was removed intact. After temporary repairs she sailed a few days later for New York. On 28 August 1941 after sailing from Liverpool in a convoy she was not so lucky being hit by two torpedoes and sunk about 330 miles (612 km) west by north of the Fastnet Light.

DONGAN HILLS — 1929 — 2030 T

251.5 × 46.1 × 18.4 feet
76,656 × 14,051 × 5,608 m

The city of New York has always had many ferry services the longest being the 5 mile (8,05 km) run from South Ferry at the lower tip of Manhattan to St. George, Staten Island. DONGAN HILLS, built for this service by the Staten Island Shipbuilding Company, was at the time of her launching on 19 March 1929 the largest ferry of her type in the world. She had a double-ended single-deck steel hull that was subdivided by five transverse watertight bulkheads. Because of ice that drifts down the Hudson in winter her shell plating was increased in thickness around her load waterline. Her main deck was arranged with two lanes for motor vehicles inboard and passenger spaces outboard; her house was devoted entirely to passengers. She could carry 28 motor vehicles and 2800 passengers for whom there were 1650 seats. DONGAN HILLS was propelled by a single screw at each end driven by two sets of 2-cylinder compound engines coupled on a through shaft so that both propellers were always turning when under way. The cylinders of each set of engines were $22\frac{1}{2}$ and 50 in. (0,572-1,270 m) diameter by 30 in. (0,762 m) stroke. Steam at 225 p.s.i. (15,819 kg/cm²) pressure was generated by four water-tube boilers but reduced to 175 p.s.i. (12,304 kg/cm²) at the engines. On trials DONGAN HILLS did better than 16 knots (29,65 km/hr.) with the engines developing 3800 (3852) i.h.p. at 150 r.p.m.

SAFETY OF LIFE AT SEA

Considering the structural envelope a ship is safe only if it can weather the normal hazards of the sea and stay afloat after a possible collision. Internal subdivision by watertight bulkheads is the usual means of providing for the latter. Watertight bulkheads were first required by the British Merchant Shipping Act of 1854. There were to be four— the two peak bulkheads and two separating the machinery from the cargo. The Act was repealed in 1862. Lloyd's Register of Shipping specified in 1882 that ships 280 ft. (85,343 m) in length and over should have a number of bulkheads which increased with length. Other classification societies added similar requirements; some limited the spacing of bulkheads. A British committee in 1890 recommended the calculation of a curve of "floodable length" which would show under certain assumptions how much of a ship could be flooded without sinking. Nothing came of this, but the sinking of ELBE in 1897 led to the first official subdivision regulations based upon floodable length which were issued by the Society of German Ship Owners.

The sinking of TITANIC in 1912 led to another British committee and in 1913 to an International Conference which agreed on subdivision requirements for two classes of ships—those primarily for passengers and those primarily for cargo. The requirements were to increase gradually with length and a "criterion of service" was to be set up to interpolate between the two classes. Negotiations on the latter were broken off by World War I. Informal conferences after the war secured working agreements that held until a new International Conference was called in 1929. The 1929 Convention for Safety of Life at Sea, later formally ratified by all the major maritime nations, provided for all ships carrying more than 12 passengers maximum and minimum subdivision curves and a means for interpolation between them by a criterion of service numeral.

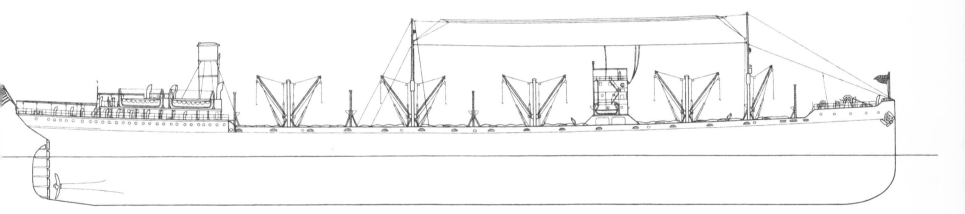

G. HARRISON SMITH · 1921

International Petroleum Company

550.3 × 72.2 × 43.7 feet ◖ 15371 T ◖ 167,730 × 22,006 × 13,319 m

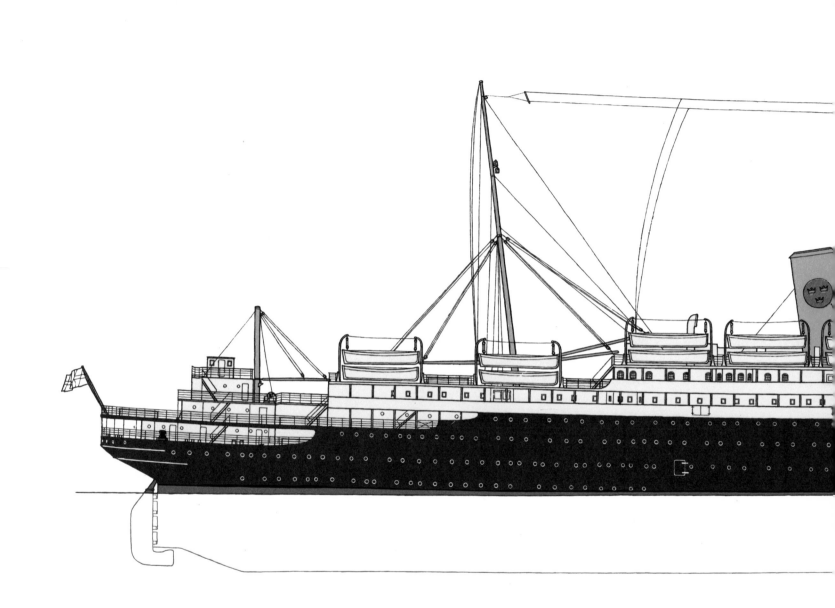

GRIPSHOLM · 1925

Svenska Amerika Linien

553.0 × 74.4 × 37.7 feet ☾ 17993 T ☾ 168,554 × 22,677 × 11,490 m

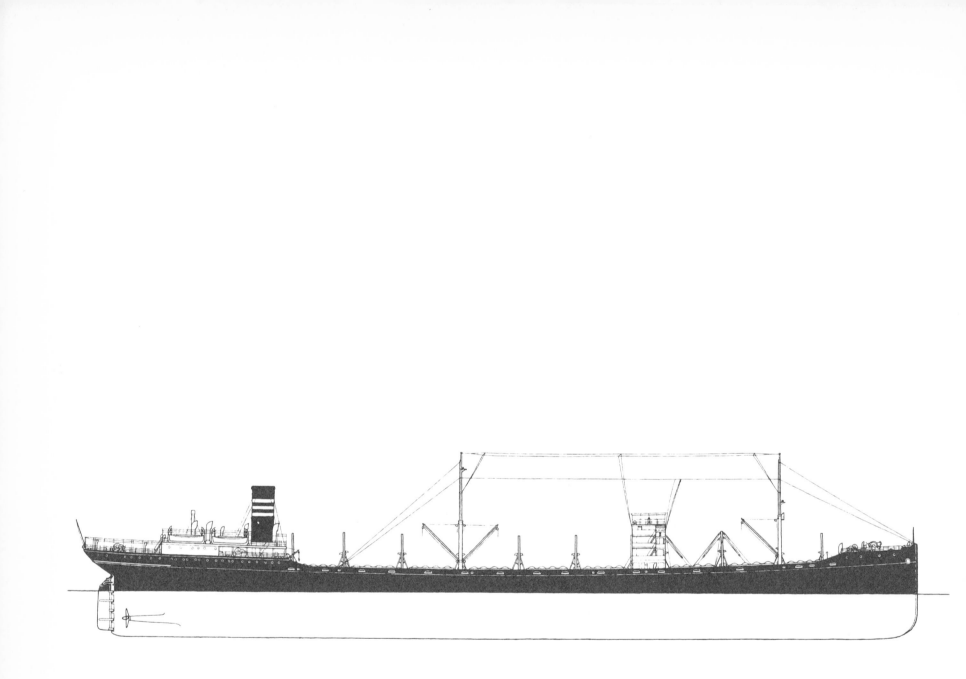

AMERIKALAND · 1925

Messrs. Axel Broström & Son

561.3 × 72.2 × 44.1 feet ☾ 15338 T ☾ 171,083 × 22,006 × 13,442 m

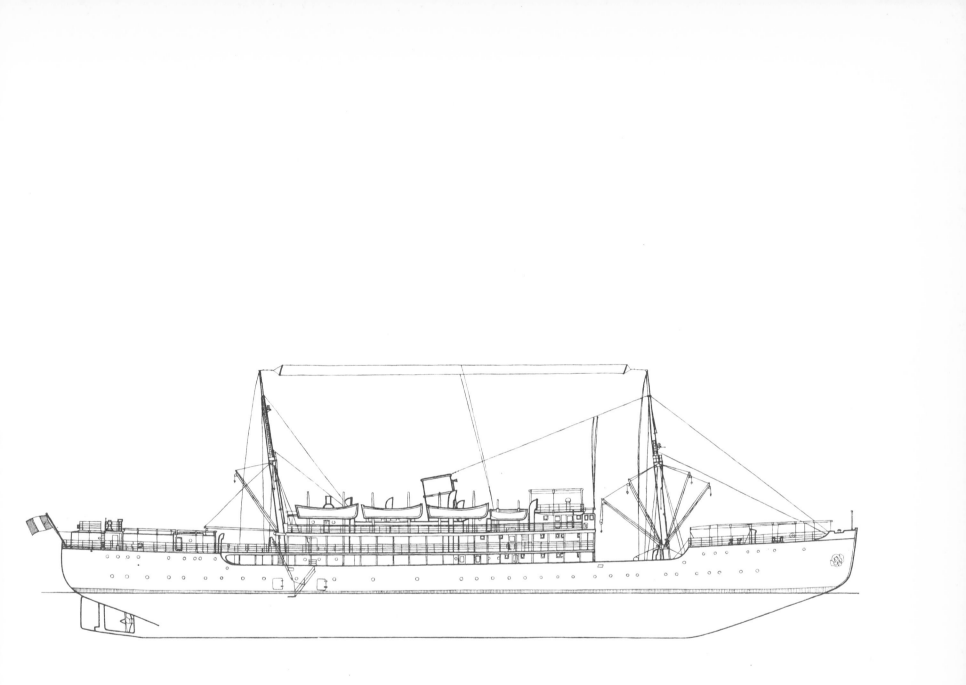

CYRNOS · 1929

Compagnie Fraissinet

293.4 × 41.1 × 23.1 feet ☾ 2406 T ☾ 89,428 × 12,527 × 7,041 m

BREMEN · 1928

Norddeutscher Lloyd

898.7 × 101.9 × 48.2 feet ℂ 51656 T ℂ 273,923 × 31,059 × 14,691 m

OTAIO · 1930

New Zealand Shipping Company, Ltd.

472.0 × 67.2 × 35.7 feet (10048 T (143,865 × 20,480 × 10,881 m

A little over 100 years after CONSTITUTIONEN's paddles first churned the waters of Norway's fjords PRINSESSE RAGNHILD was built for the coastal express steamer service. More than twice as long as Norway's first steamer her design was the result of years of experience with a service that required fast economical ships able to operate in all kinds of weather. She was constructed in 1931 by the A/S. Fredriksstad Mechaniske Verksted, Fredriksstad, Norway, with a full-length double bottom, two full-length decks, and an orlop forward. Aft the propeller shaft tunnel was plated over to form the bottom of a cargo hold. She was subdivided by transverse bulkheads into six watertight compartments. Service along the coastal route required many landings alongside wharves and to withstand the inevitable bumping PRINSESSE RAGNHILD had intermediate frames of the same depth as her main transverse frames for four-fifths of her length back from her bow.

Prinsesse Ragnhild — page 175

With a total of 207 berths for passengers, 99 first-class and 108 third, PRINSESSE RAGNHILD was allowed to carry a maximum of 400 passengers. The first-class passengers were carried in one and two-person rooms and there were two and four-person rooms for the third-class passengers. The first and third-class dining saloons, galley, and the associated spaces were all on the upper deck. In the rounded forward end of the promenade deck house was the first-class smoking room fitted with large windows to give a good view. Just abaft this to port was a reading and writing room and to starboard a music room. Aft on the upper deck was a ladies saloon and a smoking room for the third-class passengers.

The first-class saloons and the main stair well on PRINSESSE RAGNHILD were panelled with special woods but throughout the remainder of the ship Masonite was employed for joiner bulkheads and sheathing; she was the first ship to have a complete installation of this material. Five mechanical ventilation systems delivered air at the outside temperature or heated if required; a complete steam heating system was also provided. The capacity of her cargo holds and trunked hatches was 20,550 cu. ft. (582 m³)—she had refrigerating equipment for circulating cool air through the holds when transporting fresh fish and meat. For handling cargo she had two 4-ton booms forward and two 2-ton booms aft, all worked by steam winches. As part of her navigating equipment PRINSESSE RAGNHILD had the first echo-sounder to be installed on a Norwegian coastal steamer.

Although triple expansion engines were reliable and relatively economical several new types of reciprocating steam engines having better economy were developed during the 1920's. PRINSESSE RAGNHILD was equipped with a "steam-motor" designed and built by the Fredriksstad Mechaniske Verksted which consisted of two sets of compound engines mounted together on one base. The 15.36 in. (0,390 m) diameter high-pressure cylinders were at the ends with the 37.80 in. (0,960 m) diameter low-pressure cylinders together in the middle; the common stroke was 34.45 in. (0,875 m). One piston valve served each pair of cylinders with the high-pressure cylinder exhausting directly into the low-pressure cylinder which operated on the uniflow principle. As the term implies steam flowed in one direction—it was admitted at the ends of the cylinder and exhausted through a row of ports around its middle like those in a two-cycle Diesel engine. This steam-motor developed 2500 (2534) i.h.p. at 125 r.p.m. Superheated steam at a pressure of 220 p.s.i. (15,468 kg/cm²) was furnished by two coal-burning Scotch boilers. On trials PRINSESSE RAGNHILD attained a speed of 16.8 knots (31,13 km/hr.).

Delivered to her owners on 25 November 1931 PRINSESSE RAGNHILD was immediately put on the run from Bergen to Kirkenes in the far north of Norway and served regularly until the outbreak of World War II. In April 1940 she was laid up in Hjörundfjord moored close under a vertical cliff for protection against air raids; although subjected to several raids she was not damaged. She was put into service again in July 1940 and on 23 October 1940, shortly after leaving Bodö northbound, there was an explosion, probably a mine, and she sank with a large loss of life.

In addition to their first-class liners that carried the cream of the traffic the major steamship companies operating on the North Atlantic ran less spectacular ships which offered comfortable crossings at slower speeds. Thus in 1932 the Compagnie Générale Transatlantique was operating the first-class liners ILE-DE-FRANCE, PARIS, and FRANCE and the cabin-class ships ROCHAMBEAU, DEGRASSE, LAFAYETTE, and the new CHAMPLAIN. Designed for a service speed of 20 knots (37,06 km/hr.) CHAMPLAIN attained 21 knots (38,92 km/hr.) on her trials and could make the crossing from Havre to New York in about seven days.

Built and engined at the Penhoët Yard of the Société Anonyme des Chantier et Ateliers de St. Nazaire-Penhoët the twin-screw CHAMPLAIN was launched on 15 August 1931. She had an unusual profile with a curved stem, an elliptical counter stern, a single large funnel with an inclined screen designed to keep soot and gases off the after decks, and two masts, the taller located just forward of the funnel. CHAMPLAIN had the usual double bottom, one orlop forward, two aft, and four continuous

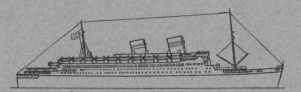

CONTE DI SAVOIA — 1931 — 48,502 T

814.6 × 96.1 × 32.4 feet
248,290 × 29,291 × 9,875 m

A notable ship for many reasons the quadruple-screw CONTE DI SAVOIA was the first Atlantic liner to be equipped with gyro-stabilizers. Constructed by the Cantieri Riuniti dell' Adriatico in Trieste for the Società di Navigazione Italia she was launched on 28 October 1931 and made her maiden voyage from Genoa to New York on 30 November 1932. She had accommodations for 500 first-class passengers, 366 special-class, 412 second-class, and 922 third-class, a total of 2200. CONTI DI SAVOIA was propelled by four sets of three-casing single-reduction geared turbines which developed a total of 100,000 (101360) s.h.p. Steam for the main turbines was generated at a pressure of 450 p.s.i. (31,639 kg/cm²) by 10 water-tube boilers; three Scotch boilers furnished steam for heating and auxiliary uses. Designed for a service speed of 26¼ knots (48,65 km/hr.) she attained a speed of 29.5 knots (54,78 km/hr.) on trials and usually made the Atlantic crossing in 6½ to 7 days. Her stabilizing equipment, designed by the Sperry Gyroscope Company, Ltd. and built by Vickers-Armstrongs Ltd., consisted of three gyroscopes having rotors 13 ft (3,962 m) diameter weighing 114 tons (115.8). Each rotor was turned at 800 r.p.m. by a 560 (568) h.p. electric motor. The total weight of the installation was 691 (702) tons. Service experience showed that the effectiveness of the stabilizers varied with the condition and direction of the seas but that in general the angle of roll was cut in half. Sunk by aircraft near Venice on 11 September 1943 CONTI DI SAVOIA was refloated in October 1945; it was expected that she would be rebuilt but in 1950 she was broken up for scrap.

Champlain — page 178

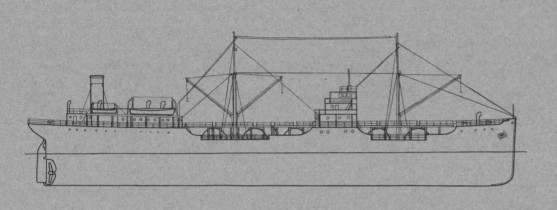

AGNITA — 1931 — 3561 T

305.4 × 50.5 × 26.3 feet
93,086 × 15,391 × 8,016 m

The mystery ship of 1931 was the single-screw AGNITA constructed by Messrs. Hawthorn, Leslie, & Company, Ltd., Newcastle, for the Petroleum Maatschappij "La Corona", one of the Royal Dutch-Shell group. Built as a normal tanker with one longitudinal bulkhead and machinery aft she had in addition twelve vertical cylindrical steel tanks with domed heads located in her regular cargo tanks, six in each side of the longitudinal bulkhead. The domed heads of these cylindrical tanks projected slightly above her single deck. While the word "acid" usually connotes an extremely corrosive liquid, one of the cargoes carried in AGNITA's cylindrical tanks was pure sulphuric acid which will not react with steel as long as no water is present. The cylindrical tanks were also designed to carry propane gas under pressure and could be employed to carry the normal petroleum products that were carried in her regular tanks. AGNITA was propelled by an 8-cylinder, 4-cycle, single-acting Werkspoor Diesel engine that drove her at 12.5 knots (23,16 km/hr.) in service. On a normal voyage she carried sulphuric acid from Europe to Curacao where she loaded petroleum products in her regular tanks. She sailed from there to Port Arthur, Texas, where she loaded propane in her cylindrical tanks and returned to Europe.

decks above which were a long bridge, a shorter boat deck, and two levels of houses. She had ten transverse watertight bulkheads which gave her three holds forward, two boiler rooms, an engine room, stores spaces, and two holds aft in addition to the usual fore and after peaks. Two 'tween-deck spaces forward were specially arranged to carry motor cars while a similar space aft was insulated for the carriage of refrigerated cargo. The total space available for the motor cars and general cargo was 345,000 cu. ft. (9769 m³) and for refrigerated cargo 14,500 cu. ft. (410 m³). For handling cargo CHAMPLAIN had ten 3-ton booms worked with electric winches.

CHAMPLAIN was arranged to carry three classes of passengers—643 cabin-class on the upper decks with 248 tourist and 122 third-class on the lower decks; the third-class quarters were forward but some of the tourist-class cabins through amidships were convertible to third-class depending on the demand for space. To minimize motion the cabin-class dining saloon was located amidships on C deck, two decks below the main weather deck. The tourist dining saloon was further aft on the same deck; the galley and all service spaces were located between the two saloons. The third-class dining saloon was down on E deck just forward of the boiler room.

The cabin-class public rooms were decorated to the usual French Line standards; the dining saloon resembling an interior court built of pink stone was entered from a white marble staircase. The grand saloon or music room on the boat deck was done in the 17th century style with gold and white panelling, mirrors, and tapestries. Also on the boat deck were a large smoking room and a verandah cafe. The cabin-class promenade, closed by windows, was 328 ft. (100 m) long and as it extended around the ends of the house it provided a continuous promenade of 820 ft. (250 m). The boat deck above provided an open promenade space. Open and closed tourist-class promenades were provided aft on the weather deck.

CHAMPLAIN's propelling machinery consisted of two sets of Parsons single-reduction geared turbines having three casings each—high, intermediate, and low pressure. The high and intermediate-pressure turbines operated at 1900 r.p.m. while the low-pressure unit turned at 1500 r.p.m.; the propeller r.p.m. was 127. The maximum power developed by the turbines was 25,500 (25847) s.h.p. CHAMPLAIN was the first French Line ship to have water-tube boilers—she had six which burned oil and supplied steam at 398 p.s.i. (28,000 kg/cm²) pressure. She also had two oil-burning Scotch boilers which furnished steam for heating and other auxiliary uses. Electric current was supplied by three direct-current turbo-generator sets rated at 900 KW each. CHAMPLAIN's fuel tanks carried 4450 (4521) tons of oil, sufficient for a round trip between Havre and New York. She sailed on her maiden voyage on 15 June 1931 and her career was ended by a magnetic mine off La Rochelle, France, on 17 June 1940.

The "1000 ft." ("300 m") ship had been the dream of ship operators and builders for years. Messrs. Harland & Wolff had designed such a ship for the White Star Line around the turn of the century revising it periodically for about thirty years to suit engineering developments. Construction was actually started on this new OCEANIC in the late 1920's but because of questions concerning the engines work was suspended and the project finally abandoned in 1929. The 1930's, however, saw not one but two ships of that size, the French Line's NORMANDIE and the Cunarder QUEEN MARY. Both companies planned to have two such ships in order to provide weekly service between Europe and New York which meant a 28 knot (51,89 km/hr.) minimum speed. Smaller ships could have attained that speed but the large size was required to give adequate comfort to those willing to pay for the fast service. The second French ship was never built but the second Cunarder, QUEEN ELIZABETH, was launched in 1938.

Normandie — page 176

The decision to build the quadruple-screw NORMANDIE was made by the French Line in October 1930 and her keel was laid on 26 January 1931 by the Société Anonyme des Chantier et Ateliers de St. Nazaire-Penhoët. She was launched on 29 October 1932 and went on trials in May 1935. The designing of NORMANDIE was a stupendous undertaking; the actual construction was equally stupendous. Such a ship is a self-contained floating community providing all the expected amenities and services and able to move at high speed. NORMANDIE complied with the requirements of the 1929 Convention for Safety of Life at Sea which covered not only subdivision but certain details of construction, fire protection, life saving appliances, and radio equipment. Her form, determined by 92 sets of tests with ten different models, was developed by V. Yourkevitch in accordance with his patent. She had a curved raked stem while her stern was a modification of the old elliptical counter. The forward end of her promenade deck served as a breakwater and terminated in something like the old-fashioned turtle back; this enabled her to run longer at full speed through rough seas. The aftermost of her three funnels was for appearance only.

NORMANDIE had a full-length double bottom, five continuous decks—A through E, and two orlops. Her "principal" deck extended from the bow almost to the stern above which were a long promenade deck, boat deck, and a large house. She was subdivided by 11 transverse watertight bulkheads; there were 61 watertight doors in various bulkheads of which 32 were hydraulically controlled from the bridge. A combination of longitudinal and transverse framing was employed, the double bottom, principal deck, and promenade deck being longitudinally framed while the remainder of the ship had transverse framing. Electric welding was used extensively but it was said that more than 11,000,000 rivets were driven. Parts of her structure subject to high longitudinal bending stresses were fabricated of special steel and to reduce stresses in her upper houses two expansion joints were fitted.

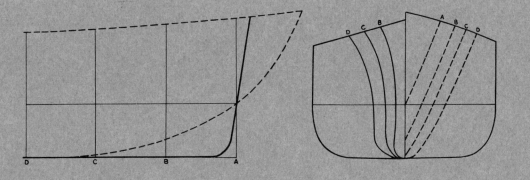

YOURKEVITCH BOW

NORMANDIE's *fore-body was designed in accordance with the principles developed and patented by Vladimir Yourkevitch who believed that the fore-body shape was the most important factor in the wave resistance of a ship. According to him wave resistance could be reduced by drawing in the fore-body sections at the load water-line so that the water-lines in that region became more or less hollow. The point of change in water-line shape from concave to convex was determined by a formula based upon ship length and speed. The displacement lost by hollowing the load water-line was regained by fitting a bulb below. As bulbous bows had been employed previously the Yourkevitch bow can best be considered as a special case of a bulbous bow. A ship having a Maier-form bow is said to have V-sections while the sections of a Yourkevitch bow are considered to be U-shaped.*

In keeping with the French Line's policy of offering the ultimate in service NOR-MANDIE was arranged to carry seven classes of passengers—28 "grand luxe", 30 "de luxe", 790 first-class, 16 intermediate, 657 tourist-class, 139 "mixte", and 315 third-class, a total of 1975. Her crew was much larger in proportion than on earlier ships—66 staff, 120 deck crew, 187 engineering department, and 972 stewards and hotel staff, a total of 1345. Great care was taken in arranging the passenger accommodations. The "grand luxe" and certain of the "de luxe" accommodations had private dining rooms; some "de luxe" and first-class rooms had small private terraces. It was said that no two first-class cabins were exactly alike. By the use of divided boiler uptakes the major public spaces were larger than otherwise possible. The first-class dining saloon amidships on C deck, the largest public room in the ship, was 300 ft. (91,440 m) long, 43 ft. (13,106 m) wide, and three decks high; it could seat 1000 persons. The main entrance hall on B deck was also three decks high; the chapel just forward of it was two decks high. First-class public spaces above the promenade deck included a main lounge, smoking room, theater, winter garden, and grill room. Tourist-class accommodations were on the upper decks aft with the third-class quarters below. NOR-MANDIE had one small hold forward for special cargo and motor cars.

Unlike most earlier ships NORMANDIE's open decks were not cluttered with ventilation cowls and fans. Special louvred intakes built into her houses admitted air to more than 160 air-conditioning units and fans below. She had about 50 miles (80,47 km) of ventilation supply and exhaust ducts. Thermostats controlled the delivery of air at constant temperature and humidity but the occupants in each cabin could control the direction, quantity, and temperature of the air supplied. The public spaces had special exhaust systems to remove smoke and the heat generated by the lighting. Because of the fire protection requirements of the 1929 Convention and fires on two then new French liners work on NORMANDIE was practically stopped for several months while fire protection methods were studied. She was divided into four main divisions in which the ventilation was independent so that upon an alarm of fire the ventilation in that section could be cut off from a safety office centrally located on A deck. A watch force of 46 specially trained men maintained a constant patrol of the ship and there were 1075 automatic detecting instruments throughout the ship. Asbestos coatings were sprayed on the joiner work, carpets and linens were fireproofed, and special paints and varnishes used. For fire extinguishing there were 504 hoses, carbonic acid gas systems for cargo and stores spaces, and foam systems for the machinery spaces.

While high power turbo-electric propelling machinery had been installed in naval vessels, NORMANDIE's was the most powerful yet installed in a commercial ship; her four shafts delivered a total of 160,000 (162176) s.h.p. Her machinery occupied six watertight compartments—four for her boilers, one for her main turbo-alternators and auxiliary turbo-generators, and one for her electric propelling motors. Each propeller shaft was driven by a three-phase synchronous motor which received electric current from an Als-Thom alternator driven by a set of high-pressure and low-pressure Zoëlly turbines. For auxiliary services there were six turbo-generators of 2200 KW each. Steam at 398 p.s.i. (28,000 kg/cm²) pressure was supplied to the main and auxiliary turbines by 29 oil-fired Penhoët water-tube boilers; four oil-fired Scotch boilers furnished steam for heating and auxiliary uses. NORMANDIE carried 8930 (9073) tons of fuel oil.

On her trials in 1935 with three-bladed propellers turning at 243 r.p.m. NORMANDIE made a maximum speed of 32.1 knots (59,49 km/hr.). In 1937 with new four-bladed propellers she won the eastbound Blue Ribbon from BREMEN crossing in 3 days 22 hours 7 min. at a mean speed of 31.2 knots (57,82 km/hr.). She was in New York at the outbreak of World War II and, not being employed by the French in war service, on 16 December 1941 she was taken over by the U.S. Maritime Commission. Renamed LAFAYETTE work was started to convert her to a troopship but she was gutted by fire on 9 February 1942 and capsized from the weight of water poured into her upper decks. Eventually refloated she was towed to Port Newark in December 1946 and cut up for scrap.

While most of the attention of the maritime world in the 1930's was focused on the new super-liners the Fredriksstad Mechaniske Versted delivered MARGIT R. on 7 March 1935, the last of the special "Fredriksstad-type" of timber carrier. A steel, single-screw, three-island ship with machinery amidships she was specially adapted for loading timber below deck and for carrying large deck loads. At first glance her single deck appeared to be all hatches and practically speaking it was. Two hatches forward and two aft filled almost the entire length of the wells between her three superstructures and about half of her breadth. Below deck she had but four bulkheads, two in the peaks and two enclosing the machinery space, which gave her two long holds. Her full-length double bottom was adapted for carrying water ballast. For trimming such bulk cargoes as coal for which she was equally well adapted the bridge ends of hatches number 2 and 3 were sloped toward the bridge. Below deck and in her spare bunkers in the bridge 134,000 cu. ft. (3794 m³) of space were available for bulk cargoes.

The cargo handling gear in MARGIT R. was located so as to leave the spaces between her superstructures available for deck cargoes. The fore and main masts were located on the forecastle and poop respectively and there were two kingposts at each end of the bridge; the cargo boom gear was worked by steam winches. Accommodations for her officers were arranged in the bridge houses; the seamen and firemen were berthed in the poop.

Margit R. — page 179

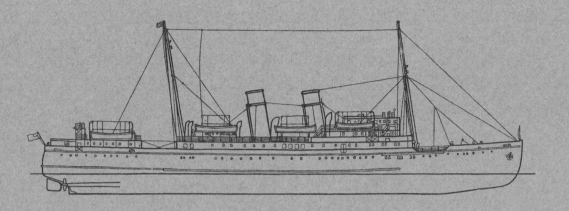

ISLE OF SARK — 1932 — 2211 T

296.7 × 42.1 × 13.9 feet
90,433 × 12,832 × 4,236 m

Designed for both day and night service in the Channel Islands fleet of Great Britain's Southern Railway ISLE OF SARK was constructed by Messrs. W. Denny & Brothers, Ltd., Dumbarton. Similar in arrangement to other cross-Channel ships ISLE OF SARK was the first vessel constructed in Great Britain to have a Maier-form bow although its shape was modified from the provisions of the patent as the ship's owners were unwilling to accept the extreme cut-up. Certified to carry 1350 passengers on day runs ISLE OF SARK had cabin berths for 117 first-class passengers; two lounges provided sleeping space for another 56. There were no berths for second-class passengers but four lounges located aft were allocated to them, two for ladies and two for gentlemen. She was propelled by twin screws driven by single-reduction geared turbines with steam furnished by two water-tube and one single-ended Scotch boiler. She entered service on 18 March 1932. In 1936 ISLE OF SARK became the first ship to be fitted with Denny-Brown activated-fin stabilizers. Proposals for such stabilizers had been made for about 50 years and in 1932 the Japanese ship KEIFUKU MARU had been equipped with Motora fin stabilizers. ISLE OF SARK's fins, one on each side, were operated by a mechanism similar to an electro-hydaulic steering gear and as they moved up and down they created a lifting force like the ailerons on aircraft. Their movement was electrically controlled by a gyroscope and in service they could reduce a 15° roll to about 3°.

One unusual feature of MARGIT R., not apparent from her exterior, was that her coal-burning Scotch boilers were on deck, an arrangement that had been tried some twenty years earlier on some of the wooden steam schooners on the Pacific Coast of the U.S.A. Her boilers were located in the after end of the bridge with the permanent coal bunkers over and abreast them; the forward half of the bridge served as a spare bunker or for additional cargo. By moving the boilers and bunkers out of the hull the below deck cargo space was increased about 6 to 10 per cent over that in a normally arranged ship.

Although the moving of the boilers and bunkers to the bridge space seems like the concentration of too much weight topside this arrangement actually improved the ship's stability characteristics. When in ballast condition a normal ship with boilers down on the tank top has too much stability which the topside boiler position in MARGIT R. reduced. When carrying bulk cargoes the additional weight of cargo below more than offset the weight of boilers and bunkers above. Unlike normal timber carrying ships which often arrived in port heavily listed—their stability became negative as coal was consumed—MARGIT R. could be loaded almost to the unstable point before leaving port as her stability improved during a voyage as coal was burned from the topside bunkers. Among other advantages were better working conditions for the firemen, easier transferring of coal, and easier dumping of ashes.

MARGIT R. was the only one of the Fredriksstad-type ships to have a Fredriksstad "steam-motor". Hers was rated at 62 n.h.p. with cylinders 11.61 and 27.17 in. (0,295-0,690 m) diameter by 25.20 in. (0,640 m) stroke. Her Scotch boilers delivered steam at 220 p.s.i. (15,468 kg/cm²) pressure. Sea speed in loaded condition was 9 knots (16,79 km/hr.).

The contract for the Cunard Line's "1000 footer" ("300 m") was placed with Messrs. John Brown & Company, Ltd., Clydebank, where she was known until her launching as number 534. Laid down in August 1930 the general business depression

Queen Mary — page 180

caused a suspension of work in December 1931. Following a merger of the Cunard and White Star Lines and financial assistance from the British government work was resumed in April 1934. Christened by Queen Mary and named QUEEN MARY she was launched on 26 September 1934. Designed for an average speed of 29 knots (53,85 km/hr.) QUEEN MARY's hull has a normal form with a straight raked stem and a cruiser stern that was the result of extensive tests with 22 models in both smooth water and artificial wave systems. The Cunard Line had stipulated that no special or unusual forms should be employed unless it proved impossible to produce an equally good normal form. Special tests were made with 24 in. (0,610 m) diameter models of her propellers, with steering arrangements, and with smoke streams to check the flow of air over the superstructure and around her three funnels.

QUEEN MARY has the usual double bottom, five continuous decks—A through E, three orlops forward, and two aft. Her main deck extends from the bow nearly to the stern and above this are the long promenade deck, sun deck, and a house. To comply with the subdivision requirements of the 1929 Convention she has 15 transverse watertight bulkheads and under the assumptions then in force she can remain afloat after damage involving any two bulkheads. Her watertight doors are hydraulically operated. QUEEN MARY is transversely framed throughout as it was believed that such framing in association with fore-and-aft girders was best adapted to resist the severe racking stresses set up in such a large structure by North Atlantic storms. It was further believed that longitudinal framing would transmit propeller vibrations throughout the ship. NORMANDIE had severe vibration problems which were cured by working in a considerable amount of steel structure around her stern and fitting new propellers with four instead of three blades. QUEEN MARY's structure is largely riveted, special steel was employed as on NORMANDIE, and there are three expansion joints in the houses above the promenade deck.

As the designation "first-class" was dropped on North Atlantic ships in 1935 the passenger classes carried by QUEEN MARY were cabin, tourist, and third. In contrast to the arrangement of tourist and third-class accommodations in the after end of NORMANDIE the Cunard Line simplified matters by stipulating that the cabin-class would be amidships, the tourist aft, and the third forward. When QUEEN MARY entered service she could carry 776 cabin-class passengers, 784 tourist-class, and 579 third-class. Her officers and crew totalled 1101. The cabin-class passengers are berthed on the main, A, and B decks with the dining saloon on C deck; the main lounge and other public spaces are on the promenade and sun decks. In laying out these spaces it was decided that the uptakes should not be divided as on NORMANDIE. The tourist-class dining saloon is also on the C deck with the main galley and service spaces located between it and the cabin-class saloon. Both the tourist and third-class cabins and public spaces are arranged in vertical zones similar to those for the cabin-class. Interchangeability between tourist and third-class accommodations is provided by devoting one side of D deck to cabins, the normal division between the two classes being about amidships. Unlike NORMANDIE, the air for QUEEN MARY's ventilating systems is drawn in through eight large and a number of small structural cowls on her house tops. Internally her ventilation provisions and those for fire protection are similar. QUEEN MARY has two cargo holds forward served by booms on her foremast and compartments for mails both forward and aft.

The machinery in QUEEN MARY is arranged in 10 watertight compartments—three auxiliary machinery rooms, five boiler rooms, and two main engine rooms. Her quadruple screws are driven by single-reduction geared turbine sets, each set having

LOAD LINES

The International Load Line Convention of 1930 established the first international standards governing the loading of vessels. A conference had been arranged for 1913 but because of world conditions it was never convened. There are historical references to load lines and in 1835 Lloyd's Register of Shipping proposed a freeboard—the height that the sides of a floating object project above the water—of 3 inches per foot of depth of hold (0,076 m per 0,305 m). The first legal requirements were contained in the British Merchant Shipping Act of 1890 and the mark on a ship's side at its legal load line became known as the Plimsoll mark after Samuel Plimsoll who promoted the legislation. German rules were established in 1904 and other countries followed suit although until 1917 in the U.S.A. an owner or master was governed only by the wishes of the insurer of ship or cargo. In that year the U.S. Shipping Board ordered that all ocean-going vessels under its control be marked in accordance with the revised British rules of 1906.

In determining how deep in the water a ship may safely be loaded consideration is given to the dimensions and shapes of her main watertight hull and weathertight superstructures, the structural strength of the hull and superstructures, and the effectiveness of the closing devices such as hatches and doors. In addition to these considerations load lines for passenger ships are governed by the subdivision characteristics in accordance with the requirements of the 1929 and later Conventions for the Safety of Life at Sea. The rules and regulations governing tonnage and freeboard are such, that a space may be legally open to the sea for tonnage purposes but legally watertight in the assignment of freeboard.

The basic freeboard tables are based on operations in average summer weather around the world. Seasonal weather zones have been determined which permit deeper loadings in tropical waters or require reduced loadings in winter. A vessel loading in fresh water may be loaded deeper as she will rise when she reaches salt water; deeper loadings are also permitted for vessels carrying timber deck cargoes. Because of the nature of their cargoes and their construction features the summer freeboard for tankers is less than for general cargo ships. Developments in ship design and features such as steel watertight hatches have indicated the need of modifications to the 1930 Convention and a new Conference is scheduled for 1966.

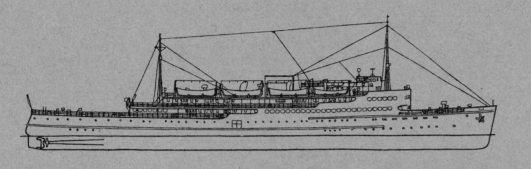

one high-pressure, two intermediate-pressure, and one low-pressure turbine. The turbines for the outer screws are in the forward engine room and those for the inboard screws in the after engine room. For her service speed of 29 knots (53,85 km/hr.) the turbines develop a total of 160,000 (162176) s.h.p. at 180 r.p.m. of the propellers. In boiler room number 1 are three oil-burning double-ended Scotch boilers supplying steam for heating and auxiliary services. The four main boiler rooms each contain six oil-burning water-tube boilers which furnish steam to the main turbines at a pressure of 400 p.s.i. (28,123 kg/cm²). Four 1300 KW 220-volt turbogenerators supply electric power for all main engine auxiliaries and three units of the same capacity generate power for all the hotel services; these generators may be cross-connected in case of emergency.

QUEEN MARY sailed from Southampton on 27 May 1936 for her maiden voyage to New York making the crossing in 4 days 27 minutes. In 1936 she set an eastbound record 3 days 23 hours 57 minutes which NORMANDIE bettered in 1937. QUEEN MARY took the Blue Ribbon again in 1938 with a crossing of 3 days 20 hours 42 minutes. She served as a troopship during World War II and was able to transport 15,000 troops at a time; she covered over 500,000 miles (926600 km) during the war years. QUEEN MARY returned to the North Atlantic service in August 1947.

The word "liner" to many still means a large passenger ship such as QUEEN MARY plying on a regular schedule between two or more ports but much of today's commerce is carried in "cargo liners" which operate on definite routes but not to such rigid schedules. TAURUS was a good example of a cargo liner as built a little before World War II. Owned by the firm of Wilh. Wilhelmsen, Oslo, she was the third TAURUS in the company's fleet. Starting with the chartering of sailing vessels in 1861 and purchasing its first steamer in 1887 the company owned 72 vessels in its centenary year. During the hundred years the company had owned 28 sailing vessels, 96 steamers, and 115 motorships. Its first cargo line was the Norge Mexico Gulf Linien in

PRINCE BAUDOUIN — 1934 — 3219 T

357.0 × 46.1 × 21.4 feet
108,813 × 14,051 × 6,523 m

The twin-screw cross-Channel motorship PRINCE BAUDOUIN was the first Diesel-engined ship to be employed on a regular Channel run and when placed in service was the fastest motorship afloat. She was built in the Hoboken yard of the Société Anonyme John Cockerill and operated by the Belgian government on the Ostende-Dover run. Her appearance varied considerably from the earlier cross-Channel steamers with a range of houses amidships, two masts only high enough to carry the required navigation lights, and a single squat funnel. She was certified to carry 1500 passengers. In accordance with the Belgian practice of entering the terminal ports stern first she was fitted with a bow rudder. The two main engines in PRINCE BAUDOUIN were 12-cylinder, 2-cycle, single-acting Diesels of the Sulzer type constructed by her builder each rated at 8500 (8616) b.h.p. maximum at 268 r.p.m. All her auxiliaries were electrically driven, there was not even a boiler for heating, and to provide electric power she had four 485 KW generators each driven by a 680 (689) b.h.p. 8-cylinder, 4-cycle, single-acting Sulzer Diesel. Designed for a service speed of 22 knots (40,77 km/hr.) PRINCE BAUDOUIN attained 25.25 knots (46,79 km/hr.) on trials.

Taurus — page 182

1907 and tankers were added to the fleet in 1913. Between 1919 and 1939 all of the company's tramp ship operations were ended and at present Wilh. Wilhelmsen operates ten major services all over the world.

TAURUS, constructed by the A/S Akers Mechaniske Verksted, Oslo, was of the shelter deck type first met in SAINT DUNSTAN; she was launched on 23 October 1935. A single-screw ship she had a straight raked stem, an elliptical counter stern, a forecastle, and a poop but only houses amidships. She had a full-length double bottom, two continuous decks, and six main transverse watertight bulkheads. The double bottom tanks were arranged to carry fuel oil and tanks built outboard of the shaft tunnel port and starboard were employed for the carriage of vegetable oil. TAURUS had four lower holds, number 2 being exceptionally long, and six 'tween deck compartments; the space over number 2 hold was divided by a bulkhead under the bridge houses and there was a compartment under the poop abaft the middle line tonnage opening. With two masts and three pairs of kingposts that also served as cargo hold ventilators her cargo was handled by one 15-ton, eight 5-ton, four 3-ton, and two 2-ton booms. All her cargo winches were electrically driven as was her anchor windlass; the cargo winch on the poop was fitted with warping heads for handling mooring lines.

The 1929 Convention provided that a ship might carry up to 12 passengers without having to comply with its special requirements. TAURUS carried that number in four two-person and four single-berth rooms. These were located in the bridge houses along with a saloon, a smoking room, the captain's accommodations, and navigating spaces. The deck and engineering officers, cooks, and apprentices were quartered in the midship houses abreast the engine casing while the seamen and greasers were berthed in two-person rooms in the poop.

TAURUS was propelled by a Burmeister & Wain-type seven-cylinder, two-cycle, double-acting Diesel engine constructed by the A/S Akers Mechaniske Verksted that developed 4000 i.h.p. at 118 r.p.m. and drove her at $13\frac{1}{2}$ knots (25,05 km/hr.) at sea. The cylinders were 17.72 in. (0,450 m) diameter by 47,24 in. (1,200 m) stroke. To provide electric power she had one 100 KW generator driven by a three-cylinder, two-cycle, single-acting Diesel and two 66 KW generators driven by two-cylinder Diesels of the same type. A combined waste-heat and oil-fired boiler provided steam for heating. TAURUS was bombed and sunk by aircraft off Montrose, Scotland, on 6 June 1941. So successful was her type for Wilh. Wilhelmsen's operations that she was replaced by the fourth TAURUS in 1948 which has the same arrangement but is 20 ft. (6,096 m) longer and one knot (1,853 km/hr.) faster.

SCHARNHORST — 1935 — 18,184 T

625.6 × 74.1 × 41.0 feet
190,683 × 22,586 × 12,496 m

The twin-screw turbo-electric SCHARNHORST and her sister-ship GNIESENAU were built for the Norddeutscher Lloyd's service to the Far East by the Deutsche Schiff- und Maschinenbau A.G. at Bremen. They were fine examples of combination cargo and passenger ships with many advanced features including Maier-form bows. SCHARNHORST had a full-length double bottom, two complete decks, orlops forward and aft, a forecastle, long bridge, and houses above. Subdivided by 10 watertight bulkheads she had three cargo holds forward and two aft. Accommodations were provided for 156 first-class and 155 tourist-class passengers; the crew numbered 264 making the total on board 575 persons. Her machinery occupied four compartments and taking advantage of one of the features of electric propulsion the engine room and the propelling motor room were separated by a compartment containing refrigerated and dry stores thus reducing the shafting length. SCHARNHORST had two main generators rated at 10,000 KW each driven by a directly-connected multi-stage turbine operating at 3120 r.p.m. Each of her two propelling motors had a normal rating of 13,000 (13177) s.h.p. Steam for all purposes on the ship was supplied by four oil-fired water-tube boilers at 735 p.s.i. (51,676 kg/cm²) pressure; this was considerably higher than normal commercial practice at the time. Auxiliary electric power was generated by two 350 KW 230-volt generators driven by M.A.N. 5-cylinder, 2-cycle, single-acting Diesels. While SCHARNHORST was designed for a speed of 21 knots (38,92 km/hr.) the Far Eastern schedule called for long passages at reduced speeds. She could operate with one main generator running at its efficient high speed rather than running two units at reduced efficiency if she had been fitted with geared turbines. SCHARNHORST was taken over by the Japanese in 1942, renamed JINYO, and converted to an aircraft carrier; a submarine sunk her in 1944.

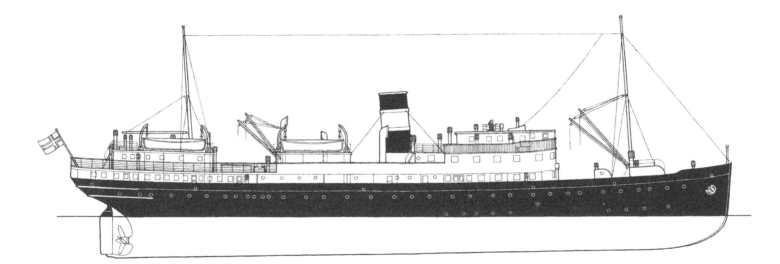

PRINSESSE RAGNHILD · 1931

Det Nordenfjeldske Dampskibsselskab

236.1 × 37.6 × 21.0 feet ◖ 1590 T ◖ 71,963 × 11,460 × 6,401 m

NORMANDIE · 1932

Compagnie Générale Transatlantique

981.5 × 117.7 × 91.8 feet ☾ 83243 T ☾ 299,160 × 35,875 × 27,980 m

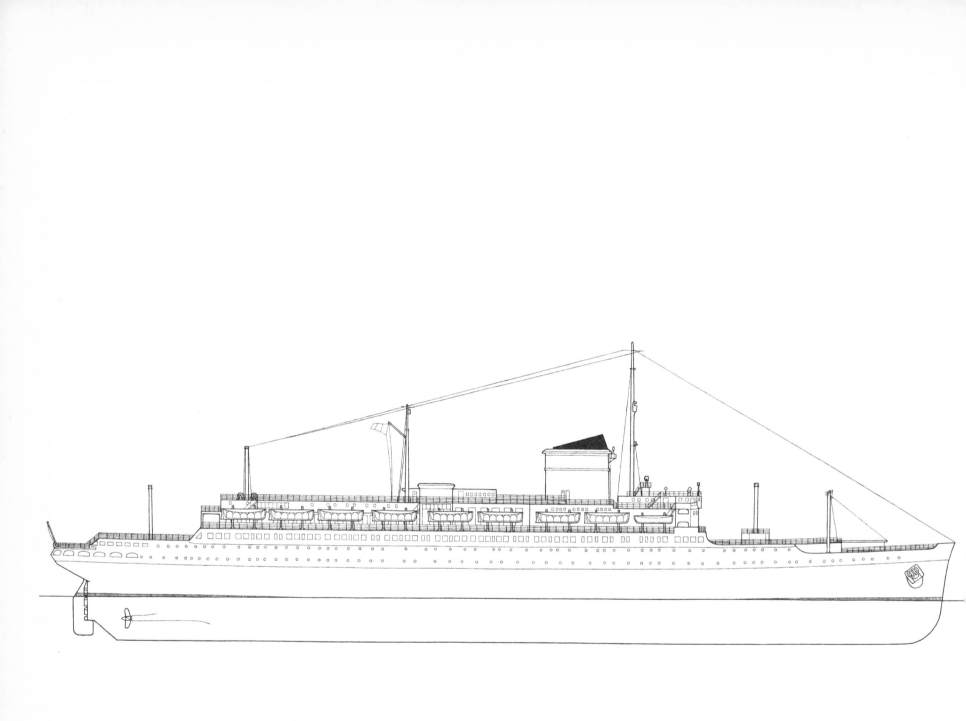

CHAMPLAIN · 1931

Compagnie Générale Transatlantique

606.5 × 83.0 × 46.0 feet ◐ 28124 T ◐ 184,861 × 25,298 × 14,020 m

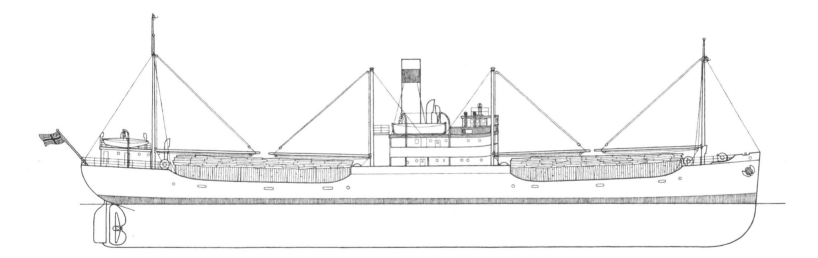

MARGIT R. · 1934

A/S Asplund (G. Rønneberg & Jens, Fr. Galtung)

244.1 × 40.1 × 16.9 feet ◖ 1597 T ◖ 74,402 × 12,223 × 5,151 m

QUEEN MARY · 1934

Cunard White Star Ltd.

975.2 × 118.6 × 68.5 feet ℂ 81235 T ℂ 297,240 × 36,149 × 20,878 m

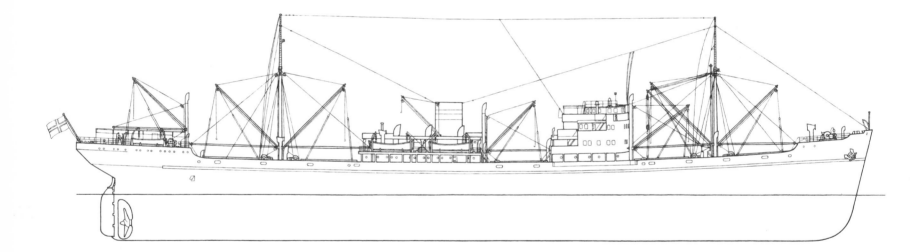

TAURUS · 1935

Wilh. Wilhelmsen

408.6 × 55.3 × 25.2 feet ℂ 4767 T ℂ 124,541 × 16,854 × 7,681 m

TOMINI — 1943 — 7233 T

422.8 × 57.0 × 34.8 feet
128,870 × 17,373 × 10,607 m

During World War II Messrs. Joseph L. Thompson &
Son, Ltd., Sunderland, designed and built a standard type
of cargo ship that differed little from SAINT DUNSTAN of
1919. Aimed at minimum cost, rapidity of construction,
and simplicity of operation this ship was the parent model
for vessels built in Canadian and U.S.A. shipyards for the
British government. With minor modifications including
the berthing of all officers and crew in one group of
houses amidships the design became the famous Liberty
Ship. U.S.A. shipyards built 2580 of the basic cargo type
and 130 special adaptations. The basic ship had two
complete decks and seven transverse watertight bulkheads; construction details varied from yard to yard. The
propelling machinery consisted of one set of three-cylinder
triple expansion engines having cylinders 24.5, 37, and 70
in. (0,622-0,940-1,778 m) diameter by 48 in. (1,219 m)
stroke. The engines developed 2500 (2534) i.h.p. at 76
r.p.m. Steam was supplied by two water-tube boilers at a
pressure of 220 p.s.i. (15,468 kg/cm²). TOMINI was
launched as GEORGE L. BAKER by the Oregon Shipbuilding Company, Portland, Oregon. Operated by the
Koninklijke Rotterdamsche Lloyd N.V. she became
KAMERLINGH ONNES in 1947 and finally TOMINI in
1950.

Sandanger — page 193

In the 1930's there was a considerable change in the structural design of tankers.
Instead of large main tanks divided by a single longitudinal bulkhead with small
summer tanks in the upper wing spaces two longitudinal bulkheads were fitted dividing
the hull into three tanks abreast. These bulkheads were usually spaced transversely
so that the capacity of the two outboard tanks was roughly the same as that of the
middle tank. Among the several advantages of this arrangement were increased
longitudinal strength, a saving in the amount of steel, a smaller area of steel subject to
corrosion, and more flexibility in loading and trimming the tanker.

A typical twin-bulkhead tanker of the period was SANDANGER constructed in the
yard of Sir James Laing & Sons, Ltd., Sunderland, for Messrs. Westfal-Larsen &
Company of Bergen. Having a straight raked stem, a cruiser stern, a forecastle, and a
poop she was built with longitudinal framing except at the very ends. As usual in
tankers a double bottom was fitted under the machinery space only. Instead of a
bridge with rectangular houses SANDANGER had on her single deck amidships four
levels of circular houses. The main deck house contained stores spaces while above
were the navigating spaces, captain's accommodations, and quarters for the deck
officers. The engineering officers and the remainder of the crew were berthed in the
poop; the galley and mess rooms were in houses on the poop.

SANDANGER's cargo space was subdivided into 18 tanks—six fore-and-aft and
three abreast. Her cargo pump room was located amidships and contained three
horizontal duplex steam pumps. Forward there was a small dry cargo tank with a

deep tank below. The capacity of her main cargo tanks was 127,240 barrels (20231 m³) and in various tanks which included the fore peak, the forward deep tank, part of the double bottom, and deep tanks just forward of the machinery space she could carry 1210 (1229) tons of Diesel fuel.

The Wallsend Slipway & Engineering Company, Ltd. constructed SANDANGER's main engine which was a seven-cylinder, single-acting Sulzer-type Diesel with cylinders 28.35 in. (0,720 m) diameter by 49.21 in. (1,250 m) stroke. Developing 4400 b.h.p. at 107 r.p.m. it drove her at 13½ knots (25,06 km/hr.) on trials and 13 knots (24,13 km/hr.) in service. Practically all of SANDANGER's auxiliary and deck machinery was steam driven. At sea enough steam was furnished for them at 120 p.s.i. (8,437 kg/cm²) pressure by a combination waste-heat and oil-fired Cochran boiler. For use in port when the cargo heating coils and steam pumps were in operation there was in addition a large oil-fired Scotch boiler to deliver steam at the same pressure. In company with the steam-driven and 19 other Diesel-driven tankers in the fleet operated by Messrs. Westfal-Larsen SANDANGER was time chartered to a major oil company. Her first voyage with cargo was from California to China, her last from the Caribbean region to England. She was sunk in the Atlantic on 12 May 1943.

Although the history of mechanically propelled vessels indicates the trend towards larger and faster vessels in accordance with economic demands and improved technology there always remains a need for small vessels to serve small coastal ports and those on restricted rivers. These services were the last stronghold of sail but the little motor coaster has ousted all but a few sailing craft even as the bigger vessels took over on the world's trade routes from deep-water sailing vessels. So small are many of the coasters that data pertaining to a large cargo ship compared to theirs seems like a compilation of astronomical information measured in light-years.

For the operations of the Ald Shipping Company, Ltd., Bristol, England, Messrs. Charles Hill & Sons, Ltd. of Bristol built the little single-screw coaster BROCKLEY COMBE. She had a single flush deck, a slightly raked straight stem, a cruiser stern, an open forecastle, and a poop. Below deck she had four transverse watertight bulkheads giving her two long holds, machinery space, and the usual two peak tanks. Transversely framed throughout, a considerable amount of electric welding was employed in her construction. She had a double bottom fitted to carry water ballast under her cargo holds only. Including the space within her two long hatches, which occupied about 70 per cent of the breadth of her deck, BROCKLEY COMBE could carry 42,000 cu. ft. (1189 m³) of cargo. For handling cargo her single mast was fitted with two 1-ton cargo booms worked by electric winches but most of her bulk cargoes such as coal would have been handled by cranes on shore.

Brockley Combe — page 196

All accommodations for the total crew of eleven were aft. The poop deck house contained the chart room, a spare cabin, and cabins for the master and mate. In the poop were cabins for two engineers, a saloon and a mess room for the officers, galley, crew's mess room, a single cabin for the boatswain, one 2-berth room, one 4-berth room, washrooms, and stores spaces.

In order to keep the engine room as small as possible BROCKLEY COMBE was fitted with a high speed Diesel engine that drove her single propeller through gearing. Messrs. Ruston & Hornsby, Ltd. constructed the seven cylinder, four-cycle, single-acting engine which had cylinders 12½ in. (0,318 m) diameter by 15 in. (0,381 m) stroke. Rated at 525 (532) b.h.p. at 430 r.p.m. it worked through an oil-operated reverse-reduction gear to turn the propeller shaft at 172 r.p.m. A Ruston & Hornsby four-cylinder 30 b.h.p. engine drove an 18 KW generator to furnish electric power for auxiliary services. On trials loaded with 900 (914) tons of coal BROCKLEY COMBE attained a speed of 10 knots (18,53 km/hr.).

In determining the characteristics of an addition or a replacement to a fleet of ships an owner must consider the relationship between the new ship and the older ships in his fleet, the qualities of his competitor's ships, and the future requirements of his service. The Netherland Steamship Company had to consider these problems in 1932 when the 16 knot (29,65 km/hr.) twin-screw motorship PIETER CORNELISZOON HOOFT of 1925 was destroyed by fire at Amsterdam. The company's existing fleet was composed of ships of about 17 knots (31,50 km/hr.) speed and at least 10 years old, other shipping lines were offering passages to India, the East Indies, and Australia on ships of 19-20 knots (35,32-37,06 km/hr.) speed, and there was the expectation of expanding traffic with higher speed ships in the future. It appeared that three 700-passenger ships having speeds between 24 and 26 knots (44,48-48,18 km/hr.) would best serve the company; length was limited to about 600 ft. (182,880 m). It was possible to design a ship of that size and speed but there would have been no room for the cargo that had to be carried on the company's route between Amsterdam and the Netherlands East Indies. After reducing the service speed to 21 knots (38,92 km/hr.) and making a large number of studies identified by letters of the alphabet design Q became the triple-screw ORANJE, the fastest motor liner of her day.

Built by the Nederlandsche Scheepsbouw Maatschappij, Amsterdam, ORANJE's keel was laid on 2 July 1937 and she was launched on 8 September 1938. Her profile shows a slightly curved stem, a cruiser stern, a forecastle, a long bridge on which the side plating is carried up two deck heights, and two levels of houses; she had one funnel and one mast. In the hull there are three continuous decks—B, C, and D—and two orlops along with the usual double bottom. Nine transverse watertight bulkheads subdivide her into fore and after peak tanks, main engine room, auxiliary machinery space, and six cargo holds. ORANJE is transversely framed throughout and electric welding was widely employed in her construction.

This description might apply equally well to many ships but an unusual feature not noticeable in a broadside view is that ORANJE's sides above her load water-line curve in so that her promenade deck is 17.5 ft. (5,334 m) narrower than her maximum breadth. There were several reasons for adopting this unusual feature. Because of restricted depths of water in ports on ORANJE's route and a general restriction on length her breadth was greater than that of older vessels in order to obtain the desired displacement. The fine hull form required for her speed meant reduced areas on lower decks for passengers and crew. Their relocation led to more weight higher up and for stability reasons the water-line breadth was further increased. On all services in the period there was a growing demand for outside staterooms and it was particularly desirable to avoid inside staterooms on tropical runs. ORANJE was arranged with no inside staterooms but if her maximum breadth had been carried up in the normal fashion the rooms would have had awkward dimensions. The breadth reduction not only gave more normal proportions to the upper staterooms but resulted in a substantial reduction in ORANJE's measured tonnage which meant lower Suez Canal tolls and port charges.

Oranje — page 194

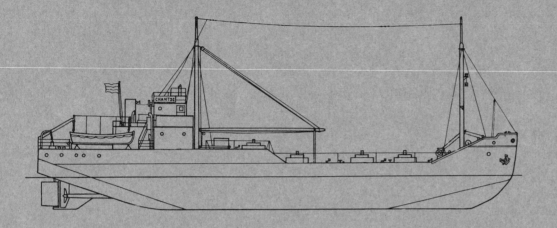

CHANT 66 — 1944 — 401 T

141.7 × 27.1 × 8.5 feet
43,189 × 8,260 × 2,590 m

Typical of a large number of small tankers constructed by several builders during World War II for the British Ministry of War Transport CHANT 66 was built by the Burntisland Shipbuilding Company, Ltd., Burntisland, and operated by Messrs. F.T. & Everard & Sons, Ltd., A single-screw vessel of simplified form and construction she has a short forecastle, a poop, and a trunk extending between the two to provide for expansion of the cargoes carried in her four pairs of main tanks. Her crew had spartan quarters in the poop and houses aft. Her main engine, built by Messrs. Ruston & Hornsby, Ltd., was a 5-cylinder, 4-cycle, single-acting Diesel having cylinders $10\frac{1}{4}$ in. (0,312 m) diameter by $14\frac{1}{2}$ in. (0,442 m) stroke which developed 210 b.h.p. Stripped of guns and other wartime gear such tankers have proved useful in commercial service.

When delivered to her owners on 15 July 1939 ORANJE had accommodations for 740 passengers and a crew of 391 making a total complement of 1131 persons. She could carry 283 first-class passengers, 283 second-class, 92 third-class, and 82 fourth-class passengers, the latter being primarily troops. The first and second-class lounges and smoking rooms were located on the promenade deck. On B deck there was a third-class deck saloon aft and a small fourth-class saloon forward. All dining saloons, mess rooms, galleys, pantries, sculleries, and the like were located on C deck; all second-class passengers could be served at one sitting as their dining saloon was the largest room in the ship. When the ship was employed for cruises or one class service it was intended that the first and second-class public spaces be used by all on board.

All living spaces on ORANJE were mechanically ventilated by a total of 42 systems. The first and second-class dining saloons and the hairdressing rooms and shop were fully air conditioned; certain of the first-class staterooms were air conditioned at night only. The arrangements for the detecting and extinguishing of fires met all the requirements of the 1929 Convention. ORANJE'S accommodations were divided into four vertical zones divided by fire-resistant bulkheads fitted with special doors; the joiner bulkheads were of double plywood construction covered on the inside with thin compressed asbestos board to retard the spreading of possible fires. The six cargo holds were provided with special smoke-detecting equipment. They could carry 280,000 cu. ft. (7929 m³) of general cargo and 2770 cu.ft. (78 m³) of refrigerated cargo. For handling cargo there were two 15-ton booms on the mast and ten 3-ton electric cranes which could be stowed down on deck when not in use. A special athwartships travelling crane working through a sideport on C deck was provided for transferring heavy machinery parts to the engine room.

A long series of model tests with twin, triple, and quadruple screw arrangements demonstrated that triple screws offered the highest propulsive efficiency for ORANJE. Her three main twelve-cylinder, two-cycle, single-acting Diesel engines were designed and built by Messrs. Sulzer Brothers, Ltd. of Winterthur, Switzerland; the cylinders

DEADWEIGHT

For shipping records the registered gross and net tonnages of ships have long been employed. Because of the exemption from measurement of spaces such as the shelter deck on dry cargo vessels and wing water-ballast tanks on ore carriers the registered tonnage figures are misleading as to the actual carrying capacity of a ship. Naval architects and shipbuilders rate ships by their deadweights and during World War II it became the practice to give statistics regarding ships built and lost in terms of deadweight tons. A ship's deadweight is what she can carry and is of prime interest to an owner or charterer. It is the difference between her full load displacement when floating at her assigned load water-line and her light weight. Deadweight includes fuel, fresh water, stores of all kinds, the crew and their effects, the passengers and their effects, and cargo. The last two items are the pay load. More cargo may be carried on a short voyage than a long one because less fuel is required but the total deadweight is the same.

are 29.92 in (0,760 m) diameter by 49.21 in. (1,250 m) stroke. For her designed speed of 21 knots (38,92 km/hr.) the engines developed a total of 23,500 (23820) b.h.p. that 125 r.p.m. but as a considerable reserve of power was necessary to maintain the schedule on the East Indies route where there were many intermediate ports of call the maximum b.h.p. was 37,500 (38010) at 145 r.p.m. On trials the engines actually developed a total of 37,635 (38147) b.h.p. giving ORANJE a speed of 26.3 knots (48,74 km/hr.). Electric power was provided by five 1000 KW 220 volt direct current generators driven by six-cylinder, two-cycle, single-acting Sulzer Diesels; three rotary converters provided alternating current for fan motors and certain of the equipment in the workshops and galley. Her electrical installation was exceeded only by those on NORMANDIE and QUEEN MARY. Although 890 (904) tons of fresh water were carried there was a distilling plant capable of producing 300 (305) tons per day. Steam for this and other uses was provided by three waste-heat boilers at sea and two oil-fired boilers when in port; all the boilers were of the La Mont forced circulation type and produced steam at 50 p.s.i. (3,515 kg/cm²) pressure.

ORANJE sailed on her maiden voyage in September 1939 and because of conditions in Europe she was laid up in Java for a time. She was eventually converted to a hospital ship and served for the duration of World War II. Restored to passenger service after the war she was reconditioned and put in round-the-world service via the Panama Canal in 1959. ORANJE was sold to Achille Lauro in 1963.

It will be remembered that G. HARRISON SMITH was built with permanent tanker features to carry iron ore from Cruz Grande, Chile, to Baltimore, Maryland, and oil from Mexico through the Panama Canal to the west coast of South America. Because the high Panama Canal tolls made oil carrying unprofitable the tanker features were omitted on AMERIKALAND. On FERROLAND, one of two ships built in 1943 by Eriksbergs Mekaniska Verkstad A/B, Gothenburg, for a subsidiary of the Swedish Broström company, the operator has his choice depending on business conditions.

The single-screw motorship FERROLAND has a raking stem, a cruiser stern, a forecastle, and a poop. Below her single deck her interior arrangement is similar to that of the earlier larger ships with two longitudinal bulkheads and a deep double bottom under the ore holds. Under and outboard of the ore holds are wing tanks normally fitted to carry water ballast; a pump room amidships contains large pumps for the rapid emptying of this ballast. By making a few changes to the wing tank fittings and obtaining a new tonnage measurement certificate the tanks may be used for oil cargoes on return trips if freight receipts and expenses, particularly those based on tonnage, are such that this would be more profitable.

Amidships FERROLAND has a tower-like structure which contains the navigating spaces, captain's accommodations, and deck officers' quarters. Separate saloons and mess rooms as well as single-berth cabins are provided in the poop and poop houses for the engineering officers, petty officers, and crew. FERROLAND's ore holds have a total of ten 2-part steel covers which are handled by lines led to two electric deck winches. The steering gear, anchor windlass, a capstan, and four special mooring winches are also electrically driven. FERROLAND is propelled at about 13 knots (24,13 km/hr.) by an eight-cylinder, two-cycle, double-acting Burmeister & Wain-type

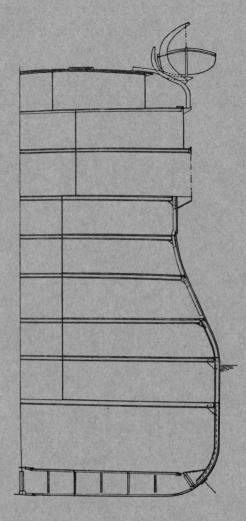

MIDSHIP SECTION—MOTORSHIP ORANJE

Ferroland — page 197

Diesel constructed by Eriksbergs Mekaniska Verkstad; the cylinders are 17.72 in. (0,450 m) diameter by 47.25 in. (1,200 m) stroke. She has one boiler furnishing steam at 80 p.s.i. (5,265 kg/cm²) for heating and other auxiliary uses.

On the Pacific Coast of North America the Canadian Pacific Railway Company has long maintained a fast passenger service linking the cities of Vancouver, Victoria on Vancouver Island, and Seattle in the State of Washington. In several respects this service is similar to many of the English Channel services which carry large numbers of day passengers. The ships employed, probably because they were constructed in British shipyards, have borne a closer resemblance to cross-Channel vessels than to those used on other coastal waters of North America. The twin-screw turbo-electric ships PRINCESS MARGUERITE and PRINCESS PATRICIA were built for the Vancouver-Victoria-Seattle route by the Fairfield Shipbuilding & Engineering Company, Ltd., Glasgow, and their delivery involved a 9500 mile (17605 km) voyage from Scotland to Victoria via the Panama Canal.

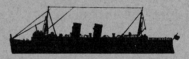

Princess Marguerite — page 200

PRINCESS MARGUERITE has a straight raked stem, cruiser stern, two funnels, and two masts with perhaps more superstructure than the average cross-Channel steamer. Having what in effect is a long combined bridge and forecastle—there is only as short length of her sides unplated at the stern—she has for all practical purposes three full length decks. Below these she has an orlop forward and aft and above two levels of houses. Eight transverse watertight bulkheads subdivide her into nine main compartments. She is allowed to carry 2000 passengers who are accommodated on the upper, promenade, and boat decks. Although designed primarily for day service she has eight de luxe staterooms and five special rooms on the upper deck, 28 double-berth cabins on the promenade deck and 10 on the boat deck. As the latter are mainly for use as private sitting rooms they are equipped with folding berths, the lower being converted into a settee.

Towards each end of PRINCESS MARGUERITE's upper deck there is a large social hall, the forward one being fitted with passenger embarkation doors at the sides; aft on this deck is the main restaurant. The forward end of the promenade deck is devoted to a large observation room with large windows giving a clear view in three directions while at the after end there is a coffee bar. The boat deck house has a smoking room forward and a ballroom aft. The accommodations for the deck and engineering officers are arranged on the boat deck, the petty officers, deck, and engine room crew are berthed forward on the orlop deck, and the stewards aft on the same deck. All mess rooms are on the main deck aft near the galley.

Most of the main deck space is devoted to the carriage of motor cars which may be driven aboard through two large gangway ports on each side. This car space is provided with a special carbon dioxide fire extinguishing system. Stairways at each end of the car space give access to the passenger spaces above. Holds forward are arranged to carry baggage and stores.

PRINCESS MARGUERITE's twin-screw propelling machinery, constructed by the British Thomson-Houston Company, Ltd., Rugby, consists of two sets of single-casing turbines directly connected to two-pole three-phase alternators turning at 3150 r.p.m. and two 2750 (2787) s.h.p. 225 r.p.m. synchronous propelling motors. The electrical connections are arranged so that either or both propelling motors can be powered by either turbo-alternator. Steam at 300 p.s.i. (21,092 kg/cm²) pressure for the main turbines is supplied by four oil-burning Fairfield-Johnson single-flow boilers.

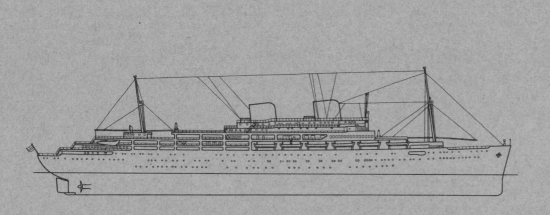

One single-ended Scotch boiler furnishes steam at 125 p.s.i. (8,789 kg/cm²) pressure for auxiliary uses. Electric power is supplied by two 400 KW and one 200 KW geared-turbine generator sets. PRINCESS MARGUERITE's service speed is 23 knots (42,66 kg/cm²).

The quadruple-screw liner UNITED STATES is the present holder of the Atlantic Blue Ribbon. On her maiden voyage in July 1952 she set new eastbound and west-bound records on the 2906 mile (5385 km) passage between Ambrose Lightship and Bishop Rock. Her time eastbound was 3 days 10 hours 40 minutes at an average speed of 35.59 knots (65,96 km/hr.) and westbound 3 days 12 hours 12 minutes for an average of 34.51 knots (63,95 km/hr.).

UNITED STATES is the largest passenger ship ever built in the U.S.A. Apart from her size and speed she is notable for three unique features—all passenger, officer, and crew spaces are completely air conditioned, a large quantity of aluminum was employed in her construction, and fireproof and fire-retardent materials were used extensively. It is said that the only wood aboard is in the pianos and butcher's blocks. Designed primarily as a mail and passenger liner she contains features making her suitable for rapid conversion to a naval auxiliary capable of carrying about 14,000 troops hence many of her details are restricted. UNITED STATES represents a new concept in overall design as the use of lightweight materials and advanced engineering practice enable her to carry nearly the same number of passengers as QUEEN MARY, only 131 less, at high speeds on about 25,000 (25400) tons less displacement.

Designed by Messrs. Gibbs & Cox, Inc. of New York, UNITED STATES was built by the Newport News Shipbuilding & Dry Dock Company, Newport News, Virginia. She presents a striking profile with a straight raked stem, a cruiser stern, a flush deck line nearly to her stern, a long range of houses, two large raked funnels, and a single mast. Her keel was laid in a large dry dock on 8 February 1950 and she was launched —floated out is more descriptive—on 23 June 1951. She has a complete double bottom, four full-length decks, and orlops forward and aft. Her compartmentation ex-

WILLEM RUYS — 1946 — 21,119 T

580.1 × 82.0 × 54.9 feet
176,814 × 24,993 × 16,733 m

The building of WILLEM RUYS by the Royal de Schelde Shipyard, Flushing, for the Koninklijke Rotterdamsche Lloyd was delayed by World War II. Her keel was laid on 25 January 1939 and she was launched in July 1946. Designed for service between Europe and the Netherlands East Indies she had when delivered accommodations for 344 first-class passengers, 301 second-class, 109 third-class, and 86 fourth-class, a total of 840. Her first and second-class dining saloons were identical and arranged to be opened into one large room when she was employed on cruises. She was arranged to carry about 5400 (5486) tons of cargo. A unique ship in many respects she has considerable tumble-home to her main hull which allows the majority of her aluminum lifeboats to be carried at a relatively low level. The most unusual feature is her propelling machinery. A twin-screw ship each screw is driven by four 8-cylinder, 2-cycle, single-acting Sulzer Diesel engines each of which develops 3750 (3801) b.h.p. at 215 r.p.m. The four engines in each group are
continued

United States — page 198

continued
connected by electro-magnetic slip couplings to the mechanical gearing that drives the propeller shaft. When cruising at low speeds one or more engines in each group may be disconnected and the others operated at their most efficient speed. Designed for a service speed of 21 knots (39,92 km/hr.) at 22,000 (22300) b.h.p. WILLEM RUYS attained a speed of 24.62 knots (45,63 km/hr.) on trials with her machinery developing 30,500 (30915) b.h.p. Since 1959 she has been employed on a round-the-world service via the Panama Canal.

ceeds the requirements of the 1948 Convention for Safety of Life at Sea which were more severe than those of the 1929 Convention. Her promenade deck, which extends to the stern, is her main strength deck and the upper limit of the steel structure. Except for the forward end all of the superstructure was constructed of aluminum which was also used for many interior bulkheads such as those around galleys, pantries, and washrooms. It is said that over 2000 (2032) tons of aluminum were employed and that it was the largest single order ever placed for the metal.

When delivered UNITED STATES had accommodations for 913 first-class passengers, 558 cabin-class, and 537 tourist-class, a total of 2008; her officers and crew totalled 1093. In general the first-class accommodations are amidships, those for the cabin-class passengers are aft, while the tourist-class spaces are forward. The crew are berthed at the ends of the ships and amidships below the passenger spaces. The officers' quarters are in the superstructure. Where not of metal the joiner bulkheads and the side and overhead sheathing throughout the accommodations are of various thicknesses of Marinite, an incombustible compressed material manufactured from asbestos. All furniture is of aluminum construction and the fabrics employed are for the most part of synthetic dynel and metallic threads. Because of air conditioning requirements the ship is completely heat insulated and there is extensive sound insulation around noisy spaces such as fan rooms.

All three classes of passengers have lounges, smoking rooms, dining saloons, theaters, bars, children's playrooms, barber shops, and beauty parlors, there being a total of 26 public spaces. The first and cabin-class passengers share a theater, gymnasium, and swimming pool but all other spaces are separate. The passenger dining saloons are all located on A deck along with their galleys, pantries, sculleries, dish, glass, and silver washing rooms, and other necessary spaces. The crew's mess rooms, galley, and associated spaces are on B deck amidships. The fireproof requirements put severe requirements on the firm of Smyth, Urquhart, and Marckwald, then, and perhaps still the only firm of women ship decorators in the world. The basic decorative motifs of UNITED STATES center around the natural elements, particularly the sea and sky and native U.S.A. subjects. Glass, enamel, and other metals are employed for decoration which feature the best modern designs of the period.

UNITED STATES has the extensive general service spaces necessary to support a floating city—hospital spaces, a tailor shop, laundry, printing shop, carpenter shop, upholstery shop, joiner and locksmith's shop, mail rooms and baggage offices. There are five holds for carrying limited quantities of cargo, three forward and two aft which have a total capacity of 148,000 cu. ft. (4191 m³) for general cargo and 48,000 cu. ft. (1359 m³) for refrigerated cargo. Cargo for number 3 hold is loaded by means of a trolley on an extensible boom working out of a side port on B deck; cargo for the other four holds is handled by booms on self-supporting kingposts.

Safety operations on UNITED STATES parallel those of a naval vessel. Near the wheelhouse is a damage control office which is manned at all times and here are located all safety controls, equipment, alarms, and means of communication for the safety of the passengers and ship in case of fire or collision. In case of accident the safety control officer can close all watertight and fire-screen doors, can shut down ventilation systems if required, and can call emergency squads for service where needed. Fires in accommodations, public spaces, or working areas, may be detected by automatic alarms or patrolling watchmen and put out by the use of portable extinguishers or water from fire hoses. The storerooms and cargo holds have smoke-detecting equipment and carbon dioxide extinguishing systems. Carbon

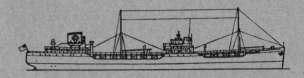

AURIS — 1948 — 8221 T

465.0 × 59.2 × 33.8 feet
141,731 × 18,044 × 10,302 m

AURIS was constructed for Shell Tankers, Ltd. by Messrs. Hawthorn, Leslie & Company, Ltd., Newcastle, as a normal 12,000 (12156) ton deadweight tanker except for her machinery. Originally it consisted of four 1105 (1120) b.h.p. at 375 r.p.m. Diesel engines driving alternating current generators which supplied power to a 3750 (3801) s.h.p. at 120 r.p.m. synchronous motor directly connected to the propeller shaft. This machinery plant was chosen to obtain experience with the burning of heavy fuel oil in moderately high speed Diesel engines and to permit the installation of a gas turbine at a later date. In August and September 1951 one Diesel generator set was replaced by a 1200 (1216) b.h.p. gas turbine-driven generator set which was the first gas turbine to be employed for the propulsion of a merchant ship. The installation was a success and operated 19,831 hours at sea during which time the Diesel engines produced almost every known defect and trouble. Occasionally the gas turbine alone made it possible for the ship to make port safely. In 1956 the propelling machinery in AURIS was again changed. All the generators and the propelling motor were removed and a 5300 (5372) s.h.p. gas turbine unit driving the propeller through double-reduction gearing was installed. This gas turbine was not reversible and to obtain a means of going astern AURIS was fitted with a hydraulic coupling to the gears for ahead rotation and a reversing torque converter for astern rotation. With her original Diesel-electric machinery AURIS had a maximum speed of 12.85 knots (23,81 km/hr.) but the more powerful gas-turbine increased it to 14.3 knots (26,50 km/hr.).

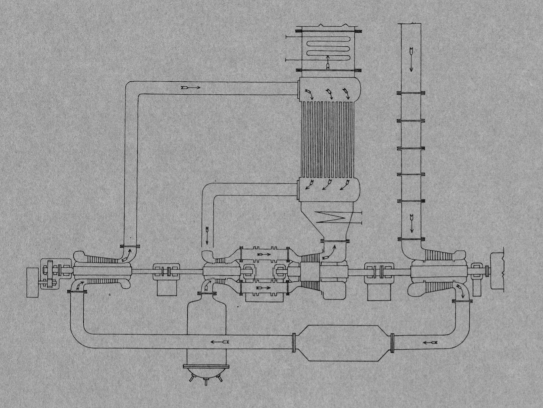

GAS TURBINES

In the early steam plants fuel was burned in a boiler to generate steam which was employed to drive a reciprocating engine that produced rotary motion by means of a crank. The steam turbine used steam to produce direct rotary motion. The gas turbine bears this same relation to the Diesel engine. Instead of burning fuel in a cylinder to drive a piston it is burned in some sort of a device and the resulting hot gases employed to drive a turbine. The hot gases used in the turbine may be the exhaust from a Diesel engine which performs other useful work or they may come from a so-called "free piston" engine in which the piston serves only to compress air. In the most efficient plants fuel is burned in a separate cylindrical chamber. Much of the power output of a gas turbine plant is used to compress the air employed in the cycle and the useful work derived depends on the relative efficiencies of the compressor and turbine.

dioxide systems are also fitted in the machinery spaces to deal with possible oil fires. All of the 24 lifeboats on UNITED STATES are of aluminum construction and are carried on aluminum davits.

The main propulsion turbines, boilers, and the associated auxiliary equipment on UNITED STATES are arranged to be operated as four independent plants. Each main propulsion unit manufactured by the Westinghouse Electric Corporation, Pittsburgh, consists of a set of high and low-pressure turbines working through double-reduction gearing. For a normal speed of 28 knots (51,89 km/hr.) the turbines develop a total of 158,000 (160150) s.h.p. In view of the speed records set by UNITED STATES it is probable that each propulsion unit develops over 60,000 (60816) s.h.p. Her boilers, probably eight in number built by The Babcock & Wilcox Company, supply steam at a pressure and temperature well above usual marine practice which required the use of special alloy steels in the boilers, turbines, and steam piping. She has about 300 pumps for various services; their total capacity is about 52,600 (53442) tons per hour. The electric service power on UNITED STATES is alternating current as experience on other vessels had shown that an alternating-current plant would be much lighter than a direct-current plant. Another important consideration was the reduced maintenance necessary on alternating-current motors.

UNITED STATES ran her official speed trials on 9 and 10 June 1952 well off the Virginia Capes in the North Atlantic nowhere near any of the standard measured-mile courses. This was made possible by the use of an electronic measuring system known as Raydist. Two buoys in the water send out impulses which are recorded by shipboard equipment; the accuracy is about one part in 5000.

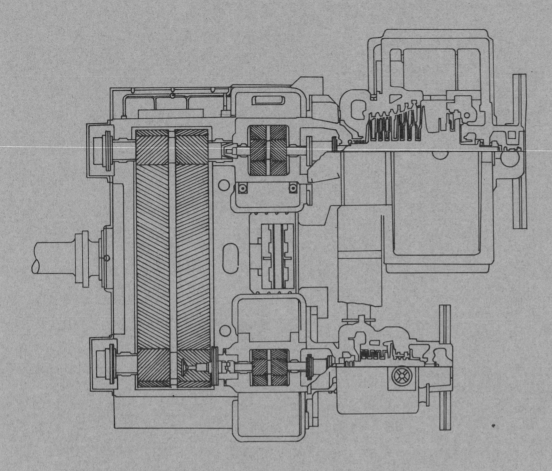

REDUCTION GEARS

For high efficiency, light weight, and minimum space requirements a steam turbine should operate at a high number of revolutions per minute. On the other hand, for best efficiency the r.p.m. of a ship's propeller should be relatively low. Dr. Carl Gustav Patrick De Laval of Sweden was the first to employ speed reducing gears for ship propulsion in a 15 h.p. experimental unit in 1892. Sir Charles A. Parsons in 1897 had a 10 h.p. turbine turning at 19,720 r.p.m. geared down to 1400 r.p.m. at the propeller to drive a 22 ft. (6,707 m) launch at a speed of 9 knots (16,79 km/hr.). In each of these units a single pinion on the turbine shaft meshed with gear wheels on two propeller shafts. In 1909 Parsons installed in the single-screw VESPASIAN a single-reduction geared-turbine plant of 1095 (1110) h. p. in which the turbine r.p.m. was 1450 and that of the propeller 53. Other geared-turbine ships followed but there were certain practical limitations on the useful speed ranges of turbines and propellers. Double-reduction gearing, introduced about 1917, had practically no limits on obtainable speed ratios thus permitting both turbines and propellers to be operated at r.p.m.'s suitable for the maximum efficiency of each. Considerable difficulties were experienced with early double-reduction gears which slowed their general use. At the present time whether single- or double-reduction gears are employed depends only on the service required, type of turbine used, and the desired performance. In general double-reduction gearing is lighter and occupies less space than a single-reduction gear of the same power.

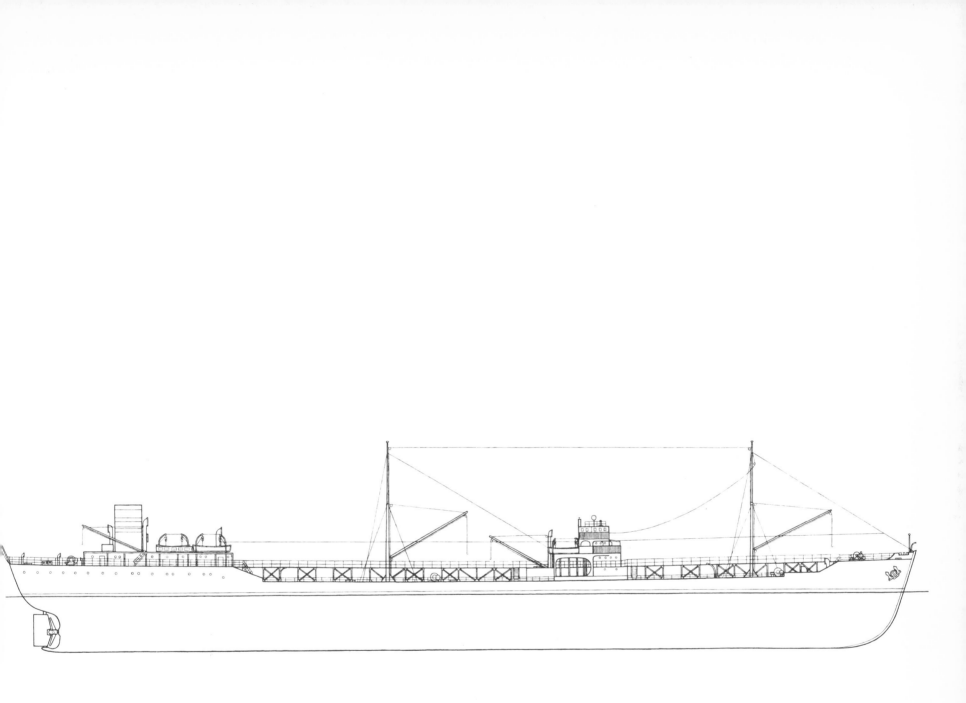

SANDANGER · 1938

Westfal-Larsen & Company A/S

483.6 × 68.3 × 36.2 feet ◖ 9432 T ◖ 147,401 × 20,817 × 11,033 m

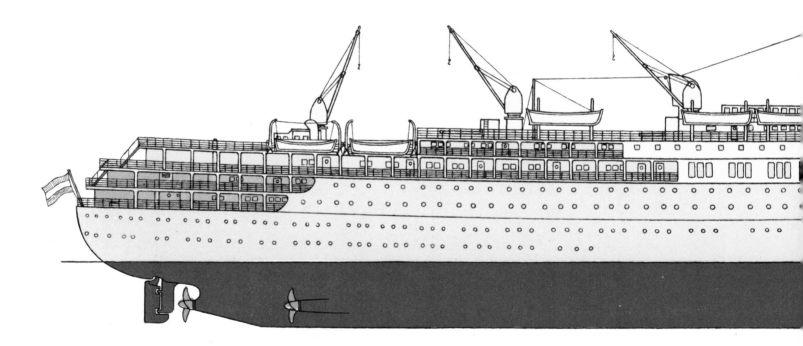

ORANJE · 1938

N.V. Stoomvaart Maatschappij Nederland
605.7 × 83.5 × 47.3 feet ℂ 19850 T ℂ 184,617 × 25,450 × 14,416 m

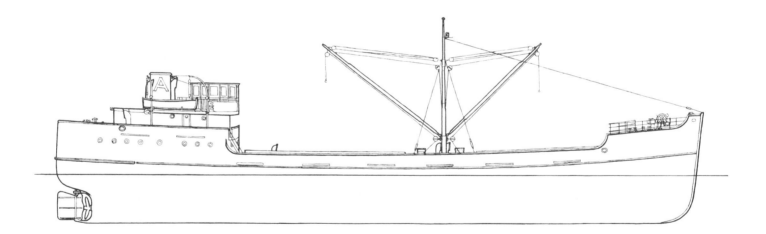

BROCKLEY COMBE · 1938

Ald Shipping Company, Ltd.

172.6 × 29.1 × 13.2 feet ◖ 662 T ◖ 52,608 × 8,870 × 4,023 m

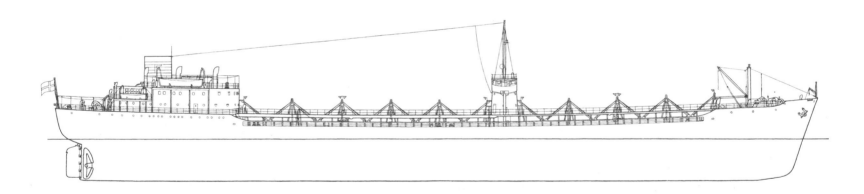

FERROLAND · 1943

Ångbåtsaktiebolaget Ferm

483.9 × 61.0 × 34.5 feet ℂ 8674 T ℂ 147,492 × 18,592 × 10,515 m

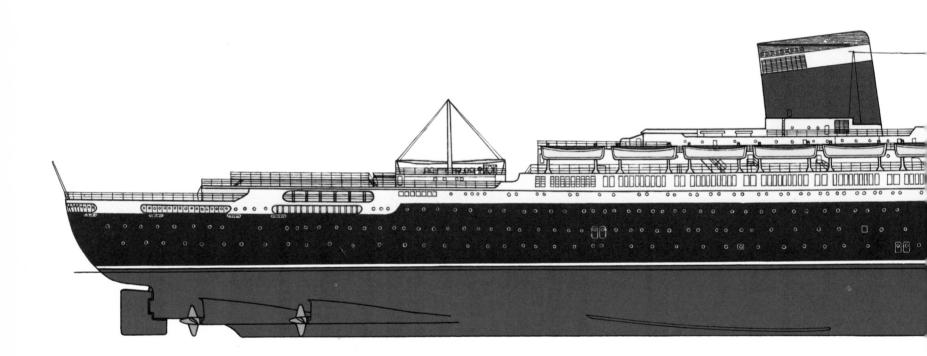

UNITED STATES · 1951

United States Lines Company

916.8 × 101.6 × 39.0 feet ❪ 53329 T ❪ 279,441 × 30,815 × 11,887 m

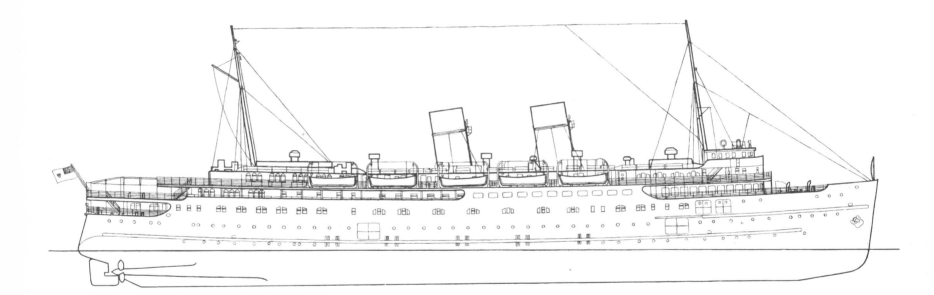

PRINCESS MARGUERITE · 1948

Canadian Pacific Railway Company

359.5 × 56.1 × 25.8 feet ◖ 5911 T ◖ 109,575 × 17,099 × 7,864 m

191.92 × 34.46 × 19.50 feet
58,496 × 10,503 × 5,943 m

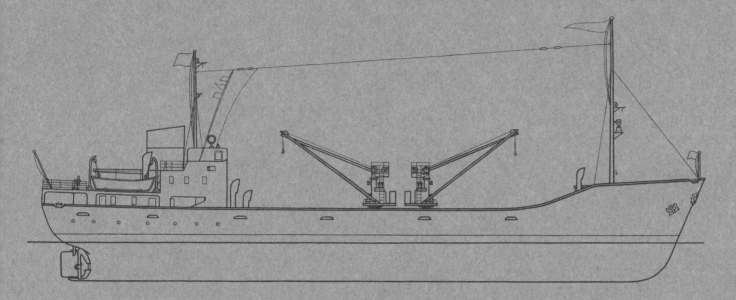

A passenger carrying service is usually considered to be a one-company operation. Occasionally two companies will alternate sailings but the daily service between Helsinki and Stockholm is maintained by three companies—the Rederi A/B Svea of Stockholm, the Finska Ångfartygs A/B of Helsinki, and the Ångfartygs A.B. Bore of Åbo. In 1950 the three companies agreed that each would build a new ship for the expected heavy traffic in connection with the 1952 Olympic games. It was further agreed that the three ships would have the same form, subdivision, and machinery but that the accommodations and profiles would vary. Different builders were chosen for the three hulls but the single-screw propelling machinery for all was furnished by the Elsinore Shipbuilding & Engineering Company, Ltd.

BORE III, the only ship of the trio to have two funnels, was built by the Oskarshamns Varv, Oskarshamn, Sweden, and launched on 1 July 1952 having been delayed by a steel shortage. As ice is encountered on the Helsinki-Stockholm route for a considerable portion of the year she has a modified ice-breaker bow and her structure is strengthened by heavy plating and extra frames to meet the Finnish ice classification requirements. Like most vessels of her size and type she has a double bottom and two full-length decks in her hull. The deck of a long forecastle continues over a long house to the stern and there are two levels of houses over this amidships. She is subdivided by seven transverse watertight bulkheads.

One thousand years ago the Vikings had specially designed wagons from which the loaded wagon bodies could be removed and stowed on suitable racks in a boat, perhaps the first pre-packaged or palletized cargoes. Their modern descendants in Denmark built AXELHUS and RIBERHUS to handle cargoes that have been stowed on small pallets or lashed together in suitable sized bundles at the manu-
continued

Bore III — page 212

continued
facturing point ready to be stowed on board a ship. Ordered by the United Shipping Company, Ltd., Copenhagen, from the Elsinore Shipbuilding & Engineering Company, Ltd., AXELHUS is a single-screw two-deck ship with machinery aft and a single long hold that can
continued

The accommodations in the three ships vary slightly BORE III having berths for 63 first-class and 185 tourist-class passengers; she can also carry 169 deck passengers. The first-class smoking room and bar extends across the ship at the forward end of the house on the forecastle deck; the first-class dining saloon is on the deck below. A large cafeteria is provided for the tourist class and deck passengers at the after end of the deck house. One hold served by two 3-ton booms is provided forward for small quantities of cargo. Her forward funnel is a dummy and it contains private quarters for her owners.

Because of the problems met in ice operations reciprocating steam engines were installed in the three ships. Of a new design developed by the Elsinore firm each ship has one set of four-cylinder, quadruple-expansion engines that develops 3400 (3446) i.h.p. at 113 r.p.m. The cylinders are 18.11, 26.77, 30.71, and 53.15 in. (0,460-0,680-0,780-1,350 m) diameter by 43.31 in. (1,100 m) stroke. The cylinders act in pairs on the Woolf compound principle—the high-pressure cylinder exhausts directly through a single valve to the first intermediate-pressure cylinder and the second intermediate and low-pressure cylinders are similarly linked. Steam from the first intermediate cylinder is passed through an exhaust turbine-driven compressor which raises its pressure and temperature before entering the second intermediate cylinder. The exhaust from the low-pressure cylinder drives the compressor turbine before passing to the condenser. Two oil-fired water-tube boilers supply steam at a pressure of p.s.i. 290 (20,4 kg/cm²). Direct current electric power is provided by two 200 KW turbo-generator sets. To cover the Helsinki-Stockholm route in about 15 hours the contract speed was 16 knots (29,65 km/hr.) which requirement all three ships successfully met on trials.

Until the late 1940's few oil tankers had lengths of more than 500 ft. (152,4 m) or deadweights of more than 16,000-17,000 (16256-17272) tons. In the years immediately following World War II the Middle East became one of the world's major oil producing regions which necessitated long hauls to the consumers in Europe, Japan, and North America. It became apparent that larger tankers would require only slightly larger crews but could carry far larger cargoes and the so-called "super tankers" were developed—ships of about 600 ft. (183 m) in length having deadweights of about 28,000 (28448) tons. The twin-screw motor tanker TAORMINA is one of this general class.

Built by the Cantieri Riuniti dell' Adriatico TAORMINA follows the standard tanker design of her period with a curved stem, a cruiser stern, a forecastle, and a poop but with a house amidships instead of a bridge. Her cargo section is divided into 32 tanks; unlike most tankers she has three instead of two longitudinal bulkheads. She has two cargo pump rooms extending her full breadth, one just forward of the midship house and the second midway between the house and the poop. The forward pump room has three steam-driven duplex pumps and the after pump room has two similar units. With this arrangement of tanks and pumps she can carry three different grades of petroleum at one time without the possibility of contamination. A 5-ton boom on a short mast forward serves the small space for dry cargo in the forecastle; pairs of kingposts at each pump room are fitted with 4-ton booms for handling the cargo hoses. Her total deadweight is 27,500 (27940) tons.

TAORMINA has a total complement of 56 consisting of 17 officers, 14 petty officers, and 25 ratings. Amidships are the navigating spaces, a suite for the owner, and accommodations for the captain and deck officers. In the poop deck house are the

continued
stow 55,000 cu. ft. (1557 m³) of cargo. Her upper deck hatch is 92 ft. (28,041 m) long and 21.4 ft. (6,523 m) wide; it is closed by a six-section folding steel cover at each end and two travelling platforms in the middle. Each platform can move at the rate of 82 ft. (24,993 m) per minute and bears a 3-ton electric crane. In addition to her crew of 16 AXELHUS has accommodations for 12 passengers. She is propelled by a 6-cylinder, 2-cycle, single-acting Burmeister & Wain Diesel engine that is rated at 1560 (1581) b.h.p. at 300 r.p.m. Fully loaded her service speed is 13¾ knots (25,53 km/hr.). As an example of the speed of loading 72 cases of bottled beer which formerly were individually handled are now packaged in a special crate that can be moved from the quay to stowed position on the ship in two minutes.

Taormina — page 213

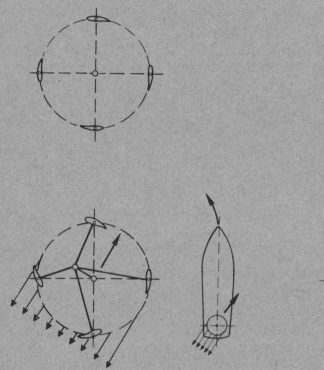

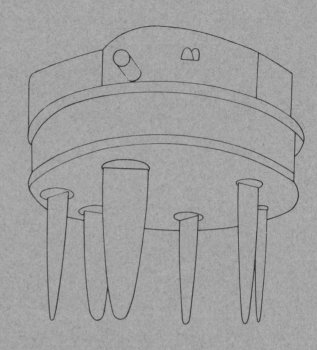

ROTATING BLADE OR CYCLOIDAL PROPELLERS

In simple terms a rotating-blade or cycloidal propeller may be described as a feathering paddle-wheel mounted with its axis vertical instead of horizontal; it serves to steer as well as propel. By means of a suitable mechanism the paddle-floats can be made to "feather" at any point in their revolution and the maximum thrust delivered in any desired direction. Such propellers were invented and tested independently about 1870 by a Mr. Moody and a Mr. Fowler. The former tried his on barges on the Clyde while the latter's was tested on the U.S.A. torpedo-boat ALARM where it proved wonderful for steering; its sole failure was the uneconomical application of the power for propulsion. The idea was revived in the 1920's when more was known about the proper shaping of the blades, the Kirsten-Boeing propeller being developed in the U.S.A. and the Voith-Schneider unit, the better known, in Germany. Both consist essentially of a number of spade-shaped blades mounted around the periphery of a large disc rotating on a vertical axis. By suitable mechanical arrangements it is possible to move the center of eccentricity of the blades while the unit is rotating thus directing the thrust as desired. As such propellers are driven from within a vessel their blades may project from any part of a vessel's underbody that is convenient.

accommodations for the engineering officers, recreation rooms for the petty officers and crew, the galley, and the messrooms. The remainder of the complement is berthed in the poop.

Each of TAORMINA's twin screws is driven by a seven-cylinder, two-cycle, single-acting Fiat Diesel engine designed to burn heavy fuel oil; the cylinders are 29.53 in. (0,750 m) diameter by 51.97 in. (1,320 m) stroke. In normal service the engines develop a total of 10,850 (10998) b.h.p. at 120 r.p.m. but their maximum rating is 14,680 (14880) b.h.p. at 133 r.p.m. Three oil-fired Scotch boilers generate steam for cargo and fuel oil tank heating, cargo pumping, and other uses. Electric power is provided by three 210 KW and one 50 KW Diesel-generator sets and one 50 KW generator driven by a steam engine. With a trial speed in a half loaded condition of 16.5 knots (30,58 km/hr.) TAORMINA's service speed is 15.3 knots (28,35 km/hr.).

The shipping company of Messrs. Shaw and Savill began business in 1859 and merged with the Albion Line in 1882. The company's steamers ARAWA and TAINUI began service on the England-Australia-New Zealand route in 1884. When such a long established company decided that combined cargo and passenger ships might have had their day on long-distance services and announced a new vessel the shipping world took notice. So did the travelling public as all of the new ship's voyages for for 1955 were sold out before she left her builder's yard for trials early that year.

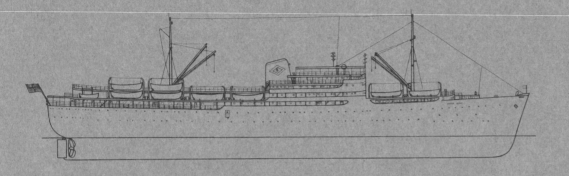

SKAUBRYN — 1951 — 9786 T

428.33 × 57.0 × 38.0 feet
180,56 × 17,37 × 11,58 m

The single-screw motorship SKAUBRYN is the modern
version of an immigrant ship. Her hull was built by the
Öresundsvarvet, Landskrona, Sweden, and she was
outfitted to carry 133 cabin class and 925 tourist class
passengers by the Kieler Howaldtswerke A/G, Kiel,
Germany; there is no space for the carriage of any cargo.
The majority of the cabin class passengers are accommodated in 3 and 4-person cabins while 4 and 8-
passenger cabins are provided for about half of the tourist
class; 442 of the tourist class passengers are berthed in 12
dormitory spaces. The only public spaces are on the
promenade deck, a recreation room and winter garden
forward and a lounge aft. The cabin class dining saloon is
amidships on the same deck while that for the tourist
class, operated as a cafeteria, is three decks below. A
separate galley and dining room are arranged for children.
With as much space as possible utilized for passenger
accommodations SKAUBRYN provides low-cost mass
transportation with some of the modern comforts.

Southern Cross — page 211

Intended to make four round-the-world voyages each year, two eastbound and two
westbound, SOUTHERN CROSS broke many of the traditions normally associated
with a large passenger ship. Her propelling machinery is located aft like that of a
tanker, she carries no cargo, and all 1160 passengers are carried as one class. Her
profile shows a slightly curved raked stem, a cruiser stern, a long range of houses for
passenger spaces, a low funnel aft, and a streamlined mast located on her bridge
houses.

Built by Messrs. Harland & Wolff, Ltd., Belfast, SOUTHERN CROSS was launched
on 17 August 1954. She has three full-length decks—main, saloon, and A—and the
side plating is carried up to her promenade deck for about three-quarters of her
length. Below there are two decks extending from the bow back to the machinery
spaces and a full-length double bottom; above are three levels of houses for passenger
cabins and public spaces. She is subdivided by nine main transverse watertight bulkheads and otherwise complies with the requirements of the 1948 Convention for the
Safety of Life at Sea.

Although the passengers are carried as one class at tourist-class standards fares
naturally vary according to the type of accommodation which ranges from a single-bed
cabin to a six-berth room; passenger cabins are located on five decks from B up. The
carriage of such a large number of passengers in relation to the size of the ship requires
a large number of inside staterooms which are acceptable on SOUTHERN CROSS
because all of the passenger spaces and a large part of the crew's quarters are fully air
conditioned. She has two large dining saloons which with the galley, pantries, and
other necessary space are located on the saloon deck. The main public spaces—lounge,
smoking room, and cinema lounge—are one level above her promenade deck. The
locating of the machinery aft has removed the noise and fumes from the passenger
spaces, allowed an arrangement of public spaces unhampered by machinery casings,
and relocated the passengers away from the movement and noise at the stern.

SOUTHERN CROSS is propelled by twin screws driven by two sets of compound
double-reduction geared turbines which develop a total of 20,000 (20272) s.h.p. at
120 r.p.m. Steam at 500 p.s.i. (35,154 kg/cm²) pressure is generated by three oil-fired

water-tube boilers of the Yarrow type; both the turbines and the boilers were constructed by Messrs. Harland & Wolff, Ltd. Electric power is provided by six 600 KW direct-current generators driven by eight-cylinder Diesel engines. When at sea the exhaust from these Diesels is utilized in two combined waste-heat and oil-fired water-tube boilers to provide steam at 80 p.s.i. (5,625 kg/cm²) pressure for all auxiliary services. Among her special equipment SOUTHERN CROSS has evaporators capable of producing 300 (304) tons of fresh water per day, a pair of Denny-Brown stabilizers, and electric deck machinery. Designed for a service speed of 20 knots (37,06 km/hr.) she attained a maximum of 21.35 knots (39,57 km/hr.) on her trial trips.

To the steady growth in tanker sizes in the years following World War II there seemed to be a sort of barrier at the 100,000 (101600) ton deadweight mark. It was inevitable that this barrier would be breached and the first to do so was UNIVERSE APOLLO constructed by the Kure Shipyard Division of National Bulk Carriers, Inc. of New York. Her keel was laid on 30 June 1958 in a dry dock in a section of the former Japanese Imperial Navy dockyard at Kure, Japan; she was floated out of the dock on 6 December 1958. At the time of delivery to her operators on 31 January 1959 the freeboard regulations permitted her to load to her 48.25 ft. (14,706 m) water-line which gave her a deadweight of 104,520 (106192) tons. A later change in rules reduced her freeboard by 30.5 in. (0,775 m) and she now carries 114,356 (116186) tons.

The total amount of structural steel employed in building UNIVERSE APOLLO was about 29,530 (30000) tons. As her light ship weight is about 31,200 (31700) tons it can be seen that the weight of machinery and outfit is but a small part of the total. The maximum thickness of steel plate used was 1½ in. (38 mm) and double thicknesses were employed extensively. Although basically an all-welded ship a few of her shell plating seams were riveted. The cargo tank section in UNIVERSE APOLLO is 640 ft. (195,072 m) long and is divided into four tanks abreast by three longitudinal bulkheads. Transverse bulkheads form 16 port and 16 starboard inboard tanks and half that number of wing tanks. There are three fuel oil deep tanks forward and four aft. The cargo tanks can carry 1,021,000 barrels (162339 m³) of oil. For discharging this cargo in about 30 hours there are four cargo pumps each driven by a 1000 (1016) s.h.p. steam turbine.

On a ship of the size of UNIVERSE APOLLO all normal items are dwarfed by the proportions of the hull but, having been built to the standards of National Bulk Carriers, Inc., the equipment and accommodations on UNIVERSE APOLLO seem extremely simple, almost austere. In small houses on the bridge that occupy about one-quarter of her breadth are the navigating spaces and accommodations for the captain and deck officers. The engineers and crew are accommodated aft; the total complement is 77.

UNIVERSE APOLLO is propelled by one set of compound double-reduction geared turbines manufactured by the General Electric Company, Lynn, Massachusetts. The normal s.h.p. is 25,000 (25340) at 100 r.p.m. with a maximum rating of 27,500 (27874), the largest yet supplied by the company for merchant service. Three Foster-Wheeler boilers, located one level above the main turbines, furnish steam at 600 p.s.i. (42,185 kg/cm²) for the main turbines and all other uses including heating and cleaning the tanks. Electric power at 450 volts is supplied by two 800 KW turbo-generators. The anchor windlass, mooring, and cargo-hose handling winches are all steam driven.

Universe Apollo — page 214

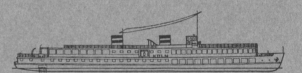

KÖLN — 1952

223.82 × 39.37 × 11.48 feet
68,22 × 12,00 × 3,50 m

Built in 1938 for the Köln-Düsseldorf Steamship Company KÖLN was sunk by German troops near the end of World War II but was raised after the war and completely reconstructed in the company's yard. Licensed to carry 2240 passengers she was recommissioned in 1952 and made a special jubilee trip to commemorate the one hundredth year of the company's operations. She was then the most modern passenger vessel of her type on the Continent. In spite of her dimensions she draws only 2.79 ft. (0,85 m) of water which makes screw propulsion difficult although not impossible. Under such a restriction the vertical-axis Voith-Schneider propeller has proved useful and as it can provide thrust in any direction rudders are not normally required for steering. KÖLN has two such propellers each driven by a Klöckner-Humboldt-Deutz six-cylinder Diesel engine capable of developing 450 (456) b.h.p. at 450 r.p.m.

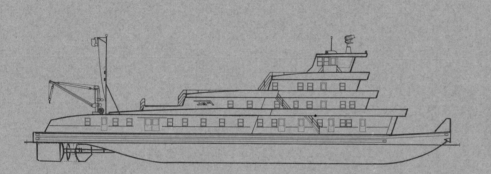

169.6 × 58.0 × 10.1 feet
51,694 × 17,678 × 3,079 m

On the Mississippi, the Ohio, and their various tributaries, "towboats" push their barges. This practice developed during the days of the stern-wheel steamers which had no convenient point of attachment for a tow-line to barges astern although some such steamers have towed from a heavy kingpost located about amidships. Since those days tunnel-sterned steam-propelled towboats were developed while the newest vessels are Diesel-propelled. The most powerful of her day, intended to work on the lower Mississippi, is the quadruple-screw UNITED STATES designed and built by the St. Louis Shipbuilding & Steel Company, St. Louis, Missouri, for the Federal Barge Lines, Inc. She is capable of pushing a fleet of 40 loaded barges carrying 40,000 (40544) tons of cargo, a "tow" that would be about 1750 ft. (533 m) long. A single-deck vessel, almost rectangular in plan view, the bow of UNITED STATES has a strong "head log" on which are mounted four huge "tow" knees for transmitting her thrust to the fleet of barges. Aft her bottom slopes up to provide a good flow of water to her propellers which work in Kort nozzles, a shrouding device that increases her pushing power about 25 per cent. In the pilot house is a control console which places all navigating equipment, engine controls, and steering controls within easy reach of the pilot. UNITED STATES is propelled by four direct-reversing Cooper-Bessemer Diesel engines driving 9 ft.
continued

Designed for a full-load service speed of 15.5 knots (28,73 km/hr.) UNIVERSE APOLLO was loaded only to a mean water-line of 27 ft. (8,229 m) for her trial trip on which she attained a speed of 17.52 knots (32,47 km/hr.). Upon delivery she was chartered for service between Japan and the Persian Gulf.

From iron sailing vessels that once carried nitrate from Chile to PRIAMOS, a modern refrigerated fruit carrier, is an indication of the way the ship-owning business can change. The Reederei F. Laeisz G.m.b.H. of Hamburg operated the famous "P" Line of sailing vessels and owned PREUSSEN of 1902, the only five-masted full-rigged ship ever built. Unlike vessels in other trades refrigerated fruit carriers have changed little in size during the years. While some have approached 450 ft. (137,159 m) in length PRIAMOS is but little larger than the steamer SAN JOSE of 1904.

Most fruit ships seem to have a clean yacht-like appearance and the 3177 (3228) tons deadweight PRIAMOS continues the tradition with her well-raked slightly-curved stem, cruiser stern, low houses, single low funnel, and two masts. Built by the Kieler Howaldtswerke A.G., Kiel, she has in her hull two complete decks, a full-length double bottom, and an orlop forward and aft. Six transverse watertight bulkheads subdivide her into four cargo holds, machinery space, and two peak tanks. A long combined forecastle and bridge is treated as a tonnage-exempt shelter deck space. Officers and crew are quartered amidships and aft.

Priamos — page 216

continued
(2,743 m) diameter propellers through 1.63 to 1 reduction gears; the total power developed is 8500 (8616) b.h.p. These engines are started on normal Diesel fuel and after being warmed up are shifted to heavy fuel oil. She is steered by six rudders forward of her propellers and four aft. Push towing is now being adopted on other continents where operating conditions are similar to those encountered by UNITED STATES.

The refrigerated cargo spaces in PRIAMOS can carry 234,000 cu. ft. (6626 m³) of chilled fruit which is handled through her hatches and cargo ports. She has eight cargo booms for working cargo through four hatches—seven capable of lifting 3 tons on a single line or 5 tons with a purchase and one hoisting 3 or 10 tons in similar fashion. Four shell ports on each side in the shelter-deck space and three each side in the upper 'tween-deck space allow the loading and unloading of cargo by means of special conveyors.

A single-screw ship PRIAMOS is fitted with an eight-cylinder, single-acting, M.A.N.-type Diesel engine constructed by the Howaldtswerke A.G. that develops 5070 (5140) b.h.p. at 122 r.p.m. and drives her at 17.25 knots (31,97 km/hr.). All deck machinery is electrically driven. To improve propulsive efficiency and to minimize vibration PRIAMOS has the so-called "clear-water" stern, the rudder being of the spade type with no bottom support.

The term "nuclear-propelled" applied to ships has led to much "science-fiction" type of reporting concerning the operation and capabilities of a ship equipped with a nuclear power plant. The nuclear part of the plant, however, is in 1965 only a heat-producing device that replaces an ordinary coal- or oil-fired boiler to generate steam. At the present stage of commercial development the steam furnished by a nuclear plant is at such a low pressure and temperature that steam turbine designers, after years of working towards ever higher steam pressures and temperatures, have had to return to the standards of the 1920's. The great advantage of a nuclear plant for generating steam is the ability of a ship so fitted to operate for long periods without refueling. There is no gain in deadweight as the total weight of a nuclear plant is about the same as that of a normal oil-fired steam plant of the same power plus a full load of fuel oil. Because of the high capital cost a commercial nuclear plant should be employed on a ship that spends little time in port such as an ore carrier or tanker.

The world's first commercial nuclear ship is SAVANNAH named for the first U.S.A. ocean-going ship to employ steam power. A joint venture of the U.S. Maritime Administration and the Atomic Energy Commission she was designed by Messrs. George G. Sharp, Inc., New York, as a demonstration ship and an experimental sea-going laboratory not expected to be competitive commercially; her deadweight is just about 10,000 (10160) tons. As safety was of prime importance first consideration was given to the location and protection of the nuclear reactor which involved studies of the weight distribution, special structure including an anti-collision barrier, and the location and arrangement of the superstructure.

Built by the New York Shipbuilding Corporation at Camden, New Jersey, SAVAN-NAH's keel was laid on 22 May 1958 and she slid down the ways into the Delaware river on 21 July 1959. In keeping with her unique concept she has an unmistakable profile with a "clipper" bow, a modified cruiser stern with a knuckled tumble-home, a long bridge, and three levels of house blended into a tear-drop shape. There is no funnel or even an exhaust pipe disguised as a mast as there are no waste gases from a nuclear reactor. Basically she is a shelter-decker with three continuous decks —A, B, and C, an orlop forward and aft, and a full-length double bottom. Ten transverse watertight bulkheads divide her into eleven main compartments—fore peak, four cargo holds forward, reactor compartment, machinery space, three cargo

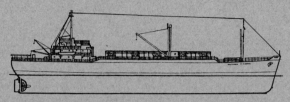

METHANE PIONEER — 1959 — 5058 T

323.9 × 50.1 × 38.5 feet
98,724 × 15,270 × 11,734 m

The world's demand for fuel has led to the development of many special types of ships. Colliers and tankers are considered normal types today. AGNITA introduced the carriage of the liquefied petroleum gases butane and propane, more commonly called LPG, while METHANE PIONEER was, as her name implies, the pioneer in the ocean transportation of liquefied methane. Because there was no convenient means of transportation enormous quantities of natural gas, which is principally methane, were burned each year at the world's major oil fields. Methane can be liquefied conveniently only by cooling— its boiling point is -258°F (-161° C). METHANE PIONEER, *continued*

Savannah — page 218

continued

a joint venture of the Gas Council of Great Britain and Constock International Methane, Inc., was converted from a dry cargo ship in accordance with plans prepared by Messrs. J. J. Henry Company, Naval Architects, of New York. Fitted with a new raised deck amidships, she carries in her hold five rectangular all-welded aluminum tanks insulated on the bottom, sides, and ends with 12 in. (0,305 m) of balsa wood and on the top with 18 in. (0,457 m) of Fiberglas. In spite of the insulation there is a continual "boil-off" of the methane. While this "boil-off" could be reliquefied with suitable refrigerating machinery or employed as fuel for a ship neither was done on METHANE PIONEER where the "boil-off" was vented to the atmosphere. Too small to be commercially practicable METHANE PIONEER proved the feasibility of the ocean transportation of liquefied methane and has been replaced by specially designed ships.

holds aft, and the after peak. SAVANNAH has normal transverse framing except for the inner bottom under the reactor compartment which has floors at every frame and many fore-and-aft girders. The reactor is further protected by two heavy longitudinal bulkheads, extra heavy plating on the decks outboard, and collision mats composed of steel plates and layers of redwood.

SAVANNAH can carry 60 passengers in 30 staterooms arranged in the bridge space on A deck. On the promenade deck above are a lounge forward and a verandah with bar aft; sliding glass doors open the verandah to a game deck and swimming pool. The accommodations for the captain, deck officers, and engineering officers are on the boat deck with the usual navigating spaces and radio officers' cabins on the deck above. Below on B deck are the main dining saloon, galley, crew's mess rooms and lounges, and some crew cabins; the remainder of the crew are quartered on C deck. All accommodations are air conditioned. For handling her 746,200 cu. ft. (21130 m³) SAVANNAH has side ports and elevators serving number 5 hold and twelve 10-ton booms serving the other six holds through hatches. In place of normal masts or king-posts she has tubular rigid frame structures; the cargo winches and other deck machinery are electrically driven. Among other equipment she has one pair of Sperry fin stabilizers.

The single-screw propelling machinery in SAVANNAH consists of one set of compound double-reduction geared turbines manufactured by De Laval Turbine, Inc., Trenton, New Jersey. This machinery has a normal rating of 20,000 (20272) s.h.p. at 107 r.p.m. and gives her a service speed of 21 knots (38,92 km/hr.). Ship's service electric power is provided by two 1500 KW 450 volt turbo-generators. Two auxiliary Diesel-driven 750 KW generator sets supply power for starting up the plant, for spare capacity in case of accident to a main turbo-generator, and to supply power to an electric motor for emergency propulsion should the nuclear reactor fail. A 300 KW Diesel-driven generator for other emergency uses is located on the navigating bridge deck. All other auxiliaries are those found with any normal steam plant.

Steam for SAVANNAH's main and auxiliary machinery is generated by a pressurized water reactor constructed by The Babcock & Wilcox Company, New York, that is rated at 74 million watts. Designed for an active life of 1230 days at average operating power it has 32 fuel elements each containing 164 stainless steel tubes filled with uranium oxide pellets enriched to an average of 4.4 per cent of uranium 235. The reactor operates on the principle that water under high pressure can be exposed to the high temperature of the nuclear fission reaction without boiling. This heated water is passed through a heat exchanger containing water under a much lower pressure which turns to steam. At the above normal turbine rating steam is supplied at 465 p.s.i. (32,693 kg/cm²) pressure. Thus far SAVANNAH's activities have included extensive trials, visits to the major U.S.A. ports, and several voyages to Europe.

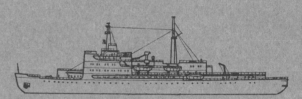

LENIN — 1957

439.64 × 90.55 × 52.49 feet
134,0 × 27,6 × 16,0 m

Designed to keep open the sea lanes in the Arctic Ocean north of Russia nuclear energy frees the icebreaker LENIN from refueling problems. It is estimated that her three pressurized-water reactors contain enough fissionable material to permit her to operate at full power for one year before having to refuel; this is equivalent to several years of normal operations at sea. The triple-screw LENIN has one 3850 KW and two 1920 KW turbo-generators providing power for a 19,600 (19866) s.h.p. motor on the middle shaft and 9800 (9933) s.h.p. motors on the two wing shafts; the middle shaft turns at 185 r.p.m. and the wing shafts at 205 r.p.m. The maximum power rating is said to be 44,000 (44598) s.h.p. LENIN's speed in open water is 18 knots (33,36 km/hr.). Displacing about 16000 (16,218) tons she is capable of working in ice up to 6.5 ft. (2 m) thick.

Vessels navigating the Rhine must operate between two evils—the bottom of the river and the underside of the fixed bridges. Their load water-lines are established in relation to the river's bottom—CALEDONIA was unable to proceed above Coblenz in 1817 because she drew 4 ft. 6 in. (1,371 m). Fixed superstructures can be limited to clear the bridges but hinged masts and funnels are common. The restricted depths of water on the upper stretches of the river make it difficult to arrange for efficient propulsion by screws, and paddle-wheels are still widely employed. A traveller waiting to

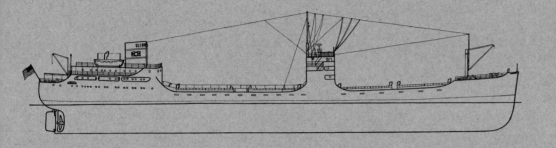

MORAR — 1958 — 6990 T

407.0 × 57.25 × 32.25 feet
124,054 × 17,449 × 9,829 m

The first free-piston gas generator and exhaust-gas turbine to be installed in a new ocean-going ship occupy the machinery space of MORAR built for the Scottish Ore Carriers, Ltd., by Lithgows, Ltd. Apart from her machinery she is a normal single-deck ore carrier with a forecastle, short bridge, and relatively short poop. Below deck she has the usual twin longitudinal bulkheads and a deep double bottom under her four ore holds. The machinery consists of three free-piston gas generators and one reversing exhaust-gas turbine driving the propeller shaft through normal double-reduction gearing. The turbine operates at 5250 r.p.m. and the propeller delivers 2500 (2534) s.h.p. at 115 r.p.m. for a service speed of 11 knots (20,39 km/hr.). This machinery installation is 220 tons lighter than steam turbine machinery installed in sister ships and it would have been possible to save about 25 ft. (7,620 m) in the length of the machinery space. The cubic capacity of the ore holds, however, was not important so the engine room was shortened only half that amount.

Berlin — page 217

board the modern Rhine passenger boat BERLIN might assume from her appearance and splashing at her side as she comes into a landing that she has paddle-wheels but her sideways motion is something that neither paddle-wheels nor screw-propellers can produce.

In November 1957 the Köln-Düsseldorf Steamship Company decided to build BERLIN for its Middle Rhine day service between Köln and Mainz and after extensive model tests her keel was laid on 1 October 1958. She was launched in April 1959. Commissioned on 14 May and licensed to carry 3000 passengers she was at the time the largest and most modern passenger vessel operating on the inland waters of western Europe. Care was taken to keep her as light as possible and when ready for a trip but without passengers she drew only 3.77 ft. (1,15 m). Her main hull, which has two continuous decks, and her lower house are of all-welded steel construction while aluminum alloys were employed for the upper structure which saved about 23 tons. Eight watertight bulkheads divide her hull into the fore peak, seamen's quarters, passenger smoking room and dining saloon, a central hall with cloak room and seven private staterooms, machinery space and engineers' rooms, galley storerooms, two compartments containing accommodations for deck officers and commissary personnel, and the after peak. Foward on the main deck is a large cafe and aft is another dining saloon; the main galley and a buffet service room for the cafe are located amidships. The forward end of the upper house is an observation lounge while the after end serves as a verandah cafe opening on to the after deck; a bar is located amidships in the upper house.

BERLIN's sideways motion, which is very useful in making the 40 landings on a round trip between Köln and Mainz, is made possible by two Voith-Schneider propellers located where one might expect to find paddle-wheels. Although these provide thrust in any desired direction this position is not as effective for steering as the after position in KÖLN hence BERLIN is fitted with three normal rudders at the stern. BERLIN's propelling machinery consists of two Deutz six-cylinder Diesel engines capable of developing a total of 1677 (1700) b.h.p. at 565 r.p.m. A Deutz three-cylinder

Diesel rated at 75 b.h.p. at 1500 r.p.m. drives a 46 KW generator and also an air compressor. On trials BERLIN made a speed of 10.34 miles (16,65 km) per hour upstream and 18.42 miles (29,65 km) per hour downstream. The effect of shallow water was shown by her speed of 11.22 miles (18,05 km) per hour when the depth was only 13.78 ft. (3,5 m) and 14.17 miles (22,80 km) per hour when the water was 23.62 ft. (6,0 m) deep.

SOUTHERN CROSS · 1954

Shaw, Savill & Albion Company, Ltd.

584.0 × 78.2 × 41.5 feet ◖ 20204 T ◖ 178,002 × 23,835 × 12,648 m

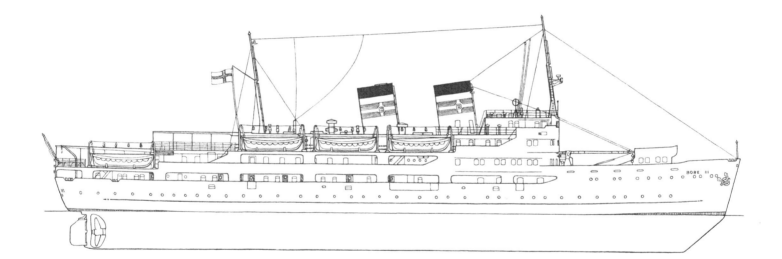

BORE III · 1950

Ångfartygs A.B. Bore

298.5 × 46.5 feet ⦗ 2797 T ⦗ 90,982 × 14,172 m

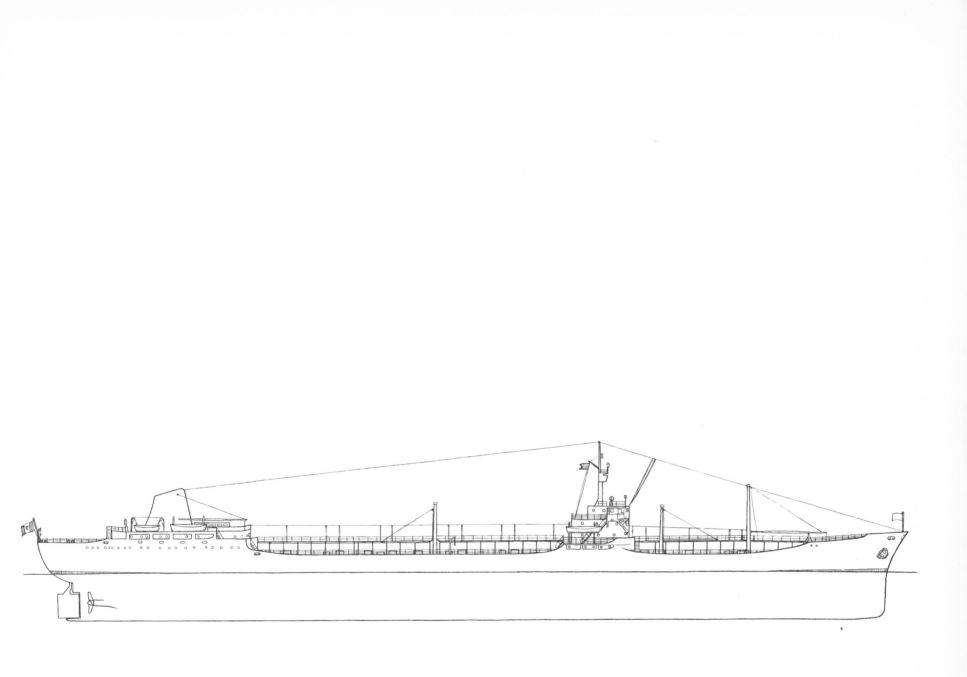

TAORMINA · 1954

Società per Azioni Antartide

630.3 × 82.3 × 45.9 feet ◖ 18566 T ◖ 192,118 × 25,094 × 14,00 m

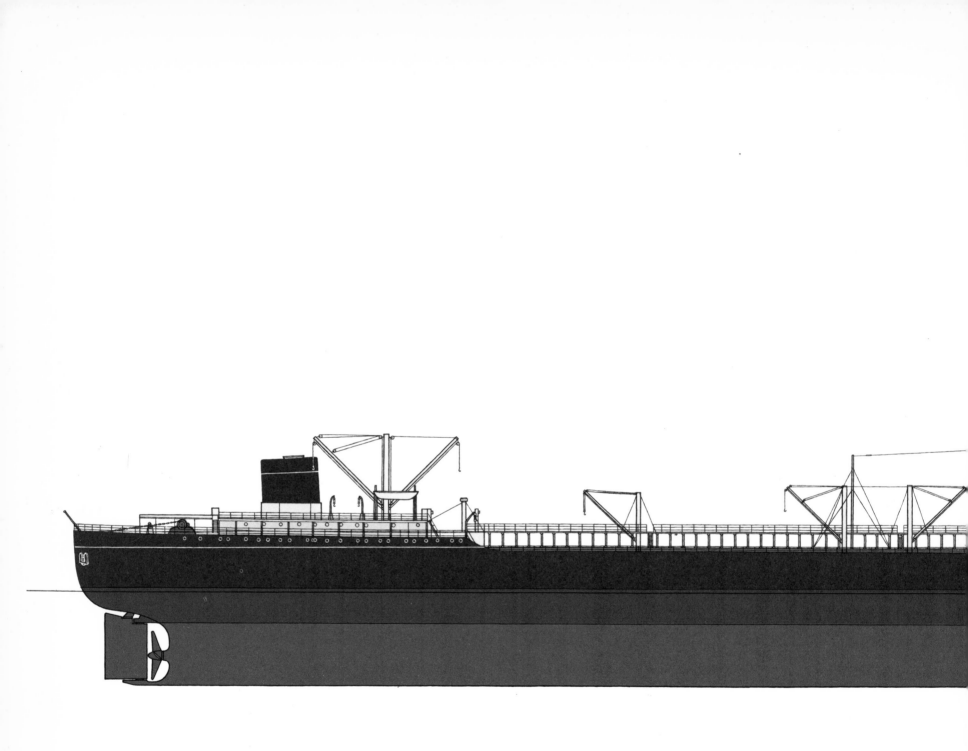

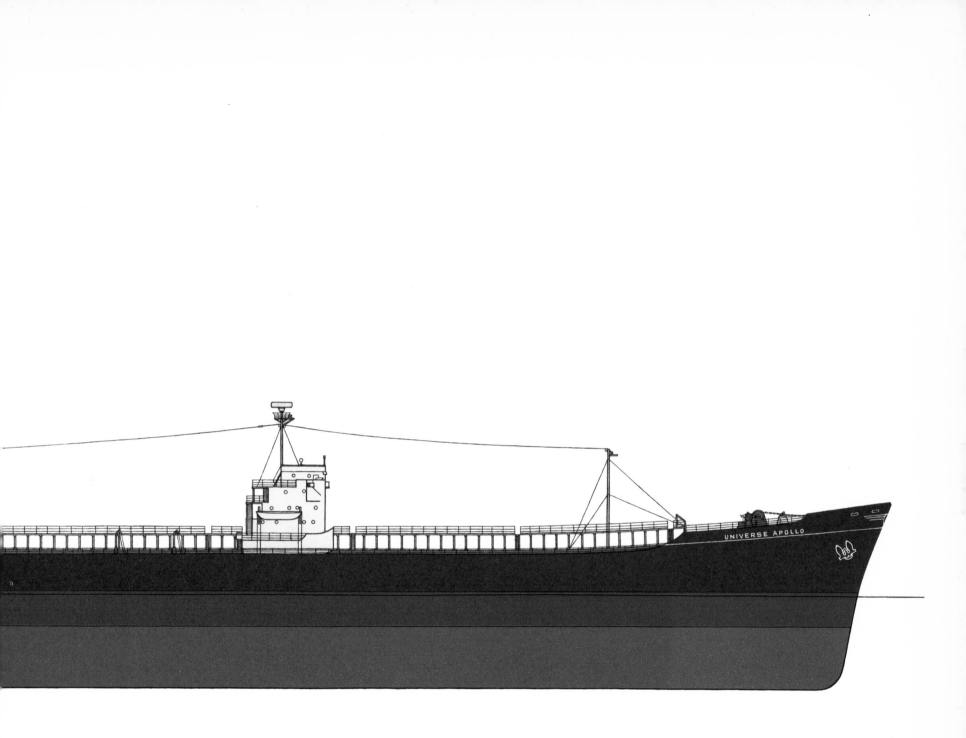

UNIVERSE APOLLO · 1958

Universe Tankships of Liberia (National Bulk Carriers, Inc.)

911.6 × 135.4 × 69 feet ℂ 72133 T ℂ 277,856 × 41,270 × 21,031 m

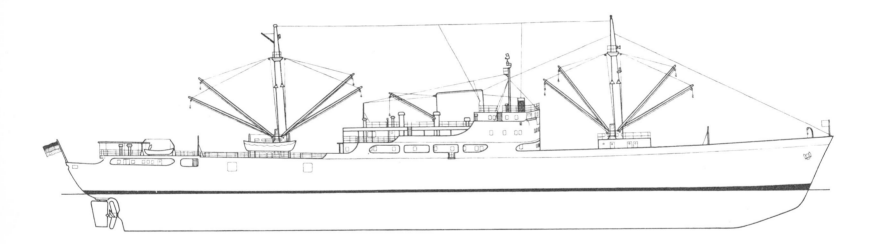

PRIAMOS · 1958

Reederei F. Laeisz G.m.b.H.

393.1 × 51.3 × 16.5 feet ℂ 3027 T ℂ 119,817 × 15,635 × 5,029 m

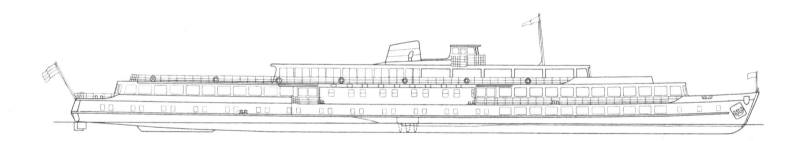

BERLIN · 1959

Köln—Düsseldorfer Rheindampfschiffahrt

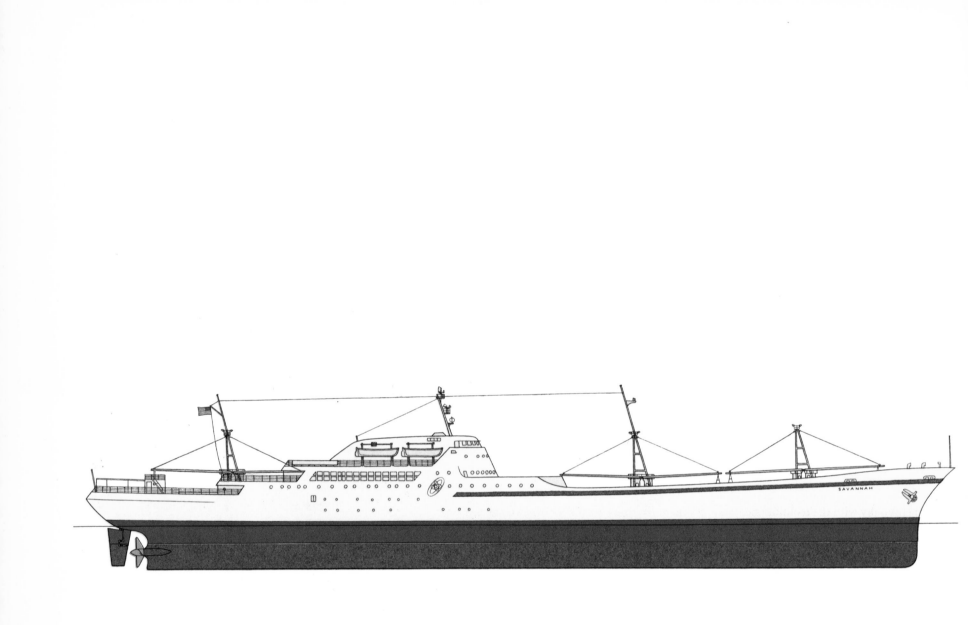

SAVANNAH · 1959

U.S. Maritime Administration

595.5 × 78.167 × 29.583 feet ℂ 13890 T ℂ 175,71 × 23,85 × 9,03 m

540.3 × 84.1 × 29.5 feet
164,683 × 25,633 × 8,991 m

SANTA ROSA and her sister SANTA PAULA operate on the year-round 12-day Grace Line cruise service from New York to Caribbean ports. Designed by Messrs. Gibbs & Cox, Inc., New York, and built by the Newport News Shipbuilding & Dry Dock Company SANTA ROSA was launched on 28 August 1957. Planned for passenger comfort her fireproof air conditioned accommodations are arranged for only 300 passengers, all one class and all in outside staterooms; her crew totals 246. Cargo is carried in six holds, three forward and three aft. General cargo in holds 1, 2, 5, and 6 is handled by eight 10-ton and four 5-ton cargo booms. Holds 3 and 4 are refrigerated but are suitable for general as well as perishable cargo which is handled in and out of them by a synchronized system of vertical and horizontal conveyors working through side ports. SANTA ROSA's twin screws are driven by two sets of compound double-reduction geared turbines having a maximum rating of 22,000 (22300) s.h.p. at 124 r.p.m. Three oil-fired watertube boilers furnish steam at 600 p.s.i. (42,185 kg/cm²) pressure and three 120 KW turbo-generators provide the ship's service alternating current electric power. SANTA ROSA's service speed is 20 knots (37,06 km/hr.). In March 1959 she collided with the tanker VALCHEM off the New Jersey coast and arrived in New York with the tanker's funnel sitting on her bow.

Rotterdam — page 232

In company with the technological improvements in ships during the twentieth century there have been startling changes in appearance. SELANDIA leads the list with no funnel. BREMEN introduced stream-lined superstructures and squat funnels. SOUTHERN CROSS was the first large passenger ship to have her machinery located aft. ROTTERDAM's machinery is not quite as far aft but her boiler gases are exhausted through twin smoke pipes stream-lined to match her single mast forward.

The flagship of the Holland-America Line, the twin-screw ROTTERDAM, was launched on 13 September 1958 from the yard of the Rotterdam Drydock Company. Her profile is quite unconventional as are many features of her interior arrangement, Constructed with three full length decks—main, A, and B—her promenade and lower promenade decks extend almost to her cruiser stern; including the navigating bridge she has five levels of houses above the promenade deck. C and D decks are broken only by the boiler and engine rooms aft and there is a short orlop through the forward third of the ship. Bottom protection is furnished generally by a double bottom but in certain locations deep tanks serve the same purpose. She is subdivided by thirteen transverse watertight bulkheads in which there are 44 sliding watertight doors all remotely controlled from the bridge. To save topside weight the houses above the sun deck, smoke pipes, mast, and lifeboats are of aluminum alloy.

For normal service across the Atlantic ROTTERDAM is designed to carry a maximum of 647 first-class passengers and 809 in tourist class; when cruising she carries 730 in one class. Her normal crew is 776. Unlike many large passenger liners where passengers of different classes are confined in vertical zones the designers of ROTTERDAM have managed to give each class a good fore-and-aft range of public spaces and promenades. Forward on the promenade deck is a two-level theater which can serve either class as required. Abaft this are the tourist-class lounge, smoking room, cafe, and promenades. The corresponding first-class spaces are one deck higher. While the extent of first and tourist-class cabins varies considerably from deck to deck those for the tourist class are generally abaft the first class. Although the cabins are arranged on the same decks access to the public spaces is kept separate by special stairs and folding partitions in foyers. The first and tourist-class dining saloons, located amidships, are separated by a vestibule which can be opened to permit using them as one space when cruising. The galley, pantries, and other necessary spaces are located below on C deck; four escalators are provided for the use of the stewards.

All passenger and crew spaces on ROTTERDAM are air conditioned. Every passenger cabin has an individual thermostat while the public spaces and crew's quarters are centrally controlled with automatic zone controls to compensate for temperature differences resulting from the heat of the sun on one side. Throughout the ship are 160 remotely controlled fireproof doors. In addition to normal fire fighting equipment the passenger and crew accommodations are protected by sprinkler systems. ROTTERDAM can stow 102,000 cu. ft. (2888 m³) of general cargo and 14,000 cu. ft. (396 m³) of refrigerated cargo in three holds. This is handled by four booms and one electric crane forward and two booms aft.

ROTTERDAM's twin-screw propelling machinery and boilers were constructed by the N.V. Koninklijke Maatschappij de Schelde of Flushing. Because of its location abaft the boiler room the engine room is relatively narrow and it was necessary to provide very compact machinery. Triple-expansion double-reduction geared turbines were finally selected; these develop a total of 17,300 (17535) s.h.p. at 131.5 r.p.m. and give ROTTERDAM a service speed of 20.5 knots (37,99 km/hr.). The maximum power rating is 19,000 (19258) s.h.p. at 135.5 r.p.m. Steam is generated at a pressure of 640 p.s.i. (44,997 kg/cm²) by four oil-fired water-tube boilers. Four 1350 KW 440 volt turbo-generator sets provide the ship's service electric power. Instead of the usual Diesel-driven emergency generator ROTTERDAM has a gas turbine unit rated at 350 KW; the turbine running at 15,000 r.p.m. drives the generator through gears at 1800 r.p.m. For passenger comfort ROTTERDAM is equipped with Denny-Brown retractable fin stabilizers. Considering that passengers in a hurry now travel by air there is no longer a need for a large number of express liners. Ships like ROTTERDAM offer comfortable Atlantic crossings at moderate speeds to travellers with enough leisure time.

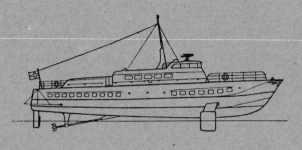

SIRENA — 1960

Modern steam- or motor-driven passenger ships require about 6 hours 30 minutes to travel from Stockholm to Mariehamn in Finland's Åland Islands. To most people the covering of the same distance in 2 hours 20 minutes implies flying but while the passengers may be in the air they are actually supported by "wings" in the water—hydrofoils. Although experimental craft were first "flown" in the early part of the twentieth century and many were developed for naval uses commercial hydrofoil craft became feasible only after World War II. Said to be the first hydrofoil craft in international service SIRENA is operated on the above mentioned run by the Finska Ångfartygs A/B Built in Italy by the Cantieri Navale Rodriguez, Messina, Sicily, she is similar to smaller craft that have "flown" across the Strait of Messina since 1956. Constructed of aluminum alloys she is powered with two light-weight, high-speed Daimler-Benz Diesel engines each of which develops 1350 (1368) b.h.p. at 1500 r.p.m. These engines are coupled to two 3-bladed counter-rotating propellers. SIRENA's cruising speed is 32 knots (59,30 km/hr.) and her top speed is about 40 knots (74,13 km/hr.). Measuring 83 ft. 8 in. (25,501 m) in length over all and 20 ft. (6,096 m) in breadth on deck she carries about 100 passengers in two saloons fitted with aircraft type seats. Bars are provided in each saloon and there is room for baggage. Fully loaded SIRENA weighs about 60 tons.

The cry of "Iceberg ahead!" meant death to the White Star Liner TITANIC but to many tough little merchant ships icebergs and pack ice are hazards met regularly during a considerable portion of their yearly operations. Some cargo ships have special strengthening forward to permit operations in broken ice but these smaller vessels have many of the special features of icebreakers. Designed to operate in Arctic

FOUNDATION VIBERT — 1961 — 236 T

90.0 × 28.8 × 11.4 feet
27,431 × 8,565 × 3,475 m

A powerful modern tug owned by the Foundation Maritime, Ltd., Montreal, Canada, FOUNDATION VIBERT was built by Messrs. P. K. Harris & Sons, Ltd. in Appledore, North Devon, England. She was designed to handle large bulk carriers in ports on the Gulf of St. Lawrence and for general towing duties around the coasts of New Brunswick and Nova Scotia; she is strengthened for operations in ice. While her above-water profile is somewhat unusual her other unusual features cannot be seen by the casual observer. She has a simplified multi-chine hull form, twin screws supported by skegs, and twin rudders. Accommodations are provided for a crew of 12—four in the houses and eight below deck. FOUNDATION VIBERT has two Fairbanks-Morse 4-cylinder, 2-cycle, opposed-piston, non-reversing Diesel engines each rated at 666 (675) b.h.p. at 750 r.p.m. Each engine drives its propeller at 187.5 r.p.m. through a flexible coupling and a 4:1 ratio reverse-reduction gear. Unlike the Doxford opposed-piston engine in which both pistons drive a single crankshaft, the Fairbanks-Morse engine has an upper and a lower crankshaft connected by gearing. FOUNDATION VIBERT has a free-running speed of 11.5 knots (20,54 km/hr.) and can develop a maximum static pull of 16.2 (16,5) tons.

Kista Dan — page 229

waters KISTA DAN was constructed for J. Lauritzen of Copenhagen by the Aalborg Vaerft and chartered to the Greenland Trading Company for service from Copenhagen to East Greenland.

KISTA DAN is a two-deck motor vessel with machinery aft. Her straight raking stem is cut away below the load water-line to give her some icebreaking capability. Aft on her cruiser stern is a horn or "ice knife" to protect her rudder when going astern in thick ice and on each side of the exterior of her hull just forward of her propeller are three fins to deflect chunks of ice from the propeller. Her hull structure is exceptionally strong with extra thick plating and intermediate frames from her inner bottom to her main deck throughout; the shell plating forward is one inch (25 mm) thick. When fully loaded her load water-line comes at about the lower deck level which provides good support and an extra ice stringer is fitted below through her two holds to aid in resisting the pressure of thick ice. She is subdivided by five transverse watertight bulkheads.

When operating as a cargo ship and drawing a maximum of 18 ft. 1 in. (5,511 m) of water KISTA DAN carries 12 passengers in addition to her crew of 25. With an increased freeboard she is permitted to carry 24 passengers. Her two cargo holds can carry 52,000 cu. ft. (1473 m³) of general cargo which is handled by four 5-ton and one 15-ton boom worked by electric winches. The two weather deck hatches are closed by steel watertight covers.

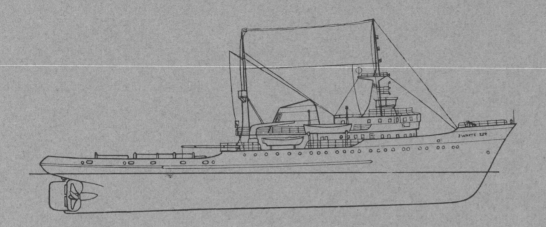

ZWARTE ZEE — 1962 — 1539 T

224.75 × 40.5 × 22.67 feet
68,504 × 12,344 × 6,910 m

As large as many small freighters and having the power of many larger ones ZWARTE ZEE is the fourth tug to bear the name for L. Smit & Company's International Tug Service of Rotterdam. The largest and most powerful tug in the world she was built by Messrs. J. & K. Smit's Scheepswerven N.V., Kinderdijke, and is fully equipped for world-wide towing and salvage work. Her towing bitts and winch are located practically amidships. For fire fighting she has one monitor on her foremast, two on her mainmast, and nine hose connections on deck. Salvage equipment which includes an air compressor, Diesel-driven pumps, anchors, diving gear, and patching materials is stowed in a special hold aft and handled by two 5-ton booms on her mainmast. Air conditioned accommodations are provided on four decks for her normal crew of 31 and an additional 20 men for manning a tow or for salvage work. ZWARTE ZEE is propelled by two 12-cylinder, 4-cycle, single-acting, turbocharged SMIT-M.A.N. Diesel engines which drive her single screw through a combined fluid-coupling reverse-gear unit. Each engine develops 4500 (4561) b.h.p. at 275 r.p.m. Electric power is provided by three 240 KW Diesel-generators. ZWARTE ZEE has a free running speed of 20 knots (37,06 km/hr.) and has an operating range of 20,000 miles (37064 km).

KISTA DAN's single propeller is driven by a six-cylinder, two-cycle, single-acting Burmeister & Wain Diesel engine that develops 1200 b.h.p. at 245 r.p.m. Its cylinders are 13.78 in. (0,350 m) diameter by 24.41 in. (0,620 m) stroke. She is equipped with a variable-pitch propeller which, for a short period, allows a 30 per cent increase in the icebreaking capability as compared with the performance of an ordinary solid propeller. The revolutions and pitch of the propeller may be controlled from the wheel-house or from the ice navigating station on the foremast, a closed crow's nest capable of holding two persons. This station is also equipped with a steering control, a rudder indicator, and a gyro compass repeater. KISTA DAN's service speed in open water is 12 knots (22,24 km/hr.). Her red paint scheme serves to make her more visible in an ice field. She transported men and supplies to the Antarctic in 1960 for the International Geophysical Year expeditions and became icebound with Sir Vivian Fuchs aboard.

Koningin Wilhelmina — page 230

The current fashion of locating machinery and funnels aft on passenger vessels extends even to those in the cross-Channel service although the main engines in the twin-screw motorship KONINGIN WILHELMINA are not as far aft as her squat funnel seems to indicate. An advanced design with a streamlined profile she was built by the N.V. Scheepswerf en Machinefabriek der Merwede, Hardinxveld, for the Hook of Holland-Harwich day service of the Zeeland Steamship Company. Her steel main hull is arranged much like that of earlier cross-Channel vessels with a double bottom, an orlop forward and aft of the machinery space, two continuous decks, and a long promenade deck extending nearly to her stern. The side plating is carried up to her boat deck for about two-thirds of her length amidships. She is subdivided into nine main watertight compartments. KONINGIN WILHELMINA's boat-deck house, navigating bridge house, and her funnel are constructed of aluminum alloy to improve stability.

Arranged to carry a total of 1600 passengers in two classes KONINGIN WILHELMINA can accommodate 1200 of them in sheltered seating spaces; her crew numbers 93. The first-class accommodations include an observation lounge at the forward end of the boat deck, ten double de-luxe cabins on the same deck, a lounge, a cocktail lounge, and a restaurant on the promenade deck, and cabins for 58 passengers on a lower deck. As special aids to travelling business men each of the ten boat-deck cabins is equipped with ship-to-shore telephones, and typewriters are available. A conference room suitable for 10-12 persons is located off the main lounge; it too is equipped with a telephone and typewriter. The second-class dining saloon, operated as a cafeteria, is located aft on the promenade deck; on the deck below is a cold buffet and bar. Dormitory spaces are provided on the lower decks for the second-class passengers. The accommodations throughout the ship are protected against fire by automatic sprinkler systems and are divided by fireproof doors. The ship's eight 60-person lifeboats are constructed of glass fiber.

In keeping with travelling trends ashore provisions are made forward and aft aboard KONINGIN WILHELMINA to carry 45 motor cars. In addition she can carry 200 (203) tons of cargo in containers or pre-stowed on pallets. She is fitted with quick-acting hydraulically-operated hatch covers but she carries no cargo handling gear and is dependent on shore-side cranes for loading and unloading.

The main propelling machinery in KONINGIN WILHELMINA consists of two twelve-cylinder, two-cycle, single-acting, turbocharged M.A.N. Diesel engines directly connected to the propeller shafts. Each is capable of developing 8000 (8109) b.h.p. at 225 r.p.m. and has cylinders 22.44 in. (0,570 m) diameter by 33.86 in. (0,860 m) stroke. Electric power is provided by three 640 KW generators driven by seven-cylinder, four-cycle, single-acting M.A.N. Diesel engines. Steam for heating and other uses is provided at 60 p.s.i. (4,219 kg/cm²) pressure by two oil-fired La Mont forced circulation boilers. Unlike earlier cross-Channel ships which had bow rudders KONINGIN WILHELMINA is equipped with a 400 (405) h.p. Voith-Schneider propeller located in a transverse duct in her bow to aid in handling alongside quays. Like many modern ships she is fitted with a pair of Denny-Brown fin stabilizers which are capable of reducing a 20° roll to 2°. Her service speed is 23.5 knots (43,59 km/hr.) and she normally makes the crossing in 5½ hours.

A familiar sight in nearly every British and West European port is a motor-driven coaster flying the horizontal red, white, and blue flag of the Netherlands. Built by the shipyard "De Vooruitgang" of Messrs. D. & J. Boot, Alphen aan den Rijn, BREEWIJD is a modern motor coaster; her home port is Rotterdam. She might best be described as a half shelter-decker as she has two complete decks except over her short forward hold which is about half the length of her second hold. Below her main deck she has the usual double bottom and three deep tanks for liquid cargoes. The fairing plates on her houses and the reverse rake of her twin smoke pipes give her a definite "forward" look. The windows of her pilot house are slanted as on U.S.A. river towboats to reduce glare on bright days.

Comfortable accommodations are arranged aft for a crew of nine—captain, mate, two engineers, cook, and four ratings. All have single rooms except the ratings but the vessel also has a single-berth hospital room and a single spare room. As the hatches on BREEWIJD extend nearly the full lengths of her two holds there is not room

Breewijd — page 231

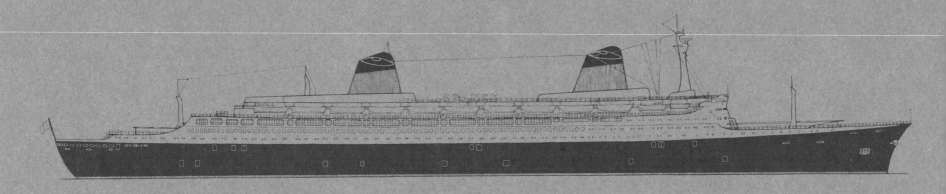

for any of the patented types of hatch covers. Her hatches are closed by the normal wood covers made watertight by battened tarpaulins. For handling cargo where port facilities are not available she has three 3-ton cargo booms worked by electric winches.

BREEWIJD's single screw is driven by an eight-cylinder direct-drive Industrie Diesel engine that develops 986 (1000) b.h.p. at 320 r.p.m. and is fully controlled from the bridge. Most of the engine-room auxiliaries are arranged for automatic operation; extensive alarm systems are connected to the bridge control console. When drawing 12.56 ft. (3,83 m) of water she has a total deadweight of 900 (1020) tons and the relatively high sea speed for her length of 13.5 knots (25,06 km/hr.).

One of the problems in designing a dry cargo ship to carry a special product in one direction is the provision of suitable arrangements for the carriage of return cargoes with a minimum of change. Another problem is the provision of sufficient water ballast capacity for stability and to give a reasonable immersion of the propeller without lifting the bow so far as to make the ship unmanageable. The latter is comparatively easy on a ship with machinery amidships but is difficult when the machinery is aft without a large reduction in cargo capacity. One solution to these problems is CONSTANTIA designed and built by Messrs. Blohm & Voss A.G. for Christian F. Ahrenkiel, Hamburg, and chartered to Volkswagenwerk A.G. for exporting motor cars. Her motor car stowage fittings are arranged so that she can carry bulk cargoes such as grain, coal, or ore on return trips.

In her general arrangement CONSTANTIA follows the modern concept of locating the propelling machinery and all houses aft thus providing the largest number of rectangular holds for the stowage of cargo. Her breadth and the lengths of her holds were determined by the dimensions of Volkswagen motor cars, her depth on the arrangement of portable decks on which the cars are carried. Basically an all-welded two-deck ship with a full-length double bottom she has a long forecastle extending over the foremost cargo hold and a long poop covering her aftermost hold. Her cargo space is divided into four holds, numbers 1 and 3 being short and served by

FRANCE — 1960 — 66,348 T

978.6 × 110.7 × 55.7 feet
298,277 × 33,741 × 17,476 m

The longest ship in the North Atlantic express service by 4 ft. (1,219 m)—she has an overall length of 1035 ft. (315,468 m)—FRANCE is the super ship of the French Line. Built by the Chantiers de l'Atlantique, St. Nazaire, she was launched on 11 May 1960 and left Havre on her maiden voyage to New York on 3 February 1962. Operating on a weekly schedule with 5-day crossings her sailings from New York alternate with those of UNITED STATES. Designed on the same principles as UNITED STATES she has the usual French decorating touches. Her most unusual exterior features are the "wings" on her
continued

Constantia — page 234

continued
funnels designed to keep her decks free from soot. Of practically all-welded construction her strength decks are constructed of high-tensile steel and the houses above are of aluminum alloy. To meet the requirements of the 1948 Convention she is subdivided into 15 main watertight compartments.

FRANCE has accommodations for 407 first-class and 1637 tourist-class passengers and a crew of 1044. The
continued

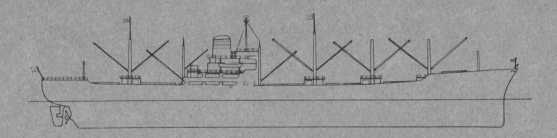

continued

joiner work and furnishings throughout are of fireproof construction and all cabins and public spaces are fully air conditioned. The first-class cabins occupy four decks amidships while those for the tourist class are arranged on seven decks forward and aft. As on ROTTERDAM each class has the full range of one deck—the tourist-class public spaces are on the promenade deck with the first-class spaces one deck higher. The two classes share a theater and a shopping center on the promenade deck. Designed for safety and reliability FRANCE's propelling machinery consists of four sets of four-casing, triple-expansion, single-reduction geared turbines that develop a total of 157,800 (160000) s.h.p. Eight oil-fired water-tube boilers deliver steam at a pressure of 910 p.s.i. (64,000 kg/cm²). Alternating current electric power is supplied by six 2750 KW turbo-generator sets; one 750 KW Diesel generator set provides power for starting the plant and for port requirements. FRANCE has two pairs of Denny-Brown fin stabilizers. Designed for a service speed of 31 knots (57,45 km/hr.) she attained 34.13 knots (65,42 km/hr.) on trials with her turbines developing 90 percent of full power.

YAMASHIRO MARU — 1963 — 10,467

492.13 × 75.46 × 42.00 feet
150,000 × 23,000 × 12,800 m

The single-screw motorship YAMASHIRO MARU is a good example of a modern economy cargo liner having some automation and remote control features. Owned by the Nippon Yusen Kaisha, Tokyo, and operated between Japan and Europe via the Suez Canal she was constructed by the Mitsubishi Shipbuilding & Engineering Company, Ltd., Nagasaki. Her form, which was developed by extensive tank tests involving more than 30 models and is classed by her builder as "epochal", features very fine water-lines forward with a moderate bulb, a short parallel body, and full stern lines. Essentially a three-deck ship she has four holds forward and two aft and can carry about 677,300 cu. ft. (19200 m³) of cargo which includes the capacity of refrigerated spaces in number 4 upper 'tween deck and strong rooms for silk and other valuable cargoes. In addition, there are two tanks for chemicals and two for vegetable oil. Cargo is handled by 6-ton, two 10-ton, and two 20-ton booms. YAMASHIRO MARU's main engine is a 9-cylinder, 2 cycle turbocharged Mitsubishi Diesel rated at 12,822 (13000) b.h.p. at 124 r.p.m. On trials in a 40 per cent load condition with the engine developing 13,139 (13322) b.h.p. she attained a speed of 22.45 knots (41,60 km/hr.) and she is expected to have a service speed of 20 knots (37,06 km/hr.) at about 85 per cent of full power.

one hatch each while holds 2 and 4 are nearly twice as long and have two hatches each. Provisions are made for carrying water ballast in the double-bottom tanks, peak tanks, a deep tank under number 1 hold, a deep tank extending to the upper deck between holds 2 and 3, and in upper wing tanks in holds 1 and 4. For handling cargo there are 12 10-ton booms on three pairs of kingposts.

While the sizes of CONSTANTIA's cargo holds were determined by the dimensions of Volkswagen cars her structural details had to be suitable for the carriage of bulk cargoes. Her classification certificate bears the notation "strengthened for heavy cargo" which means that she can carry heavy iron ore on her tank top which is longitudinally framed and has extra thick plating to resists the abrasion of grab buckets. To permit the carriage of grain with a minimum of additional fittings to keep it from shifting CONSTANTIA has partial longitudinal bulkheads in her lower holds and the under sides of the upper wing tanks in holds 1 and 4 are sloped at an angle of 30°. The "Volkswagens" are carried on portable deck sections hanging on cables from the deck above. There are three levels in lower holds 2, 3, and 4, two levels in hold 1, and one level in the 'tween-deck spaces of holds 1 and 3. The deck sections consist of steel grating on steel frames and weigh about 16 tons each. When not in use for cars the sections in the lower holds are lifted by the cables and secured under the lower deck; those in the 'tween-deck spaces are hinged and stow against the sloping bottoms of the upper wing tanks. With car decks stowed CONSTANTIA can carry 795,706 cu. ft. (22532 m³) of grain. Her total deadweight is 17,200 (17434) tons and her water ballast capacity is 5260 (5332) tons.

A single-screw ship CONSTANTIA is propelled by an eight-cylinder, two-cycle, single-acting, turbocharged M.A.N.-type Diesel engine constructed by Messrs. Blohm & Voss A.G. The cylinders are 27.56 in. (0,700 m) diameter and 47.24 in. (1,200 m) stroke and the engine develops 7250 (7349) b.h.p. at 130 r.p.m. Electric power for engine room auxiliaries, cargo winches, and other uses is supplied by three 230 KW Diesel-driven generators. With a sea speed of 15.2 knots (28,17 km/hr.) CONSTANTIA is an interesting solution to the problems imposed by the carriage of special and bulk cargoes.

SANTA MAGDALENA, the first of four combination cargo and passenger ships, is a highly developed ship specifically arranged to reduce cargo handling time and costs in the Grace Line's service between New York and the Canal Zone, Colombia, Ecuador, and Peru. In determining her characteristics extensive studies of cargoes were made. Southbound they are largely manufactured goods while bananas are the major item carried north; it was decided that such diverse items could be handled by a combination of unitized and bulk systems. Designed by Messrs. George G. Sharp, Inc. naval architects and engineers of New York, and built by the Sparrows Point Yard of the Bethlehem Steel Company SANTA MAGDALENA was launched on 13 February 1962 and delivered on 4 February 1963.

A single-screw ship of welded construction SANTA MAGDALENA has a utilitarian profile with a curved stem, a cruiser stern, a long forecastle, and a bridge with four levels of rectangular houses. Her smoke pipe—it can hardly be called a funnel—is so small that her owner's normal funnel markings are displayed on her upper houses. Prominent on her main deck forward and aft are four gantry cranes. Her form features a prominent bulbous bow and a clear-water stern; certain details of her shape above and below water were determined by cargo stowage and handling requirements. In her hull she has a full-length double bottom, three continuous decks, and orlops forward and aft. Deep tanks for liquid cargoes such as molasses are provided under her forward hold and abreast her shaft tunnel. With seven main transverse watertight bulkheads she has three holds forward and two aft, an arrangement that enables her to meet a two-compartment standard of subdivision which is in excess of the requirements of the 1948 Convention.

Primarily a cargo ship SANTA MAGDALENA has accommodations for 119 passengers and a crew of 115 in the bridge and houses; none are carried below her main deck. All of the cabins and public spaces are of fireproof construction and are fully air conditioned. Below deck SANTA MAGDALENA has one of the most varied mechanical cargo-handling systems ever installed in a ship. Holds 1, 3 and 4 are fully insulated and refrigerated for the carriage of bananas northbound which are handled by horizontal conveyors through side ports and a total of ten vertical conveyors within the holds. Southbound these same holds carry general cargo stowed on 6 ft. by 8 ft. (1,829 × 2,438 m) pallets which are loaded into the upper level of the forward hold by two 5-ton booms and of holds 3 and 4 by side-port extensible-boom cranes. They are taken over here by an automatic pallet handling system consisting of powered conveyors on each deck synchronized with an elevator that also has a powered conveyor; there are a total of five elevators in the ship but only three have this automatic feature. A master control console directs the pallets to any general location desired where a manually operated fork-lift truck is employed for precise stowage. Motor cars may also be carried in holds 3 and 4 and are driven aboard through the side ports or lowered through main deck hatches by the gantry cranes. Holds 2 and 5 and small portions of 3 and 4 have special cell structures for carrying a total of 199, 20 ft. (6,096 m) long containers; an additional 56 containers may be stowed in special fittings on the main deck. The containers are handled by the four gantry cranes which have a 15 ft. (4,572 m) outreach. The stowage fittings may be adjusted to accommodate 40 ft. (12,192 m) long containers which are lifted by two cranes linked together.

The propelling machinery in SANTA MAGDALENA consists of one set of compound double-reduction geared turbines manufactured by the General Electric Company, Lynn, Massachusetts. At their normal rating the turbines develop 18,000 (18245) s.h.p. and give the ship a service speed of 20.5 knots (37,99 km/hr.). Two

Santa Magdalena — page 235

MIDSECTION OF A TYPICAL BULK CARRIER SHOWING PORTABLE CAR DECKS

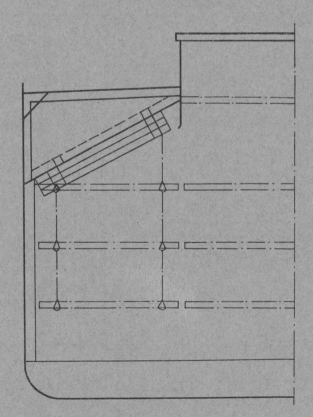

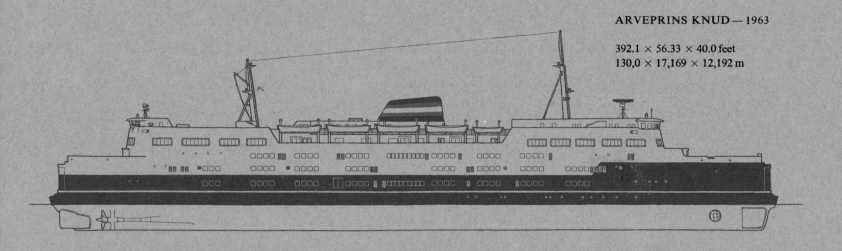

Babcock & Wilcox water-tube boilers supply steam at a pressure of 620 p.s.i. (43,591 kg/cm²). The ship's electrical system is 60-cycle alternating current which is provided by three 750 KW turbo-generators. Like most modern passenger ships SANTA MAGDALENA is equipped with fin stabilizers which in her case serve to prevent cargo damage as well as to provide passenger comfort. She is a very interesting example of the application of modern technology to the ship-board handling of cargo.

AMERICAN CHALLENGER, the first of an 11-ship class of fast freighters ordered by the United States Lines to replace ships of the World War II period, and four sisters were built by the Newport News Shipbuilding & Dry Dock Company, Newport News, Virginia, while six others were constructed by the Bethlehem Steel Company at its yard in Quincy, Massachusetts. They were designed by Messrs. Gibbs & Cox, Inc., New York, to fulfill a set of requirements established by the United States Lines. The sea speed of the new ships was set at 21 knots (38,92 km/hr.) with an ample margin of power. In order to pass through the St. Lawrence Seaway the maximum beam was limited to 75 ft. (22,859 m) and based on this the designed length was established at 529 ft. (161,239 m). A study of the characteristics necessary to meet a one-compartment standard of subdivision and stability after damage led to the designed depth of 42.5 ft. (12,953 m).

As worked out AMERICAN CHALLENGER is a six-hold ship with her single-screw propelling machinery a little abaft the normal position but not so far aft as to make trimming difficult with general cargoes. Of the four holds forward, numbers 3 and 4 are both 75 ft. (22,850 m) long and are fitted with three hatches abreast; the other holds have single hatches. Basically an all-welded two-deck ship AMERICAN CHALLENGER has a single orlop forward and aft. Her above-water profile shows a curved stem, a short cruiser stern, a long forecastle to improve her seakeeping abilities, five levels of houses, five pairs of kingposts, and a prominent raked funnel. Her officers and crew are all accommodated in the houses amidships; unlike many cargo ships there are no quarters for passengers.

In contrast to little FRITZ JUEL this 1963 car ferry is one of the largest of her type in the world. Built by the Elsinore Shipbuilding & Engineering Company, Ltd., for the Danish State Railways ARVEPRINS KNUD operates on the Great Belt service connecting the islands of Funen and Zealand. A twin-screw vessel she has, like most ferries, a

American Challenger — page 236

bow rudder and in addition a lateral thrust unit to aid in handling at the terminals. This thrust unit consists of a transverse duct containing a variable-pitch propeller driven by an 800 (811) h.p. electric motor. Her main engines are Elsinore-B.&W. Diesels which develop a total of 11,200 (11352) b.h.p. at 200 r.p.m. and drive her at 17 knots (31,50 km/hr.) in service. ARVEPRINS KNUD can carry a maximum of 400 motor cars on three decks at times of peak traffic. At off-peak hours the middle deck is raised in sections by means of hydraulic cylinders, to provide a clearance of 12.75 ft. (3,886 m) on the lower deck for the carriage of larger vehicles. Cars are driven on and off of the upper and lower decks through the ends of the ship to double-decked ramps on shore; cars on the movable middle deck are driven through a port in the ship's side from a separate shore ramp.

In her six ordinary holds AMERICAN CHALLENGER can carry 580,100 cu. ft. (16427 m³) of general cargo; holds 3 and 4 below the second deck are divided by two longitudinal bulkheads to provide spaces offering safer stowage and freedom from shifting. In the upper 'tween-deck spaces of holds 5 and 6 are refrigerated compartments for 45,130 cu. ft. (1278 m²) of perishable cargoes. Provisions are made for carrying 28 refrigerated containers on the main deck forward. In eight deep tanks built smooth on the inside and heated by surrounding water baths she can carry 1119 (1134) tons of liquid cargoes. All hatches have folding steel covers, those on the lower decks being arranged flush with the deck plating to permit the use of fork-lift trucks. For handling cargo there are twelve 10-ton booms, eight 15-ton booms, and one 70-ton boom that can serve both hatches 3 and 4.

Reliability was stressed in planning AMERICAN CHALLENGER's propelling machinery which consists of one set of compound double-reduction geared turbines manufactured by the Westinghouse Electric Corporation; the normal rating is 16,500 (16724) s.h.p. and the maximum 18,150 (18397) s.h.p. Steam at 600 p.s.i. (42,185 kg/cm²) pressure is generated by two Foster Wheeler oil-fired water-tube boilers. Alternating current power for deck machinery and other electrically driven auxiliaries is supplied by two 1250 KW turbo-generators. Although designed for a sea speed of 21 knots (38,92 km/hr.) AMERICAN CHALLENGER has averaged 24.42 knots (45,26 km/hr.) across the North Atlantic, a speed higher than that of many present day passenger ships.

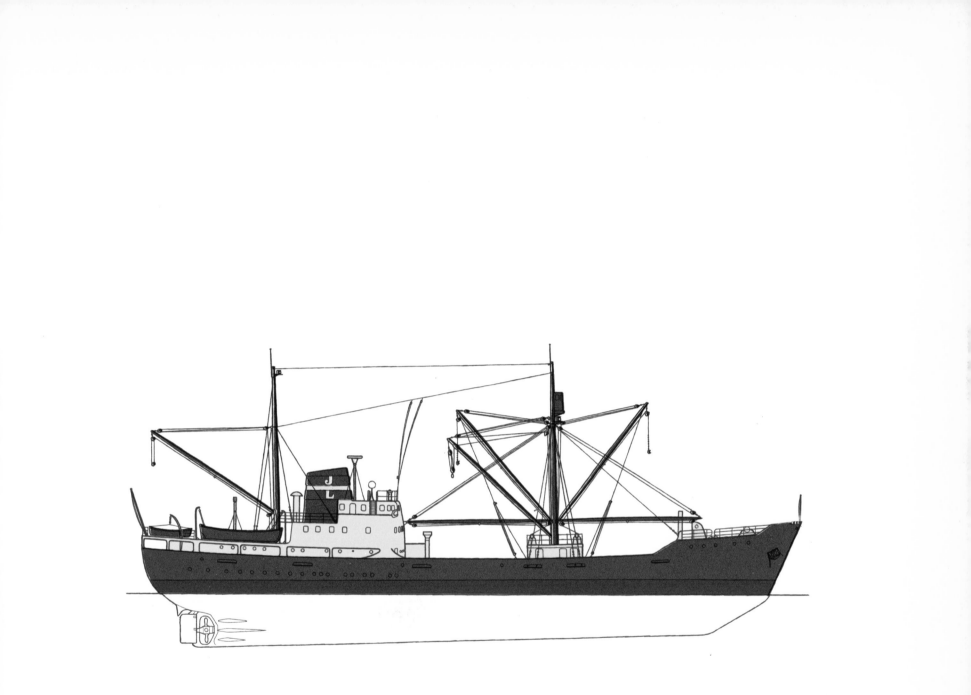

KISTA DAN · 1952

J. Lauritzen

212.1 × 36.9 × 19.7 feet ℂ 1244 T ℂ 64,651 × 11,25 × 5,997 m

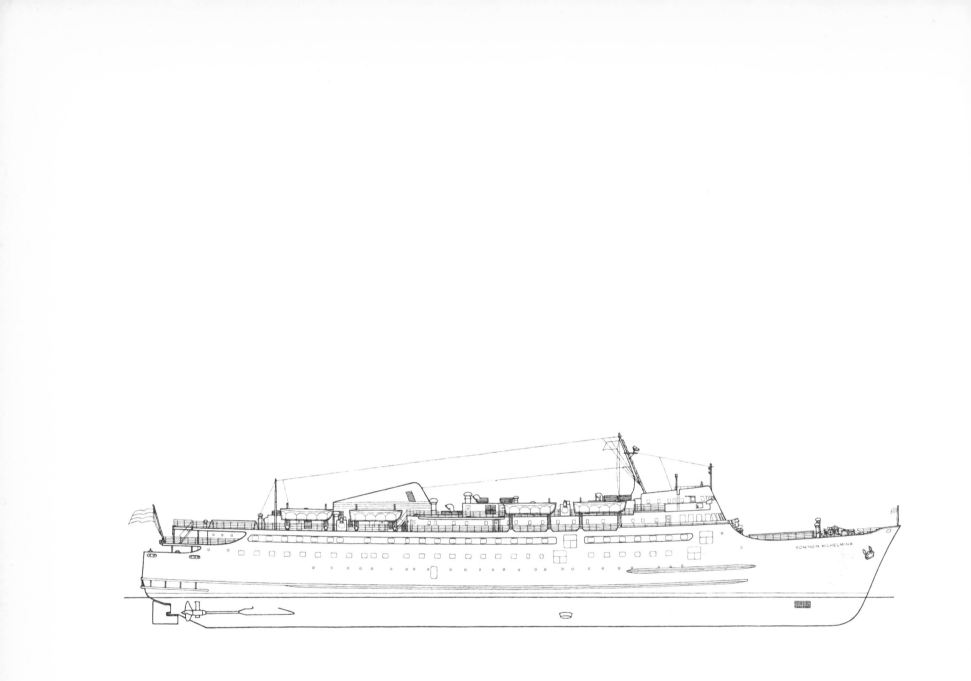

KONINGIN WILHELMINA · 1959

Stoomvaart Maatschappij Zeeland, Koninklijke Nederlandsche Postvaart N.V.

361.0 × 53.33 × 31.16 feet ℂ 6228 T ℂ 110,030 × 16,256 × 9,500 m

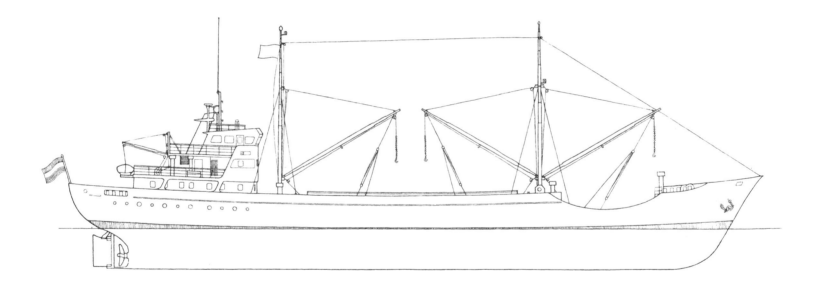

BREEWIJD · 1964

P. A. van Es & Company, N.V.

191.93 × 32.81 × 12.96 feet ◖ 494 T ◖ 58,5 × 10,0 × 3,95 m

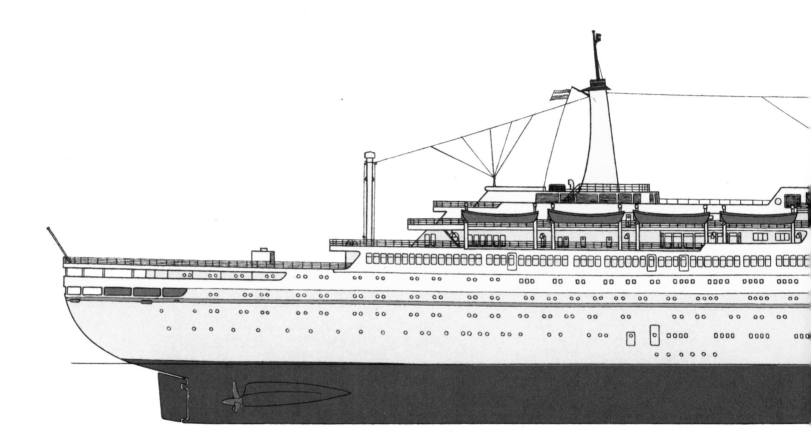

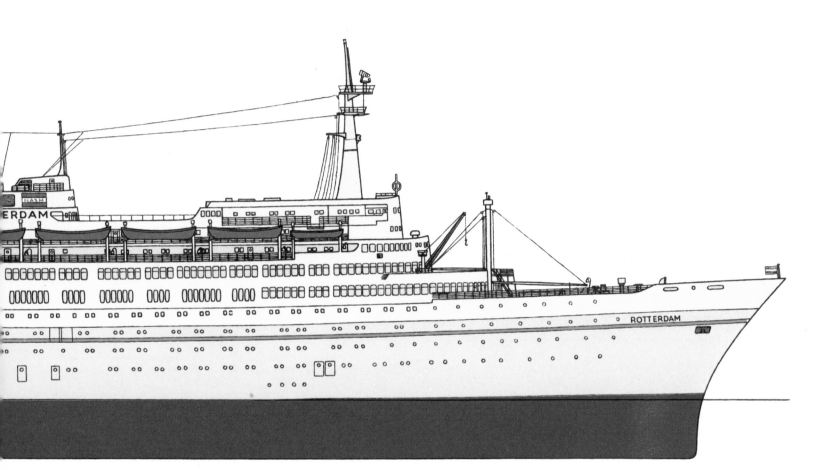

ROTTERDAM · 1958

Nederlandsch-Amerikaansche Stoomvaart Maatschappij
748.7 × 94.2 × 29.8 feet ℂ 38645 T ℂ 228,2 × 28,71 × 9,08 m

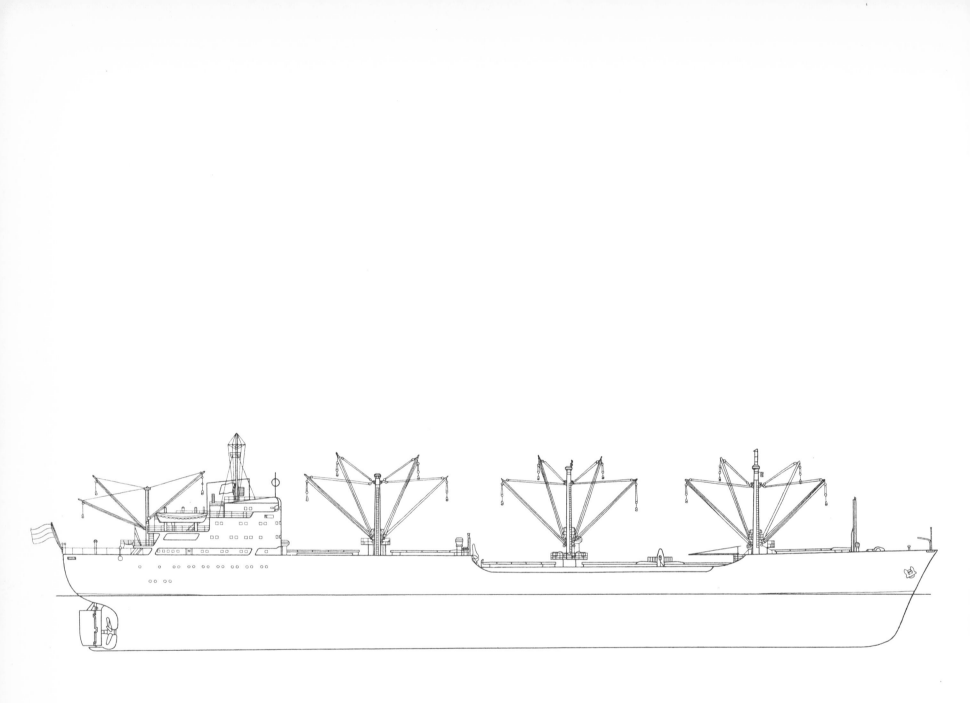

CONSTANTIA · 1961

Christian F. Ahrenkiel

475.8 × 70.3 × 40.0 feet ◖ 11406 T ◖ 145,023 × 21,426 × 12,192 m

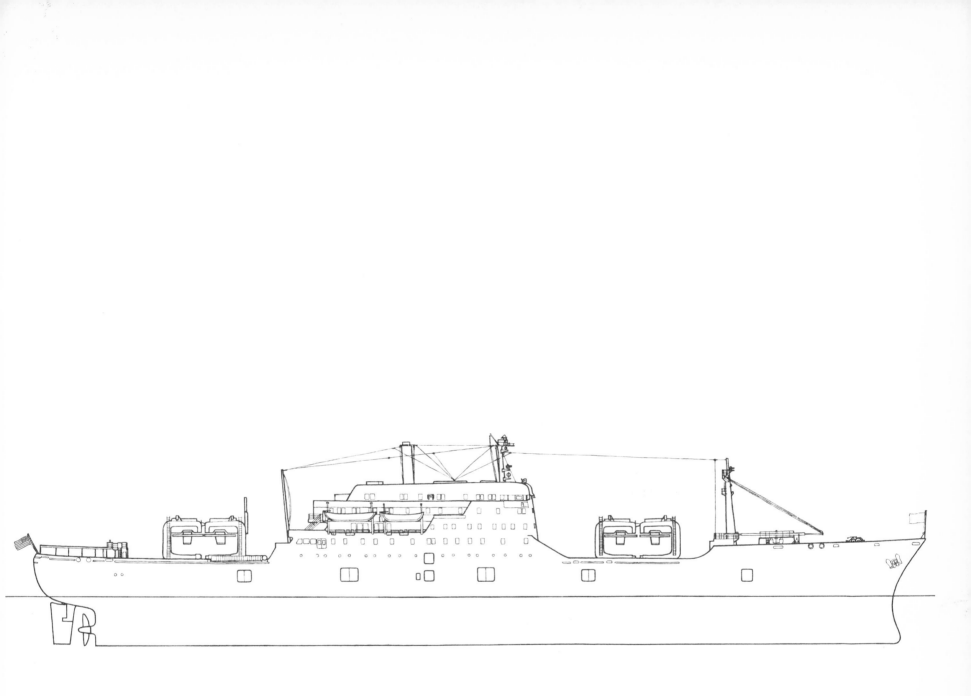

SANTA MAGDALENA · 1962

Grace Steamship Company

510.6 × 79.1 × 33.4 feet ℂ 14442 T ℂ 155,631 × 24,109 × 10,180 m

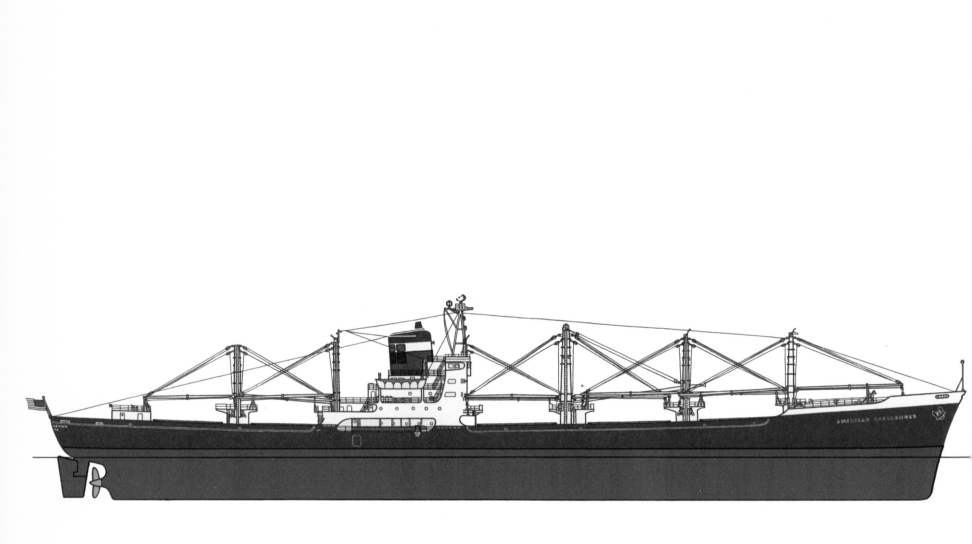

AMERICAN CHALLENGER · 1962

United States Lines Company

531.0 × 75.2 × 29.3 feet ⟮ 11185 T ⟮ 161,849 × 22,920 × 8,930 m

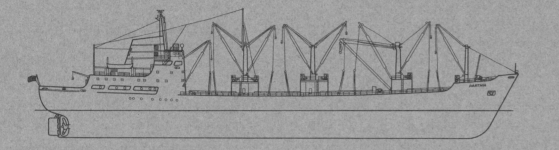

PARTHIA — 1963 — 5586 T

400.0 × 60.0 × 37.5 feet
121,920 × 18,287 × 11,429 m

Bearing the names of earlier passenger liners PARTHIA and her sister-ships IVERNA, MEDIA, and SAXONIA, are employed in the Cunard Line's cargo service between Liverpool and New York. A single-screw shelter-deck ship PARTHIA has her machinery, navigating spaces, and fully air conditioned accommodations aft. Her four holds and cargo gear are specially designed to handle and stow as fast as possible containers and cargo pre-stowed on pallets. By fitting wing tanks below the second deck in hold 2 and the third deck in hold 4 all cargo spaces except those in the forward hold are made rectangular for the easier stowage of cargo. These wing tanks are suitable for edible oils, fresh water, fuel oil, or salt water ballast. To permit the operation of fork-lift trucks the hatch covers on the lower decks are flush. For the same reason the decks of refrigerated spaces in the upper 'tween deck of holds 3 and 4 are insulated on the under side. Cargo is handled by twelve 10-ton, four 5-ton, and one 25-ton booms worked by electric winches. PARTHIA's deadweight is 7300 (7417) tons. Her main engine is a 7-cylinder, 2-cycle, turbo-charged Sulzer-type Diesel developing 7700 (7805) b.h.p. at 135 r.p.m. which has sufficient margin to enable her to maintain a 17 knot (31,50 km/hr.) service speed across the Atlantic.

Dyvi Anglia — page 247

For the long distance delivery of motor cars it would probably never prove economical to design ships of the size of CONSTANTIA for a one-way cargo only in spite of a certain amount of lost time in shifting special fittings and unloading the return cargo. This is particularly true on the North Atlantic run where good freights may be earned carrying grain or coal to Europe. On short runs where there are not suitable return cargoes it would not be economical to do otherwise. DYVI ANGLIA, built by the Trosik Verksted, Brevik, Norway, is a very special car carrier which in mid-1964 started a five-year time charter to the Ford Corporation, Dagenham, England.

Including the tank top DYVI ANGLIA has five decks connected by ramps for the carriage of cars and all possible space is employed, cars being stowed on the ramps as well as the decks. To secure the cars from shifting at sea they are hooked at their four corners to chains welded at close intervals across the decks and ramps. Because of her arrangement which allows shelter deck exemptions her registered gross tonnage is 499 although her cargo capacity is 317,500 cu. ft. (9000 m³), equal to that in a normal cargo ship of about 6000 (6082) tons deadweight. This amount of space permits the stowage of about 450 cars of normal size.

No cargo handling gear is provided in DYVI ANGLIA as the cars are run on and off and up and down the ramps under their own power. Cars are frequently damaged when loaded and unloaded by booms or cranes. Two loading ports are fitted on each side, the forward ones being about under the foremast on the main deck while the after ports are one deck higher under the funnel. This difference in level allows for variations in quay heights and the tide. To ventilate the holds during loading and unloading operations there are four supply and four exhaust fans which give six changes of air per hour. DYVI ANGLIA has accommodations for 20 persons in the houses on her boat deck although her normal crew is only 15.

A single-screw ship DYVI ANGLIA is propelled by a M.A.N. Diesel engine rated at 1844 (1870) b.h.p. Three 150 KW Diesel-generators provide ship's service electric power. On trials she attained a speed of 15 knots (27,80 km/hr.) but her normal sea speed is 13 knots (24,13 km/hr.). This speed allows her to make a round trip voyage to her normal ports of delivery—Oslo, Copenhagen, and Malmö—in 14 days. Occasionally deliveries will be made to Stockholm. On her first trip she carried a mixed cargo of 368 cars and tractors.

During the 1960's the trend towards larger tankers for more economical transportation of petroleum continues. One wonders just what to call the new ships—the "super-tankers" that appeared after World War II are harbor craft in comparison. "Mammoth" might suffice to designate those of about 100,000 (101600) tons deadweight but what is suitable to describe one of 160,000 (162560) tons? Such is the pace of construction that the honor of being the largest tanker in the world in any given category is liable to be quite fleeting.

When delivered in June 1964 the single-screw BERGECHIEF, built by the Rosenberg Mekaniske Verksted A/S of Stavanger, was the largest motor tanker constructed to that time in Norway and also in the world; her total deadweight is 92,500 (93980) tons. A glance at her profile shows that all accommodations and the navigating spaces are aft but such are her proportions that one is apt to overlook the other superstructures, the forecastle and the normal bridge located a little forward of the midship point. Of practically all-welded construction her cargo tank section is divided by transverse bulkheads and two longitudinal bulkheads into 25 cargo tanks; her only pump room is aft. By designating one pair of wing tanks amidships as permanent ballast tanks unavailable for cargo her main hull structure is a little lighter than required when all tanks carry cargo oil. Throughout the tank section the deck and side shell are joined by a rolled plate.

BERGECHIEF is manned by a crew of 54 nearly all of whom have single berth cabins; all the officers and petty officers have private lavatories as well. There are also accommodations for the owner and a superintendent. In direct contrast to the practice of some her owners have provided the crew with a study room, a library, a hobby workshop, and a swimming pool. The wheelhouse and chartroom are on the sixth level above the main deck and are arranged for a 360° view. The twin stream-lined funnels serve to support two 7½ ton booms for handling machinery parts.

The main engine in BERGECHIEF is a ten-cylinder, two-cycle, single-acting Diesel built by Messrs. Burmeister & Wain of Copenhagen having cylinders 33.07 in. (0,840 m) diameter by 70.87 in. (1,800 m) stroke; it is designed to burn heavy fuel oil. The engine's normal rating is 20,710 (21000) b.h.p. at 110 r.p.m. but it may be operated continuously at 10 per cent higher power and for short intervals at 20 per cent higher; BERGECHIEF's sea speed is 15.5 knots (28,73 km/hr.). Steam for operating the cargo pumps and deck machinery as well as for heating the accommodations, fuel oil, and cargo oil tanks is supplied by two oil-fired double-pressure boilers. The high-pressure section operates at 597 p.s.i. (42,0 kg/cm²) while the low-pressure is 179 p.s.i.

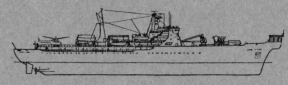

LONG LINES — 1961 — 11,326 T

461.2 × 69.8 × 40.7 feet
140,573 × 21,275 × 12,405 m

GREAT EASTERN'S activities in laying telegraphic cables were ended when FARADAY of 1874, one of the earliest specially designed cable-layers, entered service. One of the largest cable-layers in 1965 is LONG LINES owned by the Transoceanic Cable Ship Company. Designed by Messrs.
continued

Bergechief — page 250

continued
Gibbs & Cox, Inc. New York, she was launched in September 1961 by Schlieker Werft, Hamburg, but her completion was delayed until 1963 by the failure of the builder. Of practically all-welded construction she has two continuous decks and 12 transverse watertight bulkheads. Prominent forward are the bow cable sheaves, buoy racks, two 7½ ton buoy cranes, and the cable engine. Aft she has a helicopter landing platform. Her twin smoke pipes are streamlined to match her single mast. To provide the necessary control LONG LINES has twin-screw turbo-electric propelling machinery. Each of two high-speed turbines rated at 4550 (4612) h.p. at 5600 r.p.m. drives through single-reduction gearing a propulsion motor generator, a ship's service generator, and a cable engine generator. Each propulsion motor normally develops 3850 (3902) s.h.p. when turning a 5-bladed propeller at 131 r.p.m. Two water-tube boilers generate steam at a pressure of 600 p.s.i. (42,185 kg/cm²). The ship is fitted with a 750 (760) h.p. transverse bow thrust unit. Because of the control necessary during cable laying and recovery operations the machinery can be operated from the engine room, on either bridge wing, at the bow sheaves, or at the stern steering station. LONG LINES can carry about 2000 miles (3706 km) of submarine cable which is normally laid out over the stern at speeds up to 8 knots (14,83 km/hr.). The bow sheaves are employed for picking up cables.

(12,6 kg/cm²). A waste-heat boiler furnishes steam to a 600 KW turbo-generator set when the ship is under way. There are also two Diesel-driven 540 KW generators supplying 440 volt 60 cycle alternating current.

Because of port facilities these large tankers are limited to certain routes and even then the largest have to load and discharge at special offshore stations. One of their main routes is from the Persian Gulf to Japan on which BERGECHIEF operates under charter to the Tokyo Tanker Company. YAMANIZU MARU is a Japanese-built and owned tanker on the same run. With an overall length of 843.6 ft. (257,125 m), a breadth of 131.89 ft. (40,2 m), and a depth of 71.52 ft. (21,8 m) her total deadweight is 99,655 (101249) tons. With a hull deeper than normal for a tanker the usual super-structures are omitted and a lighter hull hence more deadweight is obtained. She is fitted with a twelve-cylinder Burmeister & Wain-type Diesel engine that has a conti-nuous rating of 27,200 (27600) b.h.p.; her cruising speed is 17.1 knots (31,69 km/hr.).

BERGECHIEF'S owners seem to specialize in these mammoth tankers. A duplicate tanker and one of 102,000 (103630) tons deadweight have been built by the Rosen-berg Mekaniske Verksted. In Japan four tankers of about 130,000 (132080) tons dead-weight are under construction and in the later part of 1964 a contract was signed with Mitsubishi Heavy Industries. Ltd. for one tanker of 160,000 (162560) tons deadweight to be delivered in 1967. On ships of such size longitudinal strength becomes of primary importance and this Japanese yard has proposed a jointed ship on the principle of CONNECTOR of 1863. Unlike her, however, the Japanese ship would have only one horizontal joint amidships to reduce bending stresses rather than to provide short sections for separate deliveries of cargo.

Since World War II the water-borne transportation of LPG—liquefied petroleum gas, first carried by AGNITA in 1931—has undergone a great expansion. Until recently the newly-built or converted ocean-going vessels and barges intended for river or coastal service carried LPG, propane, butane, and butadiene, only in cylin-drical tanks designed for a pressure of 250 p.s.i. (17,577 kg/cm²). Such tanks were also suitable for the carriage of anhydrous ammonia and other chemicals. The number of tanks and their arrangement in a vessel is a compromise between the maximum utilization of the space within a ship and the complexity of piping that results from a large number of small tanks. Each tank requires piping for both liquid and gas. It had long been apparent that LPG could be carried at atmospheric pressure if cooled to its boiling point thus allowing the use of non-pressurized rectangular tanks occupying a large part of a ship's interior. With the present day knowledge of the behavior of metals at low temperatures it is now feasible to transport LPG in this manner.

One of the most complicated LPG ships, four grades of LPG can be carried at one time, and the first of the type to be built in Europe PAUL ENDACOTT was construct-ed by Kockums Mechaniska Verkstad, Malmö, for the Trelleborg Steamship Com-pany. A single-deck ship with machinery, all accommodations, and navigating spaces aft she is all-welded except for a few riveted seams and has a forecastle, bridge, and poop that are connected by a wide trunk. Throughout the cargo space she has a complete double hull formed by a normal double bottom and narrow wing tanks. The cargo space is divided into five holds separated by cofferdams and thermally insulated by a total of 4 in. (0.100 m) of polyurethane plastic foam. Each hold contains a large prismatic tank constructed of special steel suitable for the intended temperature

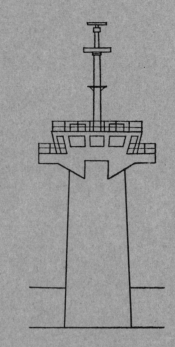

FASHIONS IN TANKER BRIDGES

In the modern tanker the bridge has developed into a tower. The picture above shows the single tower in the Norwegian tanker BORGESTEN, the picture below: the twin-towers of CARLO CAMELLI.

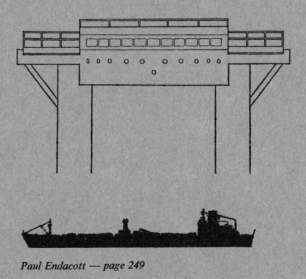

Paul Endacott — page 249

variations; for safety the hull structure through the cargo space is of the same steel. To make full use of the ship's space and deadweight capacity two vertical pressure tanks are located in the forward hold and four horizontal pressure tanks are carried on deck outboard of the trunk.

The prismatic tanks are designed for a temperature of -60° F (-51° C). Each tank has a dome protruding through the trunk through which all piping connections are made. LPG cargo is cooled on shore and loaded through insulated pipes. The tank insulation, however, is not perfect and there is always some boil off which amounts to 0.3-0.5 per cent per day. To eliminate this loss PAUL ENDACOTT has three reliquefying units. The possibility of explosions is reduced by filling the space between the cargo tanks and the inner skin with nitrogen generated on board. This nitrogen circulating outside the cargo tanks may be employed to cool cargoes that cannot be handled in the reliquefaction units. The cooled LPG cargo is unloaded by deep-well pumps while that in the cylindrical tanks is discharged by pressure. Vents from the tanks are carried to the mast amidships.

PAUL ENDACOTT is propelled by an eight-cylinder, double-acting Kockum-M.A.N. Diesel engine rated at 10,210 (10350) b.h.p. at 118 r.p.m. The ship's alternating current electric power is supplied by four 500 KW Diesel-generators. Steam for heating and other uses is generated in a waste-heat boiler at a pressure of 114 p.s.i. (8,000 kg/cm²); an oil-fired boiler is available for use in port. Her deck machinery, cargo pumps, and reliquefaction machinery are all hydraulically powered from a central unit in the control room amidships. Designed for a sea speed of 16.7 knots (30,95 km/hr.) PAUL ENDACOTT is now employed on a five-year time charter to the Phillips Petroleum Company of Bartlesville, Oklahoma.

In the not too distant past it was the North Atlantic express liners that attracted engineering attention with their ever more powerful engines and new equipment. Now it is the cargo ships, bulk carriers, and tankers. In the first decade of the twentieth century a large passenger liner required a small army of men to pass coal from bunkers to firerooms and to stoke the two dozen or so Scotch boilers. A large number of oilers were needed to keep the huge reciprocating engines properly lubricated. The change to turbine machinery and oil fuel greatly reduced the number of engine room personnel. Until recently all speed changes for the main engines have been signalled by a mechanical telegraph from the navigating bridge to an engineer on watch who opened or closed the proper valves. Now in 1965 control mechanisms have been so developed that a complete steam plant may be operated directly from the bridge with a minimum of personnel on watch in the engine room.

The single-screw steam-propelled tanker EMMA MAERSK, in 1964 Denmark's largest ship, was built by Kockums Mechaniska Verkstad, Malmö, and delivered on 13 April 1964. An all-welded ship of 60,750 (61722) tons deadweight she follows traditional tanker design in having a forecastle, bridge, and poop. Her cargo tank section is divided by transverse bulkheads and two longitudinal bulkheads into 19 tanks. Older tankers of her size would have had a larger number of tanks but classification society rules regarding the maximum length of a tank have been revised in recent years. EMMA MAERSK can load 469,373 barrels (74630 m³) of oil in her cargo tanks and her clean ballast capacity is 15,634 (15884) tons; one pair of wing tanks is employed for water ballast only. She has four turbine-driven cargo pumps located in

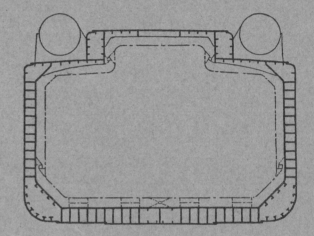

MIDSHIP SECTION—PAUL ENDACOTT

Emma Maersk — page 252

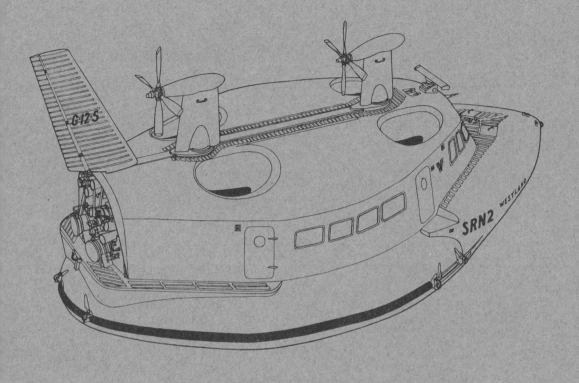

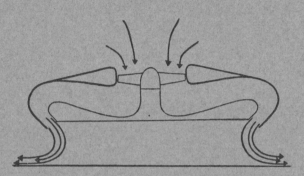

the main pump room aft each of which can discharge 1476 (1500) tons of water an hour. Although somewhat unusual for a tanker all accommodations are fully air conditioned and the crew's mess rooms are operated as cafeterias.

EMMA MAERSK's machinery plant, constructed by Kockums Mechaniska Verkstad, consists of a set of double-reduction geared turbines of the De Laval type rated at 19,726 (20000) s.h.p. at 106 r.p.m. and two water-tube boilers supplying steam at a pressure of 600 p.s.i. (42,185 kg/cm²). Alternating current electric power is provided by two 600 KW turbo-generator sets and one 120 KW Diesel-generator set. All deck machinery is driven by steam as is customary on most tankers to reduce the chance of an explosion. With a contract speed of 17.1 knots (31,69 km/hr.) when loaded to her 40.0 ft. (12,192 m) load water-line, EMMA MAERSK attained 17.46 knots (32,36 km/hr.) on trial.

Under normal conditions EMMA MAERSK is controlled by a normal appearing bridge engine telegraph connected to a completely automatic system that requires no action by personnel in the engine room. The main throttle valves are electrically operated and the boilers function automatically from stand-by·to maximum output. All engine commands set on the telegraph are executed in accordance with a predetermined series of events by an electronic selector unit. Other main components in the system are an ahead and astern electrically-driven actuators on the throttle valves, a small control panel on the bridge, and an instrumentation section in the main engine control console. Should this automatic system fail or other emergencies arise the entire plant may be operated by manual control in normal fashion.

HOVERCRAFT — GEM

One of the newest concepts for the transportation of passengers and cargo over land and sea is the vehicle known as a "hovercraft" in Great Britain and a "ground effect machine"—GEM—in the U.S.A. Basically a GEM is a platform having two fans. One is a large downdraft unit that creates enough pressure to lift the platform a short distance off the ground or the water. The second, more properly called an air propeller, drives the platform ahead on its almost frictionless cushion of air. Although still largely in the experimental stage many vehicles are being developed for commercial and military uses. They can attain the speeds of helicopters but carry far greater loads. The world's first commercial hovercraft or GEM was built by Vickers Armstrong, Ltd. The craft illustrated, SRN2, was built by the Saunders Roe Division of Westland Aircraft, Ltd., Yeovil, England. Constructed of aluminum it weighs 27 tons, can carry 57 to 76 passengers, can operate over waves 4-5 ft. (1,219-1,524 m) high, and can reach a speed of 73 knots (135,32 km/hr.). At cruising speed SRN2 can easily make the 63 mile (101,39 km) crossing from the Isle of Wight to Cherbourg in one hour. Four gas turbines developing a total of 3260 (3304) h.p. drive two lifting fans and two air propellers. There is still a question as to whether a hovercraft is an aircraft or a boat. If the waves become too high for hovering the lifting fans can be stopped and the craft settles into the water to procede as a boat driven by an air propeller.

Certain European shipping regulations make it desirable to limit the gross registered tonnage of small cargo vessels to 499. Because of the printed arrangement of these regulations setting off certain provisions in separate paragraphs these 499 tonners are known as "paragraph" ships. FLANDRIA is a paragraph ship designed especially to carry containers and general cargo, pre-slung or stowed on pallets, between Gothenburg and Antwerp. She was built by the Hatlö Verksted A/S, Ulsteinvik, Norway, and launched on 27 May 1964.

A three-deck two-hold vessel FLANDRIA is arranged so that much of her cargo can be stowed by 3-ton fork lift trucks. All hatches except that on the weather deck over the forward part of her second hold are flush to allow free use of the trucks around her decks; she is the first ship in Scandinavia to employ any flush hatches on a weather deck. Cargo for the forward hold is loaded through the hatches in the normal manner by a shore crane or the ship's 5-ton crane which can swing through an arc of 270°. In the bottom of this hold is a tank capable of carrying 346 barrels (55 m³) of liquid cargo.

Most of the cargo for the second hold is loaded through two ports in the starboard side. The doors open out and drop down to the quay to serve as loading platforms or as ramps for running fork-lift trucks right aboard. The pivot fittings at the bottoms of the doors run in vertical tracks on the ship's side to allow adjustment of the positions of the open doors. The forward door measures 19.03 ft. by 15.75 ft. (5,80×4,80 m) while the after door is 8.20 by 13.12 ft. (2,5× 4,0 m). Cargo is delivered to the door platforms by trucks equipped with fork-lifts, bale clamps, or paper roll grips and picked up by similarly equipped trucks on the ship.

The second hold in FLANDRIA is also served by two hatches each in the weather and shelter decks located on the starboard side in direct connection to the side ports. The main deck hatch, however, is on the port side abaft the large door. In this hatch is a 16.40 by 6.56 ft. (5,0×2,0 m) 5-ton elevator for moving cargo to and from the hold. A recess in the double bottom permits the level of the lowered platform to be flush with the tank top sheathing.

FLANDRIA is fitted with a single variable-pitch propeller driven by an eight-cylinder Diesel engine rated at a maximum of 1400 (1419) b.h.p. at 375 r.p.m. The main engine controls as well as those for the propeller can be operated from the bridge. Alternating current electric power for normal requirements is furnished by two 142 KW Diesel-generators; a similar 55 KW set generates power for port use. FLANDRIA's anchor windlass, capstan, cargo crane, hold elevator, side doors, and most of her hatch covers are operated hydraulically.

It is expected that cargoes such as oil and ore will continue to determine the basic characteristics of the ships transporting them but that the general cargo ships will be the pace setters for new features. Faced with a growing shortage of qualified personnel and the attractions of life ashore many owners are attempting to improve conditions afloat. Designed for service between Europe and the Far East and built by the Nakskov Vaerft in Denmark the versatile ANDORRA is an indication of things to come Certain subsidized cargo ships intended for possible use as naval auxiliaries may have higher speeds and more hatches but it is considered that ANDORRA represents an economical combination of many advanced concepts.

Flandria — page 248

LACQ — 1964

281.62 × 36.50 × 10.17 feet
85,82 × 11,13 × 3,10m

The Maas, Rhine, and Schelde rivers swarm with self-propelled and towed barges carrying almost every common commodity. With accommodations for her skipper and mate, their families, and two seamen aft over the engine room LACQ differs little in appearance from the majority of new self-propelled barges but her cargo is decidedly uncommon—molten sulphur carried at a temperature of 275° F (135° C). Sulphur is normally melted in underground deposits by steam and pumped to the surface or melted to clear the impurities after being mined or quarried. Formerly cooled and transported dry molten sulphur is now loaded directly into ships and barges and taken to local or overseas consumers or storage facilities. LACQ loads her cargo at a terminal in Rotterdam and delivers it to the growing number of chemical plants on the above named rivers. To eliminate the hull stresses that would be caused by the hot sulphur it is carried in two independent rectangular tanks that have no contact with the hull except through insulated supports on which they are free to expand or contract. The tanks are insulated with 2 in. (51 mm) of glass wool covered with aluminum foil. The sulphur is maintained in a molten condition by steam heating coils fitted in the bottoms of the tanks. LACQ is propelled by twin screws driven by two 440 (446) b.h.p. at 1430 r.p.m. Diesel engines through 3.86:1 reverse-reduction gears.

Andorra — page 254

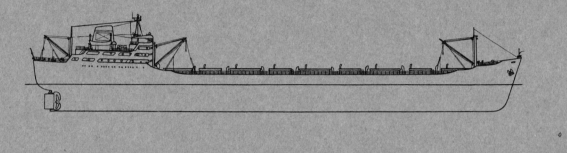

CARLTON — 1963 — 13,954 T

530.0 × 73.73 × 43.17 feet
161,544 × 22,479 × 13,158 m

CARLTON, owned by Messrs. Chapman & Willan, Ltd., Newcastle-on-Tyne, is the first vessel built in Great Britain to the patented U.B.S.—Universal Bulk Ship—design; she also proved to be the last ship built in Short Brothers yard in Sunderland. A single-deck ship she has her machinery, navigating spaces, and all accommodations aft. There are nine cargo hatches in her deck but she carries no gear for discharging her cargoes. Four 5-ton booms for handling stores or special deck cargo are fitted on pairs of kingposts forward and aft. CARLTON's cargo space is divided into five main holds and four upper holds shaped like hoppers located over the main divisional bulkheads. These upper holds are divided longitudinally into three compartments so that in all there are 17 cargo compartments of various sizes and vertical positions. Thus she may be loaded in a manner to obtain the best stability and trim for the single or mixed bulk cargoes that she may carry. All compartments are self-trimming and longitudinal girders have been arranged to eliminate the need for grain shifting boards. The wing compartments of the upper holds may be employed for water ballast. Her total grain capacity is 1,046,282 cu. ft. (29628 m³) and she can carry a maximum of 7729 (7853) tons of water ballast. CARLTON's single screw is driven by a 6-cylinder, 2-cycle, single-acting-Götaverken-type Diesel that is arranged to burn heavy fuel oil. Having a normal rating of 6700 (6791) b.h.p. at 108 r.p.m. it gives her a service speed of 14 knots (25,95 km/hr.).

A single-screw shelter-deck ship with machinery right aft to give the greatest amount of rectangular space for cargo, ANDORRA's above-water profile shows a curved raked stem, a cruiser stern, a forecastle, a block of houses amidships, and what may best be called a bridge deck extending to the stern. Below water at the bow her forefoot is cut away; the large bulb seen on many modern vessels is effective in reducing resistance only under certain conditions. Aft the propeller and rudder have the open-water configuration. In the hull are three continuous decks and a full-length double bottom that is raised in way of the forward hold and the machinery space. From the after end of the forward hold to the machinery space the decks are parallel to the keel for easier stowage of cargo. ANDORRA is subdivided by seven transverse watertight bulkheads into five cargo holds, fore and after peaks, and the machinery space. To minimize structural obstructions in the holds and to save weight all cargo space bulkheads are constructed of fluted plates.

In the upper and lower 'tween-deck spaces of hold 5 ANDORRA has eight refrigerated compartments capable of being cooled down to -13° F (-25° C); their total capacity is 24,500 cu. ft. (694 m³). One of her eastbound cargoes is frozen Danish pastry. Five deep tanks in lower holds 1 and 3 have a special coating to permit the carriage of almost all liquids but their usual cargoes are latex and vegetable oils. The liquid capacity of these tanks is 8468 barrels (1350 m²) and their contents may be heated by steam coils welded to the under side of the inner bottom. In the port side of the upper deck house abreast the machinery casing is a special compartment for carrying troublesome commodities such as paint powder and black lead. The ship's total grain capacity including deep tanks is 712,700 cu. ft. (20182 m²) and her total deadweight is 10,273 (10437) tons. All of the normal cargo spaces are mechanically ventilated.

Two or more hatches abreast are considered by some to be one of the characteristics of a modern cargo ship along with a large number of cranes. Multiple hatches were employed at least fifty years ago and all cargoes cannot be handled by cranes. ANDORRA has single hatches and although her weather deck hatches have raised coamings those in the lower decks have flush hydraulically-operated covers. For handling the great variety of cargoes transported on the Far Eastern route she has eight 12½-ton, five 3/5-ton, and one 60-ton cargo booms and two 5-ton cranes. By means of a special lifting yoke two 12½-ton booms may be employed to handle 24-ton loads. The two cranes are normally operated from their cabs but they may be controlled from a push-button panel worn by the operator who is then free to walk around the deck and observe conditions in the hold and on shore.

ANDORRA's fully air conditioned accommodations are arranged with no cabins alongside or over the machinery space. The navigating spaces, cabins for the officers and four passengers, a smoking room, and a dining saloon are located in the midship houses. The crew's quarters, galley, and messrooms are located in the upper deck house outboard of trunked hatches 4 and 5. Single-berth cabins are provided for nearly the entire complement.

The main engine in ANDORRA is an eight-cylinder, high-pressure, turbo-charged Burmeister & Wain Diesel engine developing 12,000 (12163) b.h.p. at 115 r.p.m. and designed to burn heavy fuel oil. Steam at 100 p.s.i. (7,031 kg/cm²) pressure for heating the ship is generated by a waste-heat boiler when under way or any oil-fired boiler in port. Three 560 KW Diesel generator sets provide 440 volt 60 cycle alternating current to drive her engine room auxiliaries and deck machinery. To aid in handling in port ANDORRA has a transverse bow thrust unit consisting of a variable pitch propeller driven by an 800 (811) h.p. electric motor set in a duct under the raised double bottom. On trials with the main engine developing 10,800 (10947) b.h.p. ANDORRA attained a speed of 18.4 knots (34,10 km/hr.) and at the end of the trials was easily berthed in Copenhagen with the aid of only one small tug.

ANDORRA's propelling machinery is completely controlled from the bridge and there are no watch-keepers in the engine room. The engineers perform their maintenance and routine duties during the day but no one is on duty during the night although when entering port or sailing in restricted waters one engineer is on watch in the engine room control booth. The main engine rotates continuously in one direction and speed changes including reversing are made by controlling the variable pitch propeller, the most powerful of its type yet installed in a merchant ship. Although the main engine can be reversed the controls are normally locked in the ahead position. If in an emergency it must be operated from the engine room control booth three push-buttons marked Ahead, Stop, and Astern rather than a normal engine telegraph are employed on the bridge. With this high degree of automation and certain changes in deck operations ANDORRA is able to sail with a crew of only 33 instead of the normal 41. Thus with the best part of her hull devoted to cargo space, versatile cargo handling gear, attractive accommodations, and highly automated machinery she points to the features that will become common on newer cargo ships.

And now, what of the ship of the future? For every trade the answer will be different but there are certain fundamentals that will govern the answer. The size, shape, and living requirements of human beings are not apt to change radically in the foreseeable future, not all goods to be transported can be stowed in convenient containers at the point of manufacture, fossil fuels will continue to be available for a considerable period,

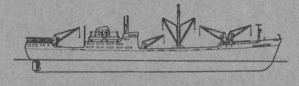

SHAHRISTAN — 1964 — 9469 T

470.0 × 67.5 × 39.0 feet
143,256 × 20,574 × 11,887 m

The Strick Line's single-screw two-deck motorship SHAHRISTAN is designed for versatile cargo handling but in particular for heavy lifts. She is arranged with one hold abaft her machinery space and four forward; holds 2 and 3 have a common 'tween-deck space which is served by a 60 ft. (18,287 m) long hatch. Hold 2 only has a lower 'tween deck which is the top of a deep tank; the long forecastle extending over the forward hold provides additional cargo space. All lower deck hatches are flush and are reinforced to permit the use of fork-lift trucks. SHAHRISTAN's heavy lift gear consists of a pair of heavy kingposts and a 180-ton boom built in accordance with the German Stulcken patent; this boom can serve either the long hatch forward or hold 4. The kingposts also carry four 10-ton booms. Hold 1 is served by a 3-ton crane mounted on athwartship tracks; it can also handle cargo from hold 2 which has a fixed 7-ton crane. Fixed 3-ton cranes port and starboard serve hold 4 while hold 5 has a fixed 7-ton crane. SHAHRISTAN is operated by a total complement of 71 and the accommodations are arranged for European officers and petty officers and a Lascar crew. Her main engine, which may be controlled from the bridge, is a 6-cylinder Doxford Diesel rated at 10,000 (10136) b.h.p. at 120 r.p.m. which gives her a service speed of 17 knots (31,50 km/hr.).

and man probably will not be able to control the oceans' waves and the winds. As with dry architecture ashore much connected with naval architecture is affected by the whim or fashion of the moment. From the technical point of view every new ship of any size is at least two years old when delivered; a new passenger ship may be as much as five years behind current thinking. There will be new shapes, new materials, new methods of handling cargo, and new methods of propulsion but the successful ship of the future will be a careful blend of the traditional and the new. The laws of economics and the hazards of the sea do not brook ill-considered experiments.

KOLEJARZ — 1964

472.45 × 66.93 × 41.00 feet
144,00 × 20,40 × 12,50 m

This Polish-built ship is primarily a bulk carrier with provisions for handling general cargoes. A single-screw shelter-deck ship of 12,700 (12903) tons deadweight she is arranged in the modern "all-aft" fashion and is subdivided into five cargo holds. She is specially strengthened for carrying full loads of iron ore and for navigation in ice. Longitudinal bulkheads in the 'tween-deck spaces and deep girders under the main deck meet shifting board requirements for the carriage of grain. The foremost hold has single hatches while the remaining four have two abreast; the covers in the lower deck are flush and are designed to support ore cargoes. The lower deck hatch covers and the inner bottom under the hatches are reinforced to withstand the abrasion of grab buckets when unloading. Cargo is handled at the forward hold by two-5-ton booms on a pair of kingposts while four 5-ton cranes serve the other holds; these cranes operate on athwartship tracks between the hatches. KOLEJARZ is powered by a 5-cylinder Sulzer-type Diesel engine which develops 6500 (6588) b.h.p. at 119 r.p.m.

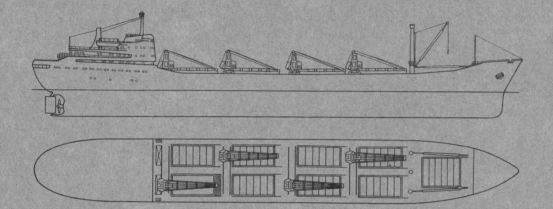

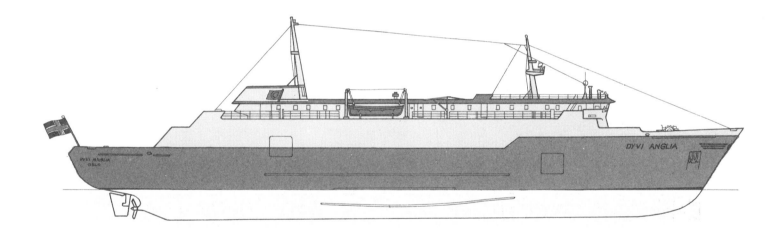

DYVI ANGLIA · 1964

I/S Car Carrier (Jan-Erik Dyvi)

288.9 × 48.4 × 12.3 feet ◖ 499 T ◖ 88,1 × 14,75 × 3,77 m

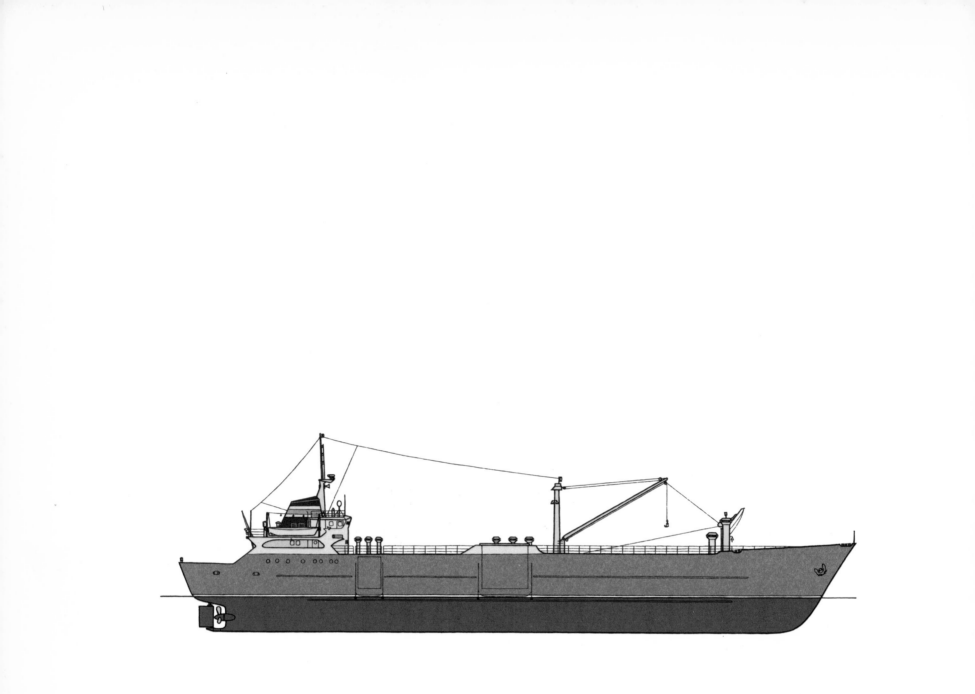

FLANDRIA · 1964

A/B Broker (Erik Kekonius)

248.4 × 34.10 feet ℂ 500 T ℂ 75,71 × 10,39 m

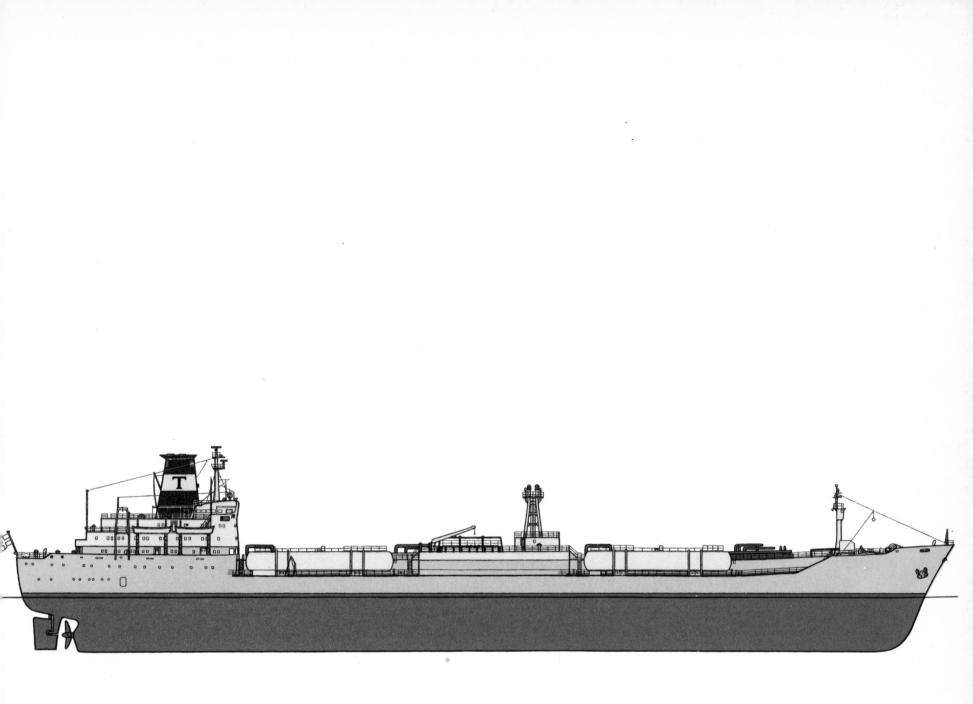

PAUL ENDACOTT · 1964

Rederi Trelleborgs Ångfartygs A.B.

586.5 × 82.1 × 45.8 feet ℂ 19077 T ℂ 178,765 × 25,024 × 13,960 m

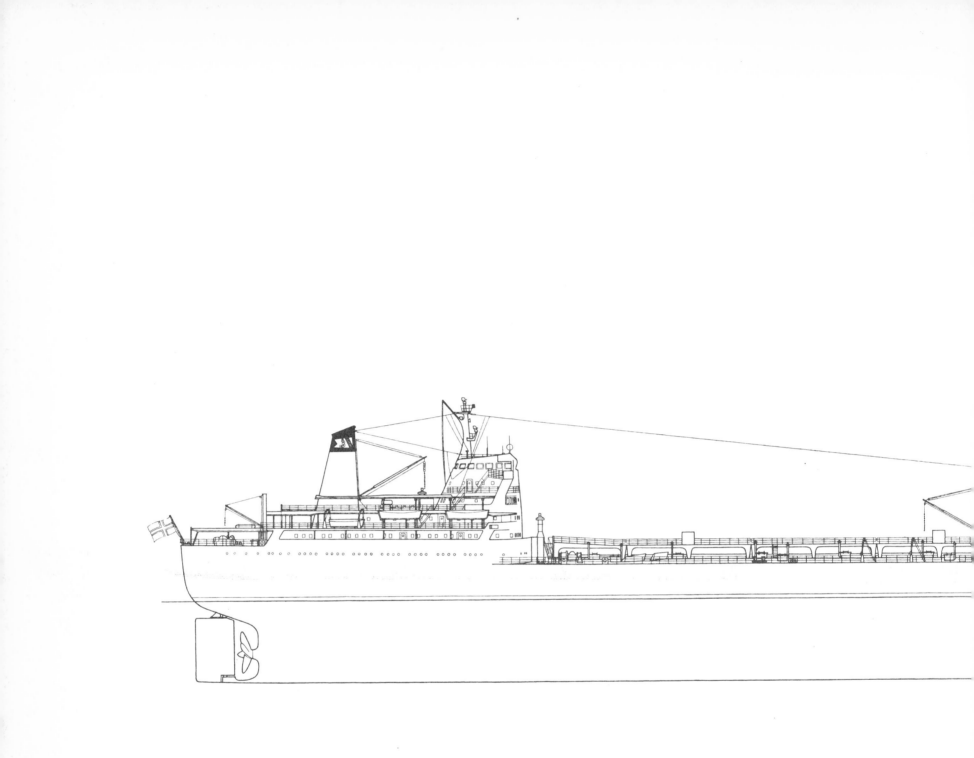

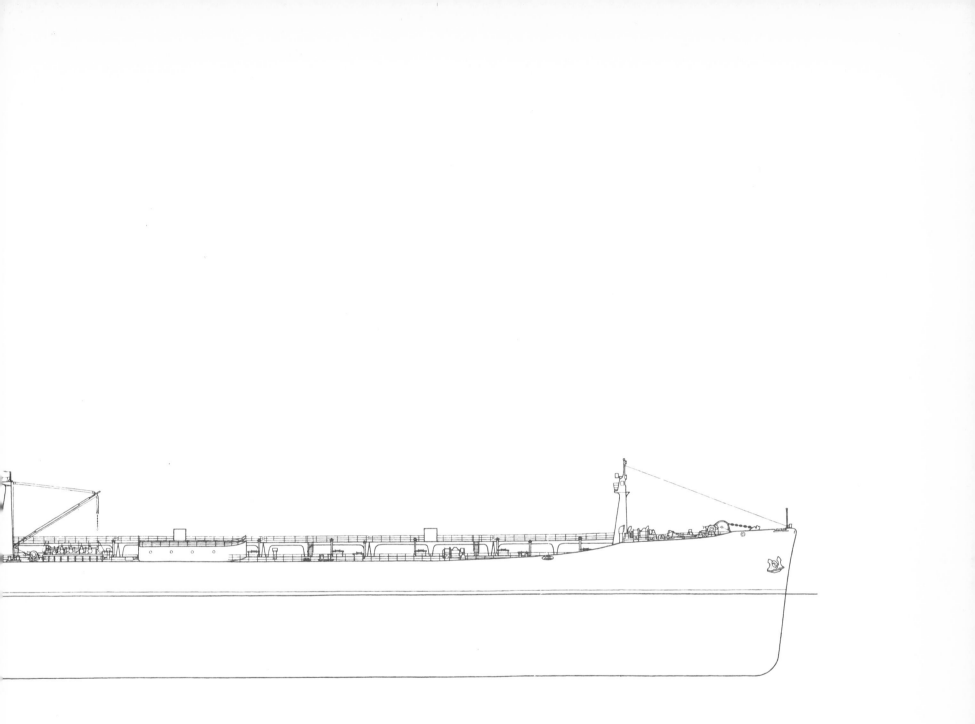

BERGECHIEF · 1964

Sig. Bergesen d.y. & Co

868.8 × 122.0 × 46.8 feet ℂ 53375 T ℂ 264,81 × 37,19 × 14,31 m

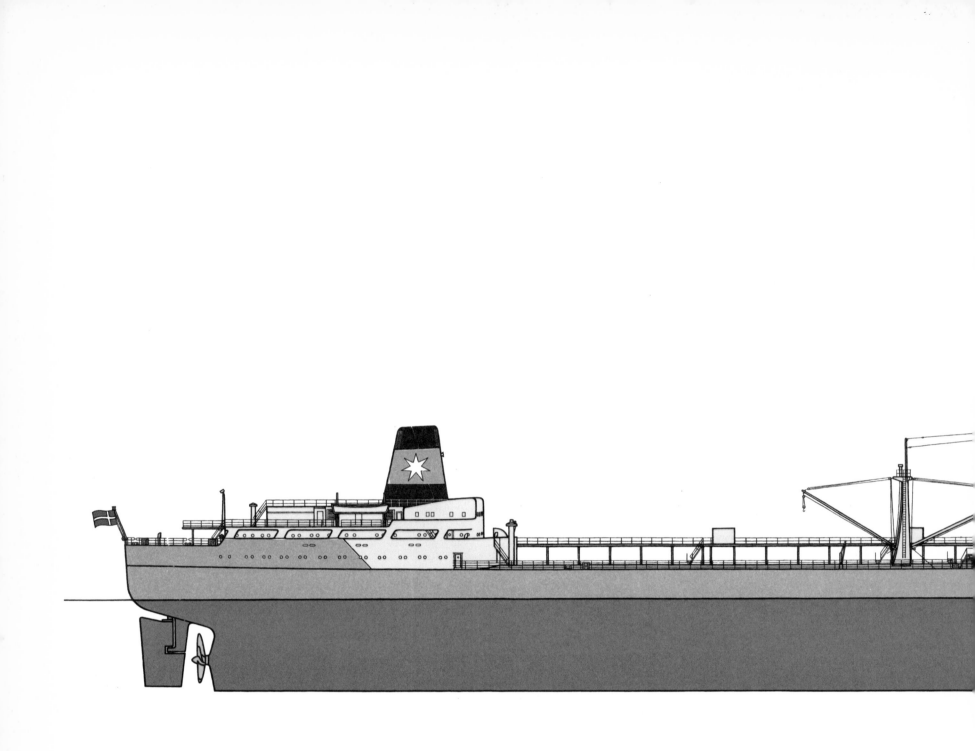

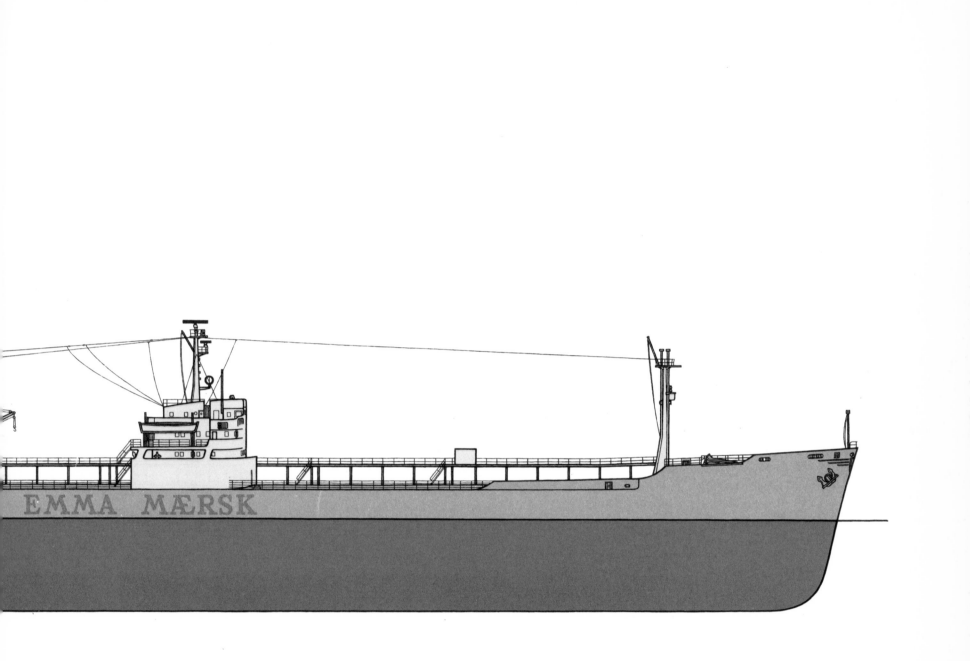

EMMA MÆRSK · 1964

Messrs. A.P. Möller

775.0 × 109.3 × 40.0 feet ' ℂ 36440 T ℂ 236,22 × 33,31 × 12,19 m

ANDORRA · 1964

Det Östasiatiske Kompagni A/S

480.1 × 67.3 × 41.2 feet ℂ 7610 T ℂ 146,33 × 20,52 × 12,57 m

INDEX

MERCHANT NAVIES IN VARIOUS COUNTRIES 1890-1964

Gross tonnage data of sailing vessels—motorships 1890-1930; also same data according to various types of ships 1950-1964.

	1890	1900	1910	1920	1930	1950	1960	1964
BELGIUM								
Sailing vessels		420	3.725	4.689	7.035			
Motorships		162.493	295.913	410.423	546.002	481.656	728.981	796.133
TOTAL		162.913	299.638	415.112	553.037	481.656	728.981	796.133
Thereof: Passenger ships								
Tankers						*33.000*	*169.096*	*214.297*
Refrig. carriers							*12.892*	
Others						*448.656*	*546.993*	*581.836*
DENMARK								
Sailing vessels	120.993	106.738	64.734	83.967	16.485			
Motorships	159.072	412.273	671.828	719.444	1.071.521	1.269.011	2.269.847	2.431.020
TOTAL	280.065	519.011	736.562	803.411	1.088.006	1.269.011	2.269.847	2.431.020
Thereof: Passenger ships							*77.000*	
Tankers						*142.000*	*830.185*	*883.853*
Refrig. carriers							*134.035*	
Others						*1.127.011*	*1.228.627*	*1.548.167*
ENGLAND & NO. IRELAND								
Sailing vessels	2.467.212	1.727.687	748.796	219.771	116.524			
Motorships	7.774.644	11.513.759	16.767.683	18.110.653	20.321.920	18.219.247	21.130.874	21.489.948
TOTAL	10.241.856	13.241.446	17.516.479	18.330.424	20.438.444	18.219.247	21.130.874	21.489.948
Thereof: Passenger ships							*2.162.686*	
Tankers						*3.690.000*	*6.422.326*	*8.002.303*
Refrig. carriers							*3.383.723*	
Others						*14.529.247*	*9.162.139*	*13.487.645*
FRANCE								
Sailing vessels	235.504	298.369	434.108	281.965	60.288			
Motorships	809.598	1.052.193	1.448.172	2.963.229	3.470.591	3.206.504	4.808.728	5.116.232
TOTAL	1.045.102	1.350.562	1.882.280	3.245.194	3.530.879	3.206.504	4.808.728	5.116.232
Thereof: Passenger ships							*646.122*	
Tankers						*545.000*	*1.762.358*	*2.208.763*
Refrig. carriers							*590.005*	
Others						*2.661.504*	*1.810.243*	*2.907.469*

	1890	1900	1910	1920	1930	1950	1960	1964
GERMANY								
Sailing vessels	640.400	490.114	373.868	253.233	30.139			
Motorships	928.911	2.159.919	3.959.318	419.438	4.199.096	459.530	4.536.591	5.159.186
TOTAL	1.569.311	2.650.033	4.333.186	672.671	4.229.235	459.530	4.536.591	5.159.186
Thereof: Passenger ships							*218.437*	
Tankers						*1.000*	*598.700*	*838.740*
Refrig. carriers							*186.329*	
Others						*458.530*	*3.533.125*	*4.320.446*
HOLLAND								
Sailing vessels	161.762	63.068	32.144	20.004	7.315			
Motorships	217.022	467.209	983.049	1.773.392	3.079.000	3.108.574	4.888.049	5.110.022
TOTAL	378.784	530.277	1.015.193	1.793.396	3.086.315	3.108.574	4.888.049	5.110.022
Thereof: Passenger ships							*686.046*	
Tankers						*485.000*	*1.275.745*	*1.638.419*
Refrig. carriers							*223.051*	
Others						*2.623.574*	*2.703.207*	*3.471.603*
ITALY								
Sailing vessels	515.942	443.306	333.094	123.964	69.304			
Motorships	300.625	540.349	987.559	2.118.429	3.261.922	2.580.392	5.122.240	5.707.817
TOTAL	816.567	983.655	1.320.653	2.242.393	3.331.226	2.580.392	5.122.240	5.707.817
Thereof: Passenger ships							*648.942*	
Tankers						*513.000*	*1.641.660*	*1.982.485*
Refrig. carriers							*319.952*	
Others						*2.067.392*	*2.511.686*	*3.725.332*
NORWAY								
Sailing vessels	1.337.686	876.129	592.527	239.828	5.052			
Motorships	246.669	764.683	1.422.006	1.979.560	3.663.237	5.455.704	11.203.246	14.477.112
TOTAL	1.584.355	1.640.812	2.014.533	2.219.388	3.668.289	5.455.704	11.203.246	14.477.112
Thereof: Passenger ships							*148.000*	
Tankers						*2.131.000*	*5.928.000*	*7.664.000*
Refrig. carriers							*423.500*	
Others						*3.324.704*	*4.703.746*	*6.813.112*
SPAIN								
Sailing vessels	119.994	52.549	18.712	59.750	24.644			
Motorships	414.817	642.231	746.748	937.280	1.207.093	1.189.672	1.800.721	2.047.715
TOTAL	534.811	694.780	765.460	997.030	1.231.737	1.189.672	1.800.721	2.047.715
Thereof: Passenger ships							*266.613*	
Tankers						*137.000*	*382.688*	*590.882*
Refrig. carriers							*38.369*	
Others						*1.052.672*	*1.113.051*	*1.456.833*

	1890	1900	1910	1920	1930	1950	1960	1964
SWEDEN								
Sailing vessels	294.183	218.722	135.571	76.502	29.625			
Motorships	181.781	418.550	782.508	996.423	1.594.313	2.048.033	3.746.866	4.308.042
TOTAL	475.964	637.272	918.079	1.072.925	1.623.938	2.048.033	3.746.866	4.308.042
Thereof: Passenger ships							*218.000*	*231.100*
Tankers						*374.200*	*1.273.000*	*1.462.750*
Refrig. carriers							*452.000*	*504.000*
Others						*1.673.833*	*1.803.866*	*2.110.192*
USA								
Sailing vessels	1.306.488	1.156.498	1.229.536	1.472.612	843.547			
Motorships	517.394	878.564	3.788.688	14.524.691	13.103.299	27.513.385	24.837.069	22.430.249
TOTAL	1.823.882	2.035.062	5.018.224	15.997.303	13.946.846	27.513.385	24.837.069	22.430.249
Thereof: Passenger ships							*579.080*	
Tankers						*4.736.000*	*4.446.033*	*4.505.274*
Refrig. carriers							*787.000*	
Others						*22.777.385*	*19.024.956*	*17.924.975*
GREECE								
TOTAL		178.137	499.184	496.996	1.390.899	1.277.008	4.529.234	6.887.624
JAPAN								
TOTAL	138.431	488.187	1.146.977	2.995.878	4.316.804	1.871.276	6.931.436	10.813.228
LIBERIA								
TOTAL						245.457	11.282.240	14.549.645
PANAMA								
TOTAL					75.497	3.361.339	4.235.983	4.269.462
USSR								
TOTAL						2.320.000	3.359.523	6.957.512
WHOLE WORLD								
Sailing vessels	9.133.156	6.521.043	4.593.428	3.376.112	1.583.840			
Motorships	12.985.372	22.369.358	37.290.695	53.904.688	68.023.804	84.583.155	129.769.500	152.999.621
TOTAL	22.118.528	28.890.401	41.884.123	57.280.800	69.607.644	84.583.155	129.769.500	152.999.621
Thereof: Passenger ships							*8.209.000*	
Tankers						*15.824.000*	*38.824.000*	*50.563.315*
Refrig. carriers							*8.040.989*	
Others						*68.759.155*	*74.695.601*	*102.436.306*

LIST OF SOURCES

Bowen, Frank C.
A CENTURY OF ATLANTIC TRAVEL,
1830-1930. *Boston 1930.*
MAIL AND PASSENGER STEAMSHIPS.
London 1928.

Buchanan, Lamont
SHIPS OF STEAM. *New York 1956.*

Bucknell, Rixon
BOAT TRAINS & CHANNEL PACKETS.
London 1957.

Bureau Veritas
REPERTOIRE GÉNÉRALE DE LA MARINE
MARCHANDE. NAVIRES À VAPEUR.
Paris 1888-89.

Chapelle, Howard I.
THE NATIONAL WATERCRAFT
COLLECTION. *Washington 1960.*
THE PIONEER STEAMSHIP SAVANNAH:
A STUDY FOR A SCALE MODEL.
Washington 1961.

Chatterton, E. Keble
STEAMSHIPS AND THEIR STORY. *Toronto
and Melbourne 1910.*

Dayton, F. E.
STEAMBOAT DAYS. *New York 1939.*

Deutsche Werft, Hamburg.
MOTORSCHIFFE SVEALAND UND
AMERIKALAND

Dugan, James
THE GREAT IRON SHIP. *New York 1953.*

Eskew, G. L.
THE PAGEANT OF THE PACKETS. *New
York 1929.*

Evans, I. O.
THE OBSERVERS BOOK OF FLAGS.
London 1959.

Fincham, John
A HISTORY OF NAVAL ARCHITECTURE.
London 1851.

Fletcher, R. A.
STEAMSHIPS—THE STORY OF THEIR
DEVELOPMENT TO THE PRESENT DAY.
Philadelphia 1910.

Flexner, J. T.
STEAMBOATS COME TRUE. *New York 1944.*

Fry, Henry
THE HISTORY OF NORTH ATLANTIC
STEAM NAVIGATION. *New York 1896.*

Gibbs, C. R. Vernon
PASSENGER LINERS OF THE WESTERN
OCEAN. *London 1952.*
BRITISH PASSENGER LINERS OF THE
FIVE OCEANS. *London 1963.*

Halldin, Gustaf
SVENSKT SKEPPSBYGGERI. *Malmö 1963.*

Hambleton, F. C.
FAMOUS PADDLE STEAMERS. *London 1948.*

Hardy, A. C.
THE BOOK OF THE SHIP. *London.*

Jackson, G. G.
THE BOOK OF THE SHIP. *London.*

Kannik, Preben
FLAGGOR FRÅN HELA VÄRLDEN.
Copenhagen-Stockholm 1957.

King, G. A. B.
TANKER PRACTICE. THE CONSTRUCTION,
OPERATION AND MAINTENANCE OF
TANKERS. *Wokingham 1956.*

Landström, Björn
SKEPPET. *Weert 1961.*

Lane, Carl D.
AMERICAN PADDLE STEAMBOATS.
New York 1943.

Lawson, W.
PACIFIC STEAMERS. *Glasgow 1927.*

Lehmann, Johannes
M/S SELANDIA 1912-1937. *Copenhagen
1937.*
BURMEISTER & WAIN GENNEM
HUNDREDE AAR. *Copenhagen 1943.*

Lindqvist, Sune
SVENSKT FORNTIDSLIV. *Stockholm 1944.*

Lindsay, W. S.
HISTORY OF MERCHANT SHIPPING AND
ANCIENT COMMERCE. *London 1876.*

Lindström, Claes
SJÖFARTENS HISTORIA. *Stockholm 1951.*

Lisle, B. O.
TANKER TECHNIQUE 1700-1936. *London
1936.*

Ljungzell, Nils J.
SNABBARE OCH ÄNDAMÅLSENLIGARE
PASSAGERARBÅTAR FÖR STOCKHOLMS
SKÄRGÅRD.

Maginnis, Arthur J.
THE ATLANTIC FERRY, ITS SHIPS,
MEN, AND WORKING. *London 1893.*

Marestier, J. B.
MEMOIR ON STEAMBOATS OF THE
UNITED STATES OF AMERICA. *Mystic 1957.*

Morrison, J. H.
HISTORY OF AMERICAN STEAM
NAVIGATION. *New York 1903.*

Murray, Andrew
THE THEORY AND PRACTICE OF SHIP-
BUILDING. *Edinburgh 1861.*
SHIP-BUILDING IN IRON AND WOOD.
Edinburgh 1863.

Nordenskiöld, A. E.
VEGAS FÄRD KRING ASIEN OCH EUROPA.
Stockholm 1880.

Parker, H. & Bowen, Frank C.
MAIL AND PASSENGER STEAMSHIPS OF
THE 19TH CENTURY. London 1928.

Preble, G. H.
ORIGIN AND DEVELOPMENT OF STEAM
NAVIGATION. Philadelphia 1895.

Reed, E. J.
TRANSACTIONS OF THE INSTITUTION OF
NAVAL ARCHITECTS. London 1860.

Roentgen, Gerhard M.
VERHANDELING OVER DE STOOMBOOTEN.

Russell, J. Scott
NAVAL ARCHITECTURE. London.

Smith, E. W.
PASSENGER SHIPS OF THE WORLD.
Boston 1963.

Spratt, H. P.
OUTLINE HISTORY OF TRANSATLANTIC
STEAM NAVIGATION. London 1950.
MERCHANT STEAMERS AND
MOTORSHIPS. London 1949.
MARINE ENGINEERING. London 1953.
THE BIRTH OF THE STEAMBOAT.
London 1958.

Stanton, Samuel W.
AMERICAN STEAM VESSELS. New York
1895.

Svensk Litteratur
STOCKHOLMS SKÄRGÅRD. Stockholm 1954.

Svensson, Sam
SEGEL GENOM SEKLER. Amsterdam 1961.

Tenac, De M. van
HISTOIRE GÉNÉRALE DE LA MARINE.
Paris.

Thomson, P. W.
UNPUBLISHED LETTER TO VICE ADMIRAL
E. L. COCHRANE, U.S.N. 1 MARCH 1950.

Tre Tryckare
THE LORE OF SHIPS. Göteborg 1963.

Tute, Warren
ATLANTIC CONQUEST. Toronto 1962.

Tyler, D. B.
STEAM CONQUERS THE ATLANTIC. New
York 1939.

Underhill, Harold A.
MASTING & RIGGING THE CLIPPER
SHIP & OCEAN CARRIER. Glasgow 1958.

Van Nouhuys, J. W.
DE EERSTE NEDERLANDSCHE
TRANSATLANTIC STOOMVAART IN 1827
VAN ZR MS STOOMPAKKET CURAÇAO
—VOL. L III WERKEN DER LINSCHOTEN-
VEREENIGING.

Vigeland, Nils P.
NORGE PÅ HAVET. Oslo 1953-54.

Walton, Thomas
STEEL SHIPS; THEIR CONSTRUCTION
AND MAINTENANCE. London 1908.
PRESENT-DAY SHIPBUILDING. London
1921.

Weber, I. C.
FRA HJULSKIBENES DAGE. Copenhagen
1914.

Wedge, Philip L.
FLAGS AND FUNNELS. Glasgow 1958.

PERIODICALS

THE AMERICAN NEPTUNE
DIE DEUTSCHE HANDELSFLOTTE
THE ENGINEER
ENGINEERING
FORENINGEN BERGENS SJØFARTSMUSEUM
  ÅRSHEFTE
HANSA
HOBBY
THE ILLUSTRATED LONDON NEWS
THE INSTITUTE OF MARINE
ENGINEERS (TRANSACTIONS)
THE MARINE ENGINEER AND NAVAL
  ARCHITECT
MARINE ENGINEERING
MARINE REVIEW
THE MARINER'S MIRROR
MERCHANT SHIPS: WORLD BUILT
THE MOTOR SHIP
NATIONAL GEOGRAPHIC MAGAZINE
NORWEGIAN SHIPPING NEWS
SCHIFF UND HAFEN
SCHIP EN WERF
THE SHIPBUILDER AND MARINE
  ENGINE-BUILDER
SHIPBUILDING AND SHIPPING RECORD
THE SOCIETY OF NAVAL ARCHITECTS
  AND MARINE ENGINEERS
  (TRANSACTIONS)
SVENSK SJÖFARTS TIDNING
SVERIGES HANDELSFLOTTA
TEKNISK TIDSKRIFT
ZEITSCHRIFT DES VEREINES DEUTSCHE
  INGENIEURE

In the event of another edition the editors would appreciate any suggestions readers might have for improvements to the book. Please mail them direct to: Tre Tryckare, Box 13110, Gothenburg 13, Sweden.

Despite vigorous research work the editorial staff has not always succeeded in obtaining accurate information concerning the older vessels. In such cases reconstructions have been made on the basis of available pictures. These have, however, often displayed contradictory details. Primarily this is applicable to the following main illustrations: pages 17, 22, 23, 24, 33, 35, 37, 39, 40, 51, 55, 67, 68, 72, 73, 86, 88, 91, 121, and 123 as well as to some text illustrations. The Nederlander on page 36 was drawn from a plan by Gerhard Roentgen. This purports to show the essential characteristics of the vessel.

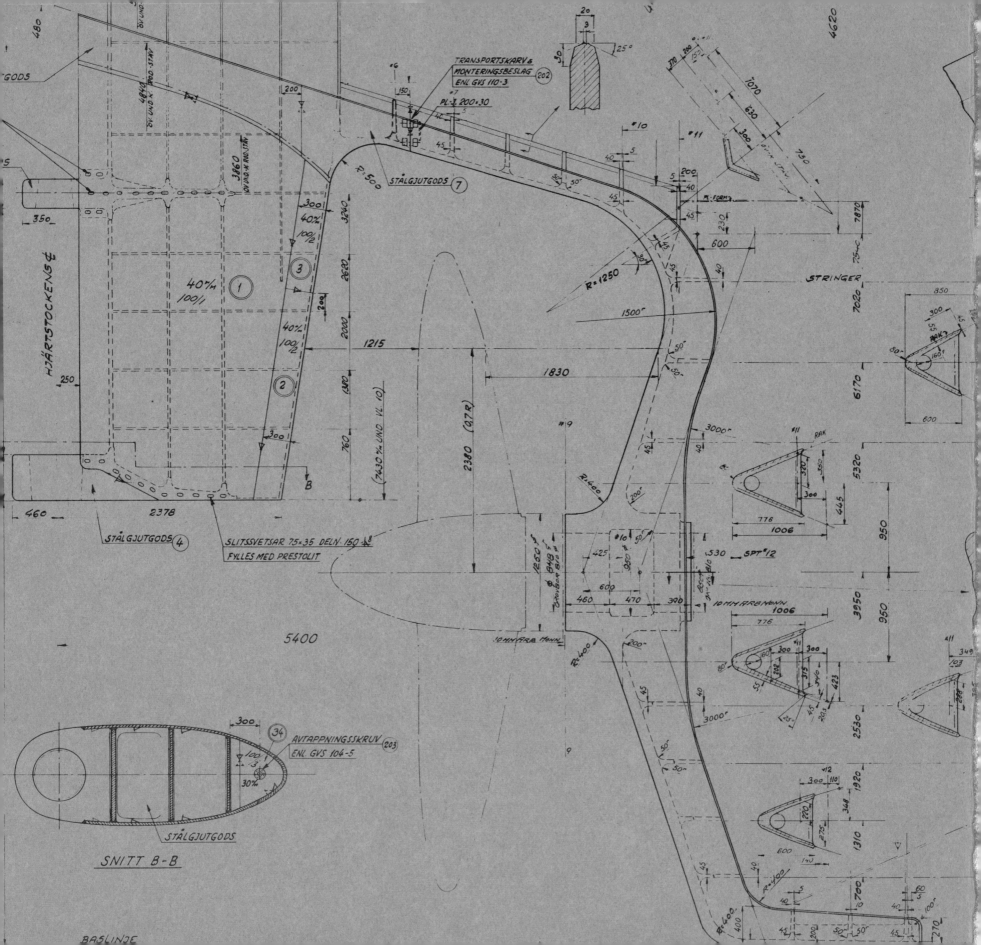